LIBRARY SCIENCE AND DOCUMENTATION
A Series of Texts and Monographs

JESSE H. SHERA, *General Editor*

Volume I
TOOLS FOR MACHINE LITERATURE SEARCHING

Volume II
PUNCH-CARD METHODS IN RESEARCH AND
  DOCUMENTATION
    with Special Reference to Biology

LIBRARY SCIENCE AND DOCUMENTATION
A Series of Texts and Monographs

JESSE H. SHERA, *General Editor*
Dean, School of Library Science, Western Reserve University, Cleveland, Ohio

Editorial Advisory Board

VOLUME II

PUNCH-CARD METHODS IN RESEARCH AND DOCUMENTATION

With Special Reference to Biology

First English Edition
based on Second Revised German Edition by
DR. MARTIN SCHEELE
Hydrobiologische Anstalt der Max-Planck Gesellschaft (Plön/Holstein)

Translated from the German by
J. E. Holmstrom, Ph.D
Member of the Institution of Civil Engineers. Fellow of the Institute of Linguists. Fellow of the Institute of Information Scientists

1961

INTERSCIENCE PUBLISHERS, INC., NEW YORK
INTERSCIENCE PUBLISHERS, LTD., LONDON

This book is translated from the second edition of M. Scheele:

Die Lochkartenverfahren in Forschung und Dokumentation mit besonderer Berücksichtigung der Biologie

Interscience Publishers, Inc., 250 Fifth Ave., New York 1, N.Y.

For Great Britain and Northern Ireland:
Interscience Publishers Ltd., 88–90 Chancery Lane, London W.C.2, England

Printed in Great Britain by Richard Clay and Company, Ltd., Bungay, Suffolk

PREFACE TO THE SECOND GERMAN EDITION

During the five years, more or less, that have elapsed since the appearance of the first edition of this book, the applications of punch-card methods and of electronic computing machines have shown a very notable expansion and the related literature a corresponding growth in volume.

The author too has enjoyed opportunities for further studies in the methodology of applying punch-cards in research, in documentation and in neighboring fields of interest such as nomenclature, terminology, classification and notation, as well as opportunities for learning the experiences of other users. These have come to him in his capacity first as leader of the documentation center for limnology in Hannover-Münden, then as specialist for documentation in the Deutsche Forschungsgemeinschaft at Bad Godesberg, and finally through a special research assignment given him by the Hydrobiological Institute of the Max-Planck-Gesellschaft.

As the first edition of this book was well received and out of print, both publishers and author had to consider the question of a new edition. In view of what has been said so far the author felt compelled to decide in favor of practically a new work as being the only way satisfactorily to cover the varied and extensive material that has become available from new experience, in order to bring this monograph right up to date without having to enlarge it too much.

It is more impracticable than ever to attempt to cover the whole range of questions that relate to punch-card methods in either their general or their research applications. Moreover, it would be wrong in a book such as this to aim merely at an uncritical listing of a great many individual experiences. The author therefore has felt bound, even more than in the first edition, to trace out those features in punch-card methods which are of common application, seeking to establish general rules and finally to summarize the individual concrete examples in a separate part of the book. He hopes that this endeavor to systematize the varied material will provide the reader with as complete a survey of the subject as is possible, and with the necessary groundwork for developing and combining the rules and principles here set forth in whatever special directions he may need. There is, however, no lack here of special references, which different users may find to be significant from very different angles.

Points of special importance are brought out several times over in different parts of the book, for such repetition should not be thought of as a disadvantage and something to be avoided. Other points of view, such as for instance the commercial uses of the punch-card method, do not, however, fall within the scope of this book and have been completely disregarded here; these are the subjects of separate publications produced by the

Committee for Economic Administration (Ausschuß für Wirtschaftliche Verwaltung, AWV). Nor has it seemed advisable to give detailed information and special operating instructions, such as are to be found in the appropriate trade literature.

Once again, the author's thanks are due to the persons and institutions mentioned in the preface to the first edition. Besides these he now feels specially indebted to the following whose help and support have made this second edition possible:

To Professor Dr Dr h.c. Thienemann, Director of the Hydrobiological Institute in the Max-Planck-Gesellschaft, for his support in the establishment of the documentation center for limnology in Hannover-Münden which was the pre-requisite for the work which the author carried out.

To the Sales Community of German Potash Works (Verkaufsgemeinschaft Deutscher Kaliwerke) in Hannover for generous financial support, which enabled the field-punching method and the codes for biology and physiography described in Part III of the book to be worked out.

To Mr Gurtmann, Dipl. agr. Hansen and Mr Storm who were collaborators in the documentation center at Hannover-Münden already mentioned.

To the Deutsche Forschungsgemeinschaft which made it possible for the author to obtain a bird's-eye view of documentation throughout the Federal Republic of Germany.

To the general management of the Max-Planck-Gesellschaft and to the new director of its Hydrobiological Institute, Dr Sioli, for the grant of a research assignment to carry out the work, as well as to Dipl.-Ing. Heimerdinger and Mr Körber of the Hollerith Department in the Max-Planck-Gesellschaft at Göttingen, for their loyal cooperation which has now continued for ten years.

To the IBM (Deutschland) Corporation and its branch in Bonn, for their constant support.

To the presidency and management of the Deutsche Gesellschaft für Dokumentation for much help and advice; and finally but not least to the publishers Schweizerbart, for once again having achieved so good a presentation of the book.

August 1959   M. SCHEELE

ADDENDUM TO THE FIRST ENGLISH EDITION

The author is particularly grateful for the suggestion made by Dr J. E. Holmstrom to publish an English version of the second edition of his book on punch-cards. Dr Holmstrom himself undertook the translation into English and Interscience Publishers, Inc., New York, the publication of this edition. The opportunity is taken to thank both translator and publishers very heartily for their interest and their efforts.

September 1959   M. SCHEELE

PREFACE TO THE FIRST GERMAN EDITION

The tremendous rate of advance in science and technology has brought about developments commonly denoted by catchwords like 'electronic brain' and 'thinking machines', and it is to this category of technical developments that modern punch-card methods belong.

Such catchwords are, however, very dangerous, being all too apt to throw a false light on things and problems which, whether we are scientists or technologists, still baffle us. Yet science has now reached a stage where, unless it fosters the further development of these machines and methods, it cannot but block its own progress along the chosen road—which is not an alternative that falls for discussion here. In this context it must, however, expressly be emphasized that if methodology and machinery are to retain any sense and purpose at all they must still, as heretofore, be looked upon simply as tools and aids for use by a human being capable of thought and feeling.

Be it noted, also, that punch-card methods are not limited to those which depend on the availability of machines: simple and inexpensive hand-operated devices also exist, the use of which involves no great material commitment, but which up to the present are hardly known at all.

Meanwhile, here in Germany, punch-card methods in general have aroused a growing amount of interest largely through the initiative of Professor Dr E. Pietsch, Director of the Gmelin Institute for Inorganic Chemistry and Related Fields, which is affiliated to the Max-Planck-Gesellschaft; and it may be permissible to suggest, as a task incumbent perhaps on German science, the development of those punch-card methods which in America, up to now, have predominantly been looked at from the side of technology.

The author's own approach to modern methods of using cards has been from both these aspects of their application. On the one hand, in pure research, he has found these modern methods to be outstandingly effective in his own ecological work. On the other hand he has been led to appreciate their importance in the field of documentation—a field which in relation to such a science as limnology (the study of inland waters) raises many problems because of the great diversity of disciplines over which the literature ranges.

In 1951 the Deutsche Gesellschaft für Dokumentation set up a committee for mechanized documentation under E. Pietsch, in which the present author assumed responsibility for biology, that being a branch of science which hitherto had presented only few openings for the introduction of punch-card methods. Although an attempt to raise the matter through Unesco in the spring of 1950 met with no positive response, it is precisely in biology that so many possibilities for applying these new methods arise.

Experience shows that all innovations encounter skepticism and this is particularly true of punch-cards. Such skepticism is to be overcome only by arguments of manifest cogency supported by facts of experience. It was on these grounds that the author decided to put together such experiences as were already available, in the field of biology, with a view to publication. At first he did so only in the form of typewritten manuscript, but this led inevitably to the more detailed and general appreciation of punch-card methods which here appears in book form. No attempt can, however, be made in the present book to cover the whole range of questions which relate to the possibilities of applying punch-cards in scientific research. The most that can be hoped for is to systematize the more salient of the facts and experiences that have come to light in the course of applying these methods to research and documentation, and to impart to those newly interesting themselves in these matters as much information as is necessary to enable them to decide whether punch-cards should be considered for possible application in their own work, either generally or in special directions.

Anyone who is seriously turning to punch-cards must begin by handling the cards in actual practice. It is essential for him to carry out trial runs and it is desirable that he should himself work on the machines, studying the instructions supplied by their manufacturers and the advice given by appropriate specialists as regards particular applications.

Finally, the author thanks those who have given him advice and help in punch-card work. Above all he wishes to thank Professor Dr E. Pietsch as the initiator of mechanized documentation in Germany, Dipl.-Ing. Heimerdinger who is in charge of the punch-card department and Mr H. Fuhrmann who is responsible for the documentation centre of the Max-Planck-Gesellschaft in Göttingen. This book owes much to Mr H. J. Knigge for the bibliography, to Dr H. Hörnicke and Dr J. Illies for their kindness in providing material and to the firms concerned as well as the Deutsche Gesellschaft für Dokumentation who have provided blocks for the illustrations. Lastly, his special thanks are due to Messrs Schweizerbart, the publishers, for the interest they have shown in this work and for their excellent presentation of the book.

April 1954　　　　　　　　　　　　　　　　　　　　　　　M. SCHEELE

CONTENTS

INTRODUCTION AND ARRANGEMENT

Science is only made possible through, and indeed it consists mainly of, a process of fitting together multiple concepts under certain general headings and of inter-relating these concepts by means of theories. It is thus that science has been defined as 'a systematic orientation of man in his environment'.

The object of natural science is thus to 'tidy up' the limitless variety of natural phenomena. Its basic method consists of the derivation of general statements from a multitude of isolated observations. The farther science advances, the more difficult does it become to discover this underlying generality; but, if research is not to stagnate, the methods which science uses for apprehending and evaluating the isolated facts must be matched with the status to which it has attained. In our own times, the methods can to a great extent be none other than those of technical statistics, applied through punch-card and similar techniques.

Here is an example. It is required to discover the laws relating climate to the population of organisms in an extensive region. Now, each of these two factors, climate and organisms, is itself a complex of many. We do not even know which of the individual climatic factors are significant nor which kinds of organisms react with them. In practice, the question is even more complicated. For us to be able to solve the problem, a method is required which makes it possible for all relevant data about climate and population to be continuously recorded in maps by many observers at many places, and for these data later to be arranged and combined from any desired points of view so that their true interconnections can be perceived. Using only the traditional methods, however, this is a problem which either cannot be solved at all or requires a great expenditure of time.

But today it is not only from this point of view of the research work itself that the purely technical organization of science is decisive. What now occupies the center of interest is rather what is called the literature problem. Our existing knowledge of nature has grown to such enormous dimensions that even specialized scientists are no longer able to grasp the whole range of experience falling within their special fields. Often the simple consequence of this fact is that valuable knowledge runs to waste and that many potentially valuable pieces of work are overlooked. What makes the problem really baffling is when it becomes a question of cross-connections permitting the data from various disciplines to be combined into a synthesis or a general picture of a large area to be obtained.

This is a perfectly general problem, not confined to biology and the natural sciences, which in its classical form has already been treated elsewhere in full detail (Pietsch, 1951–52), as the following two quotations show:

> The execution of research works and the progress of technical
> developments—indeed even the presentation of data relating to the

moral sciences—is growing so constantly in volume that it becomes more and more difficult every year to take proper cognizance of the newly published international literature, or even to be aware of it. According to a survey made in 1937 there then existed in the world at least 40 000 newspapers and 80 000 periodicals, including some 15 000 relating to technology and the natural sciences, this last group carrying at least a million separate publications every year. In the special field of chemistry alone, the volume of publications is overwhelming. Merely to index the dates, authors and subjects of papers which have been noticed during the fourth decade of this century in the great American referencing organ, *Chemical Abstracts*, takes up about 8 km (5 miles) length of small type! A further example may serve to show the desperate situation which exists in the field covered by the Gmelin undertaking: in order to survey the literature for the 'Sulfur' volume of the Gmelin *Handbook* (relating only to elementary sulfur and its combinations with hydrogen and oxygen and excluding the sulfide and sulfate salts) about 30 000 publications covering about half a million pages have had to be registered, procured, examined, analysed and related to the existing state of knowledge. Even when a team of scientific collaborators for such work is available, the necessary editorial mastery of this huge mass of material approaches the limit of what is possible. From this single chosen example relating to the structure of the literature it may at once be seen how powerless the individual research worker has become, in recent decades, to avoid the necessity of basing his own experimental and theoretical investigations on a merely arbitrary selection from what has already been published. The consequence is that he builds upon partial knowledge and a considerable duplication of work is bound to occur. This is another way of saying that important social resources are being used wastefully and indeed perversely. The lack of economy in intellectual work is thereby manifest (Pietsch, 1952 b).

To conclude these remarks on new ways to master the problems of documentation in science [in which the punch-card method had been discussed—Author], there is a further question which calls for mention, relating to the stage now reached in these endeavours to systematize intellectual material. That question is the following: What is the place of this development within the morphology of our cultural development as a whole? It is one which cannot be answered here, but which must be raised in order to show that what has been said is not merely accidental or spasmodic. Rather does it serve to illustrate how the manifold directions in which the human intellect is spreading its efflorescence compel us to explore methodically the new possibilities for coping with it, so as to cope with all the knowledge which mankind is opening up—unless indeed we are prepared to contemplate the human spirit being overwhelmed by the very growth of the subject content. Of course we feel a strong repugnance to the idea of abandoning the use of accepted procedures, which served us well enough until a few decades ago, in favor of new methods which are not yet fully matured. But we must take the decision to consider them, and to collaborate in perfecting them, if we are to fashion the tools we need for the intellectual work of the future. And if, from now on, we can hold this aim in view, then I feel entitled to expect from these new methods so marked an improvement in the economy of our intellectual output, and such great possibilities for intercorrelating the separate regions in the universe of science, that a new creative period will ensue for the spirit, influencing human development and influenced by it (Pietsch, 1951 b).

There are, then, two great fields for applying the punch-card method in science: namely research and documentation, the latter being defined by the Deutsche Gesellschaft für Dokumentation as follows: 'To document means to collect documents systematically, to make them accessible and to render them useful. This activity constitutes documentation'.

The application of punch-card and similar methods to documentation has been named 'mechanized documentation', but the term 'mechanical selection' also is used where literature searching is meant. As in all newly developing areas the terminology is still somewhat uncertain, but the concept denoted by 'punch-card method' is nowhere the same as that implied by 'mechanized documentation'.

The designation 'punch-card method' applies unequivocally only to the various methods which in fact make use of punch-cards.* In commerce and industry these have now achieved a firm status, but in science their application is quite new, relating—be it once again repeated—on the one hand to research and on the other to documentation. The expression 'mechanized documentation' implies reference both to methods and to the fields of their application, but documentation is only one of the fields in which the punch-card method can be applied. On the other hand, methods falling under the head of mechanized documentation are not limited to punch-cards: they include also those based on the use of films such as the 'Rapid Selector' and those based on television such as 'Ultrafax', electronic methods which do not use punch-cards (these, too, are applicable in research) and yet others. This note on nomenclature is necessary here in order that the reader may clearly understand the following pages and may be on guard against forming a wrong picture of the relation between particular details in them.

The present book relates exclusively to the punch-card method, but it includes also the necessary references to electronic computing machines. In discussing applications, the natural sciences and especially biology are in the foreground, but to a great extent the principles brought out in that

---

* Throughout this book I have rendered *Lochkarten* by 'punch-cards' in preference to 'punched cards' so as to be able to distinguish 'machine punch-cards' from manual systems without implying that the former are always punched by machine, and so as to avoid the awkwardness of referring to them as 'punched cards' before they have in fact been punched.—Translator.

context are capable of being transferred to other areas. The arrangement of the whole work is governed by the idea of proceeding, as follows, from the general to the particular:

Part I, entitled 'The punch-card method', is concerned purely with the technology and methodology of the method, applications not being mentioned at this stage, or mentioned only by way of example. In the first ('General') chapter a few quite general situations and rules for the punch-card method are discussed. These are followed by a historical survey of the development of punch-cards and then by two sections providing a complete terminology and classification for what the method involves, under the headings of 'manipulatory technique' and of coding or 'intellectual technique'. Herein the basic consideration has been that an adequately defined terminology, and a classification worked out at the start, will obviate the need for interpolating explanations into later text.

This general chapter concludes by reviewing the fields of application for the various punch-card methods that exist. In this review, questions of costs and estimating are discussed and comparisons are made in order that the reader may be enabled from the very beginning to form some idea as to which method appears *prima facie* the most appropriate to his particular purpose and may pay special attention to that method in his further reading.

After this comes a discussion of those punch-card methods which are actually the most important. Machine punch-cards are considered at the beginning of the second chapter, needle punch-cards in the third and visual cards in the fourth.

The two chapters which relate respectively to machine punch-cards and needle punch-cards are further sub-divided so as to describe on the one hand the machines and apparatus used ('manipulatory technique') and on the other hand rules for coding ('intellectual technique'). The chapter about the 'visual' or 'feature card' method calls for no further sub-division, as this method is one of great simplicity, and is based on principles altogether different from those of machine punch-cards and needle punch-cards.

In *Part II* of the book, a whole range of general rules and experiences relating to *applications* of the punch-card method in research and documentation is discussed. In this context it has been found that research and documentation cannot be considered in isolation from one another. In fact the experience obtained to date makes it manifest that the punch-card method can be exploited to full advantage only on condition that questions and problems relating to nomenclature and terminology, to classification and notation and to everything that is involved in publication are re-examined. For this reason it has been deemed necessary that, in considering applications for the punch-card method, all these questions should be raised.

Finally, *Part III* of the book presents a number of more or less detailed examples of such applications to research, documentation and systematics. From these quite specialized and concrete examples the reader will be able to appreciate the extent to which the general principles and rules developed in *Part II* have in fact been followed up within the various disciplines and by the various authors quoted.

PART I

THE PUNCH-CARD METHODS

1. GENERAL

One of the main arguments raised against proposals for using punch-cards in research and documentation is that here we have reached the point where even the human spirit is to be 'mechanized'; for when one hears of 'mechanized thought' one automatically goes on to the defensive.

As against this, it must be said that the antithesis of 'spirit' and 'machine' rests on false assumptions. No machine can ever replace the creative thinking of a human being; but what machines can do is to contribute very notably to lessening the load on the human brain and thereby to freeing it for truly creative thought.

Just because machines and other such aids cannot be substitutes for human thought, the preliminary work for using punch-cards is of quite special importance. Referring to the punch-card method a distinction needs to be drawn between 'manipulatory technique' and 'intellectual technique', and the preparatory work involves familiarity with both. Here the expression 'manipulatory technique' covers all the material pre-requisites such as the cards themselves, the associated devices and machines, their mode and possibilities of use, whilst 'intellectual technique' is an expression which may be used to denote the establishment of the code (that is to say, to denote the principles that should govern the attribution of significance to the holes or the perforatable positions in the punch-cards) and the process of coding. For applying the punch-card method this intellectual technique of 'keying' or 'coding' is central and decisive. The method cannot yield any more than has been put into it through the intellectual work of establishing its code system. It is the failure to appreciate this fact that accounts for the disappointment one occasionally hears about in cases where the punch-card method has been applied. Familiarity with the cards themselves, with the apparatus and machinery and with all the possibilities for arranging the holes and for interpreting the patterns of meaning they may be made to represent, as well as with the possibilities that may exist for rationally combining different methods, demand appropriate experience, and may involve considerable work at first.

Finally, it is a mistake to expect miracles from the punch-card method. Do not expect a 100 per cent solution to every problem that may occur, but be content with 98 per cent. Experience shows that the remaining two per cent can be disregarded as being an overhead cost without significance for success. In this context, it should be stressed also that not every kind of work is suitable for handling by punch-cards and that in some cases the attempt to use them can be a mere waste of time which brings the whole thing into discredit. Before deciding to adopt the punch-card method, both the manipulatory and the intellectual techniques must be properly studied so that the right way may be found and no unforeseen

B

difficulties be encountered at a later stage. The simpler and less complicated the better: such is the golden rule.

Nearly all beginners fall to the allurement of the manifold possibilities offered by this technical game. The result may be arrangements and fanciful ideas leading to more or less complicated solutions; the initial enthusiasm may cause these to be published, and later on, in the light of longer experience they may be seen to be unsound. The author can say this with a good conscience, for he has himself had that experience and felt compelled, step by step, greatly to simplify a complicated plan (see page 212).

(1) HISTORY OF THE PUNCH-CARD METHODS

What occasioned the discovery of the punch-card method was the U.S.A. census of population in 1880. At that time, processing of the census data

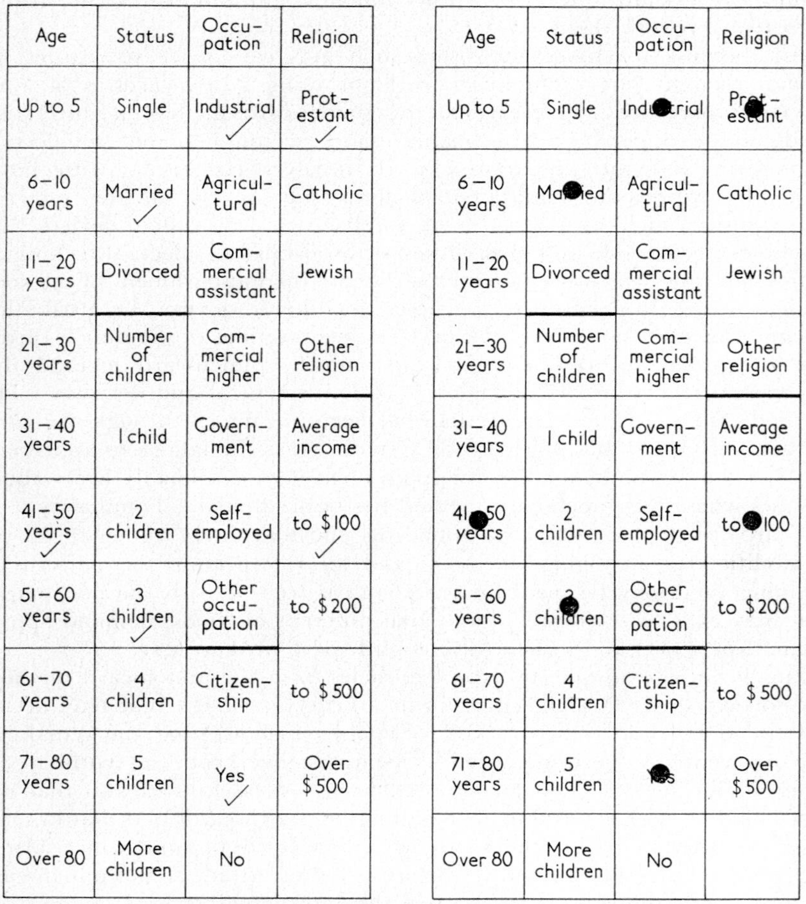

Age	Status	Occupation	Religion
Up to 5	Single	Industrial ✓	Protestant ✓
6–10 years	Married ✓	Agricultural	Catholic
11–20 years	Divorced	Commercial assistant	Jewish
21–30 years	Number of children	Commercial higher	Other religion
31–40 years	1 child	Government	Average income
41–50 years ✓	2 children	Self-employed	to $100 ✓
51–60 years	3 children ✓	Other occupation	to $200
61–70 years	4 children	Citizenship	to $500
71–80 years	5 children	Yes ✓	Over $500
Over 80	More children	No	

Age	Status	Occupation	Religion
Up to 5	Single	Industrial •	Protestant •
6–10 years	Married •	Agricultural	Catholic
11–20 years	Divorced	Commercial assistant	Jewish
21–30 years	Number of children	Commercial higher	Other religion
31–40 years	1 child	Government	Average income
41–50 years •	2 children	Self-employed	to $100 •
51–60 years	3 children •	Other occupation	to $200
61–70 years	4 children	Citizenship	to $500
71–80 years	5 children	Yes •	Over $500
Over 80	More children	No	

FIG. 1. Small census check cards and punch-cards (IBM).

used to take seven years and lead to results which during that long period
of gestation had become out of date and largely worthless (see Placzek
in Hosemann, 1951).

At this census the characteristics noted in the returns were transferred
on to small cards, all printed with the same layout (Fig. 1), by making
checkmarks in the appropriate fields, after which the cards were
accordingly sorted and counted by hand. These processes had to be
gone through for each of the characteristics in turn, so that naturally
miscounts occurred and it is no wonder that the work took so long to
complete.

Dr Hermann Hollerith, son of a German who had migrated to America,
thereupon conceived the idea of so constituting the cards that they could
be sorted into statistical groups and be counted mechanically. He replaced
the checkmarks on the cards by holes and he designed machines able to
detect the presence of the holes. In this way the punch-card method
was born.

Even the first U.S.A. census to be carried out by this new method, that
of 1890, needed only one year to work out the results and these were sur-
prisingly free from error. As described by Mikat (in Hosemann, 1951),
its success caused a sensation.

In this historical summary it would be wrong not to mention that the
rapid developments of automation and electronic computing which have
taken place in our own day run closely parallel to that of the punch-card
method. In that context a quotation from Aikele (1956) may be of interest
regarding the course of evolution from the original discovery of the principle
until the present day.

It is very interesting and exciting to contemplate the increasing rate
at which the art and science of computing has developed since 1694,
the date when Leibniz completed his first calculating machine based
on the same principles as our modern desk calculators. Until the
present century, however, the desk calculator was not generally looked
upon by professional computers as a 'must'. Machines able to read off
information automatically from punch-cards came into use in 1893;
for the first 30 years they were scarcely noticed, but then they became
popular. The development and generalization of non-electronic
automatic scientific computing machines, based mainly on already
known principles and components, took place in the two decades
between 1925 and 1945. The decade since then has seen the development of the electronic computer from its exploratory stage into a revolu-
tionary tool of science. In the 'NORC' the latest fulfilment of the
hopes of the last ten years may be perceived: here microsecond impulse
circuits operate many billions of times without error, electrostatic
accumulators and magnetic tapes work in combination, new and simpler
logical conceptions are predominant. The range of problems which
today can be worked successfully has multiplied during the last ten
years by 10000 and everyone now engaged in computing excitedly
looks forward to developments in the next decade.

Needle punch-cards and visual or feature punch-cards have a history of their own which, however, began later than that of machine punch-cards. Without going into details about this, it may be remarked that in general neither of these two kinds of methods met with any appreciable notice at first, although their discovery dates from much farther back than is generally assumed.   Practically speaking, they did not become widely adopted and used until after 1945.

(2) TERMINOLOGY AND SUBDIVISION OF THE METHODS

A suitable terminology for the punch-card method is needed here to serve the purposes both of classification and of survey.   An incidental object of this terminology will be to create, or at least to propose, a conceptual apparatus as simple as possible, applicable to the whole field in which the punch-card method is of interest.

Indeed it is in a field as broad as this that the value of a proper terminology may best be illustrated, for the application of punch-cards leads quite generally to clearer conceptualization and (in documentation) to a better picture of the nature of our knowledge.   It is proper, therefore, that the punch-card method itself should be endowed with really simple and definite terms, that this relatively compact and methodical field of work should not become fogged by a needless and ambiguous multiplicity of technical terms and that generally intelligible subject matter should not thereby be rendered abstruse.   This is especially important for users whose own special backgrounds are so very varied and who ought not to be burdened, on the methodological side, with a complicated terminology.

As regards terminology and classification of the punch-card method, it is desirable first of all to draw a distinction between the 'method' and the 'punch-cards' themselves.   Here the word 'method' should be defined as covering the various possible working principles whereas 'punch-cards' refers to the material, the concrete objects, which enable these principles to be realized. At first sight this distinction may seem somewhat abstract and superfluous, but closer thought and practical application will show that it enables the whole of the terminology to be appreciably simplified.   This is so because experience has demonstrated that the working principles here called the 'method' are not closely connected with the 'punch-cards' themselves.   That is to say, different working principles can be combined with one another, as desired, on one and the same punch-card.   For instance, the principle of machine punch-cards can be combined with that of needle punch-cards or of the visual or feature punch-cards, and combinations are possible also within particular types of method.

This point is purposely stressed here in order that the proposed distinction may be drawn between 'method' and 'punch-cards' from the beginning; but in what immediately follows we shall confine our attention to the terminology of 'method', from which that applicable to what might be described as 'pure strains' of card types can be derived directly.   Thus the designation 'machine punch-card method' leads to the term 'machine punch-cards', and correspondingly for the other methods.

Purposely, no terminology will be worked out here for uses of punch-cards in which two or more of the recognized methods (or working principles) are applied in combination with one another. In certain particular cases (for instance, that of 'notched visual cards') this might indeed be useful, but in others it could easily lead to mistakes or to stillborn expressions.

The following terminology is based on publications and proposals by Draheim (1957), Gröttrup (1957), Kistermann (1957/58), Scheele (1956 c) and Ühlein (1958).

(A) Methods

Punch-Card Methods

Methods based upon the use of perforatable index cards in which certain information may be recorded by mechanically altering the cards (as by making holes, notches or slits in them) so as to render them more or less amenable to mechanical processing.

Machine Punch-Card Method

Punch-card method in which the handling of the cards is entirely mechanical, the cards passing through the machines separately and in succession. Before use they are unperforated.

Needle Punch-Card Method

Punch-card methods in which the cards are handled mainly by hand with the aid of needles or needling devices. A multiplicity of cards can be handled at the same time. The cards are already perforated before use.

Notched card method—Needle punch-cards in which the holes are convertible to notches open to the edge of the card.

Slit card method—Needle punch-card methods in which the holes can be connected to one another, thereby forming internal slits, but the edges of the cards remain intact.

Visual Punch-Card Method

Punch-card methods in which the cards are examined visually by looking through the holes. As regards the recording and retrieving of information this method works on a principle fundamentally different from that of the other punch-card methods, being in fact the exact contrary. A multiplicity of cards can be handled at the same time. Before use, the cards are unperforated.

Explanation

It seems desirable to add some further notes on this terminology in order that the user may be clear why it and the corresponding subdivisions have been chosen, especially as other terms occur, to some extent, in the literature and in practice, the significance and synonymy of which need to be understood.

The triple division of punch-card methods is based on the indisputable fact that there do exist these three major groups of methods, as to which specialists and authors are in the main agreed.

As regards the meaning of the expression 'machine punch-card methods' there are practically no differences of opinion, but some authors (for instance, Draheim, 1957) have proposed combining needle punch-card methods and visual or feature punch-card methods under the higher collective expression 'hand punch-card methods'. Though it is true that this proposal corresponds to a mode of expression already in use to a varied extent, there are two reasons why it nevertheless appears undesirable, the main argument against the combination being that the 'visual' or 'feature' punch-card methods are different in principle from the other two groups of methods. It is a fact of experience that the principle of feature punch-cards demands, from the uninitiated, an effort of re-thinking which is always rather a difficult one. Therefore it seems expedient to differentiate this method quite clearly from either of the other groups of methods by the place allotted to it in the scheme of subdivision, and to assimilate it with the needle punch-card method is neither desirable nor necessary. The second of the arguments against doing so is that the corresponding two German terms '*Handlochkarten*' and '*Randlochkarten*' are very similar in sound.

The German designation *Nadellochkarten-Verfahren*, here translated as 'needle punch-card methods', was originated by Draheim. After long reflection, the present author has adopted this term as it is a good and revealing one which serves to avoid unnecessary discrepancies between different terminological proposals that have been made. The German term *Sichtlochkarten-Verfahren* (here rendered as 'visual' or 'feature' punch-card methods) has become current in Germany with a welcome unanimity.

Synonyms

The following German terms (of which English translations are here given in parentheses) are in use also:

Binnenlochkarten ('interior' or 'field punched' cards): applicable both to 'machine punch-cards' and to 'slit punch-cards'.

Flächenlochkarten ('surface punched cards'): used in the same sense as *Binnenlochkarten*.

Handlochkarten ('hand punched cards'): used as a higher collective term embracing both 'needle' punch-cards and 'visual' (or 'feature') punch-cards, but sometimes restricted to 'needle' punch-cards.

Randlochkarten ('edge punched cards'): used instead of either 'needle punch-cards' or 'notched cards'.

Remark

Personal and trade names (such as Cordonnier, Allform, etc.) have not here been listed as synonyms. It is to be wished that in future the manufacturers concerned may use the correct terms along with their own special designations of the firms or inventors. It is further to be hoped, in the general interest of a unified terminology, that current synonyms may gradually fall out of use. The author feels doubtful, however, whether that hope will be realized in regard to *Randlochkarten* (edge punched cards) as this is doubtless as good a term as *Nadellochkarten* (needle punched cards) and both terms are now firmly rooted.

(B) Layout

Perforatable area (*Lochfläche*): portion of a card in which holes can be punched.

Punching position (*Lochstelle*): place on a punch-card in which a single hole can be punched.

Row of holes (*Lochreihe*): a straight alinement of punchable positions.

Punching column (*Lochspalte*): a row of holes parallel to the direction in which the cards move during the process of selection.

Line of holes (*Lochzeile*): a row of holes at right angles to the direction of movement of the cards during the process of selection.

Punching field (*Lochfeld*): a combination of several holes or columns of holes considered as a unit.

Writing field (*Schreibfeld*): area in which to record information by hand or typewriter.

(C) Handling

Punching (*Ablochen*): recording of information by means of holes, notches or slits.

Marking (*Markieren*): indication of the positions or holes to be punched (or pencil writing on machine punch-cards when using the mark-sensing method).

Selecting (*Selektieren*): the process of searching out the required punch-cards from a collection.

Sorting (*Sortieren*): arrangement of a selection of punch-cards in accordance with pre-determined characteristics.

(D) Application

Indication (*Aussage*): a collective term for a characteristic, such as subject content, significant content, catchword, keyword, figures, letters and symbols—a term applicable to any kind of information which is to be stored on punched cards.

Working unit (*Bearbeitungseinheit*): entity to which the indications on a punched card relate (e.g. a publication, a biological specimen, a person, etc.).

Coupling number (*Kopplungsnummer*): a number which is to be punched in the cards so as to make it possible for several of these relating to the same working unit to be brought together. On all such cards the coupling must be the same.

Punching instructions (*Lochbeleg*): graphical representation of all the indications to be recorded on punch-cards, as nearly as possible ready for punching.

Combination cards (*Verbundkarten*): punch-cards whose own function is combined with that of a punching pattern. The indications to be punched, and others, are marked directly in the writing fields of the connecting cards and are read off directly therefrom when punching. (Cards in which the significance of the punching positions, or of the holes, is ready printed so that no system of notation is necessary, also are to be regarded as combination cards.)

(3) TERMINOLOGY AND SUBDIVISION OF CODING

The general terminology and subdivision of coding techniques will now be discussed in accordance with the distinction between the 'manipulative' and the 'intellectual' techniques already explained above, the latter of which refers to coding. Here again the terms proposed are suitable for use throughout the whole range of punch-card methods and the introductory explanations, given above, can equally well be applied to the terminology and classification of coding. The terms are:

Code (*Schlüssel*): rules for matching indications with holes or perforatable positions in punch-cards.

Important remark—In order to make such matching of indications with holes at all possible, it is necessary in all punch-card methods that the perforatable positions or the holes should somehow be capable of being specified. For this purpose numbers, letters or coordinate systems are used. Basically, however, the manner of their specification has nothing to do with what indications are to be recorded; it is merely an aid to coding. Where the indications, too, are expressed in the form of figures or letters, either these represent purely quantitative values or they are notations (regarding which see page 128). Such indications can be identical or correlated with the hole designations, but need not necessarily be so. The distinction made here between notation on the one hand and coding (including hole designations) on the other is no mere hair-splitting of only theoretical importance, but is what opens up the way to the almost unlimited possibilities of the punch-card method.

Simple code (*einfache Schlüssel*): a code which serves for the recording or matching of simple indications (in the form of figures, letters or other conceptual unit symbols).

Direct code (*Direktschlüssel*): a simple code in which each individual hole or perforatable position corresponds to one indication.

Abridged code (*Kurzschlüssel*): a simple code in which not each individual hole or perforatable position but a combination of two or more holes or perforatable positions corresponds to one indication.

Compound code (*zusammengesetzte Schlüssel*): code which serves for the recording or incorporation of compound indications—that is, complexes of numbers or of letters, or of associations of concepts—or of other symbols which are themselves compounded from symbols representing indications coded with the help of simple codes.

Hierarchical code (*hierarchische Schlüssel*): a compound code whose components are hierarchically related to one another (each individual component having its definite position value subordinate to another).

Associative code (*assoziative Schlüssel*): a compound code in which the individual components of the compounded indications are *not* hierarchically dependent on one another, having *no* definite position values).

Comments

In reference to coding, Draheim, Kistermann and other authors have proposed still further terms. As the various proposals differ considerably from one another they would be more difficult to unify than would the terminology for the punch-card method discussed above. The present author is of opinion that the terms already in use, which have been explained here, are sufficient for designating the various codes, and that it is not desirable to try to anticipate now the designations that may be required for possible future developments.

The differentiation between simple and compound codes has here been made by the author for the first time, so far as he is aware. A thorough study of the coding problem suggests that this differentiation is almost a necessity if the simplest possible and most intelligible classification of codes is sought.

The designations of the two possible kinds of simple codes ('direct code') and 'abridged codes') were originated by Draheim and seem to the author well conceived to express their meanings. It has, however, been deemed necessary to contrast simple codes with compound codes. In this way a needlessly complex terminology—such as *Gruppenschlüssel* (group code), *Mischschlüssel* (mixed code), *Mehrfeldschlüssel* (multiple field code), etc.— is avoided, and with it the risk that the normal user would not understand it or that it would merely become an object of contention among specialists in punch-card techniques. On the other hand, the designation 'compound codes' makes it clear to everybody that such codes are composed of several simple codes. As there are two kinds of simple codes, the construction of a compound code may be either homogeneous or heterogeneous, but this possibility offers no justification for further subdivisions or for new terms. If any such further subdivision is to be made, it ought rather to be dependent on the nature of the relationship between the individual components.

The designations for the two kinds of compound codes ('hierarchical' and 'associative') have been introduced and defined by the present author. The necessity for this differentiation, and its meaning, cannot be made fully apparent until later in the book, as it calls for practical examples, so that meanwhile it would be pointless to enter into further and more detailed explanations.

Finally, some general observations and rules in reference to coding may be apposite. In every case, the development of a code raises a clear and definite problem. It is rightly said that what characterizes a true scientist is his having the art of asking the right questions. This is equally true here as regards applying the punch-card method. Any lack of clarity in stating the problem or of familiarity with manipulative technique leads to unusable codes and thereby to failures in the work as a whole. Without any doubt, it is an advantage of the punch-card method that its use compels clearer and more definite conceptualization so as to be able to make use of this in constructing the code system.

Coding can be made considerably easier if the punching pattern which is to be imposed on the cards has already been subdivided and arranged in accordance with the conditions which the punch-card method requires. It is important that this operation should be so planned that the sequence of the indications corresponds with that in which they are to be recorded on the cards; for otherwise one's eyes have to be continually wandering here and there over the pattern during the process of punching it, which is very tiresome, slows up the work and introduces unnecessary risks of error. For the same reason it is desirable that the punching pattern should be marked out in columns or cells to receive the respective code symbols, in accordance with the concepts to which they relate.

The task of devising the code system should be left for the user of the punch-card system in every case where general applicability is not being sought.

The more important of the special rules for code construction will be explained in the course of describing particular methods. But an absolutely fundamental requirement, whatever the method and whatever the code, is perfect unambiguity. Also, no code once established must ever be altered later. For this reason it is desirable, before a code is definitely established and the actual work is begun, to carry out a small run of trial codes whereby the coding system can be tested. Experience shows that codes built up purely from theory are hardly ever perfect. Finally, care should be taken, when making up a code, to leave a sufficient reserve of unused columns and holes in which later additions (not changes) can be accommodated.

It is after all these preparations have been completed that the actual work with punch-cards begins. The following general plan may be followed:

(1) Determining from the code schedule the pattern of holes to be punched corresponding to the indications that are to be recorded (coding).
(2) Marking or punching the cards (with holes, notches, slits, etc.).
(3) Manipulating the cards (by hand, sorting apparatus or punch-card machines).
(4) Interpreting the results in the reverse direction by reference to the code schedule (decoding).

In conclusion it should be stressed, if the fullest success is to be obtained in using punch-card methods, that coding requirements link up with the general necessity to have regard for the structure of the scientific (or commercial) organization as a whole.

(4) FIELDS OF APPLICATION FOR PUNCH-CARD METHODS

When the layman asks which punch-card method to adopt for his particular work the answer has of course to be based on existing experience. In what follows, therefore, some general advice will be given in this respect, having regard to the following considerations which need to be weighed in the choice of method:

(a) Nature of the work: research or documentation.

(b) Scope of the work or estimated number of cards needed.

(c) Available staff and financial expenditure.

Let us now deal with considerations (a) and (b) as inter-related.

(A) Research

Calculations of Very Extensive Scope

When the research involves extensive and complicated calculations, with which it has not previously been possible to cope, only electronic computers can be envisaged. Generally speaking, the case for using these becomes stronger according to the amount of material to be handled. The costs are very high but without such machines they would be still higher. Where it is not worth while having one's own installation, because the work will not be repetitive or for other reasons, such processing may be entrusted to appropriate firms under contract. Further information can be obtained from such firms.

Scope of Calculations Medium to Small

For moderate or small amounts of calculation the ordinary punch-card machines may be considered (such as multipliers, statistical machines, tabulators, according to the nature of the work). Here again contract arrangements are possible.

(B) Statistical and Correlational Work

Scope Large to Very Large (exceeding about 500 000 punch-cards)

A distinction needs to be drawn between work which is aimed at the establishment of statistics once and for all and work which is aimed at creating the means to deal with repeated problems and combinations of problems, or to go on accepting new material over an indeterminate period of time in the future. In either case, either the normal punch-card machinery or electronic computers may be chosen. If large numbers of cards are to be handled in the ordinary punch-card machines, what is called 'pre-sorting' may be adopted; by this is meant that the total number of cards is broken down into several runs, each able to be looked after by a different operator. For the same purpose, the stock of cards may be partially or completely duplicated.

Medium Scope (about 10 000 to 500 000 punch-cards)

Normal punch-card machines including statistical machines may be used, or, in suitable cases ranging from 10 000 to 100 000 cards, needle punch-cards in conjunction with the more elaborate kind of auxiliary apparatus or machines (as, for instance, the Keysort method). Needle punch-cards, being punched with holes beforehand, are always more expensive than machine punch-cards which are not punched before use: hence it should be appreciated that after a certain number of cards is exceeded the needle punch-card method becomes uneconomic as compared with the machine punch-card method. The present author, as well as others, believes the critical point to lie somewhere around 10 000 cards. He does not consider the needle punch-card method suitable for statistical applications save in exceptional cases.

Small Scope (under 10 000 cards)

Normal punch-card machines, or in exceptional cases needle punch-cards or visual punch-cards, may be used. In research work of his own the author obtained good results using about 2 000 edge-notched cards (see page 199) but in that instance the number of working units was limited to between 300 and 350 biological specimens, for each of which six notched cards were provided, so that manual statistical counting of the cards for the purpose of evaluating the results was still acceptable.

Kistermann and Ühlein (1957 a) have reported good results from using notched visual punched cards. They have written as follows:

It is not only in literature appraisal, but above all in the evaluation of research data, that we have been able to obtain very successful results from the combined cards. This system made it possible to answer questions which at the planning stage of the experiments were not even contemplated. For instance, when the complicated question: 'In the experimental denaturation using serum albumin in phosphate with $pH = 7.0$, ion concentration 0.1, temperature range between $65°$ and $75°$ C with an addition of sodium sulfite, was the reaction checked or accelerated?' was posed, the answer to it—'accelerated'—was found simply by picking out and superimposing eight cards.

It should, however, be remembered here that the working principle for visual punch-cards is the opposite of that for notched cards, and because of this the economic limit for using the former cannot be fixed at 10 000 cards. As exemplified above, the proper criterion does not depend on the statistics of large numbers but rather on the possibilities which this method offers for discovering correlations between more or less numerous particular characteristic features (a separate visual punch-card being provided for each such feature).

(C) Documentation

Reference Cards

Scope large to very large—Opinions vary greatly as to the minimum numbers which make it rational or necessary to instal electronic computers for the purpose of indicative documentation. The lowest suggested minimum of which the present author is aware is 50 000 and the highest 600 000 working units, each corresponding to one machine punch-card. Although not enough experience is available to be definite about this, it seems certain that for very large numbers of cards the substitution of electronic computers in documentation would be both possible and justifiable.

Contract work is suitable for purposes of documentation except at the initial stage of establishing the collection of cards, because a reference index composed of machine punch-cards or of a magnetic tape record is worth its cost only if continually in use. Hence installations of electronic computers are not worth considering for documentation unless an initial stock of data is already available in the appropriate form.

Medium scope (10000 to 500000 cards)—Either machine punch-cards using the ordinary machinery or visual punch-cards may be appropriate. Ühlein (1958) has written as follows in reference to a report by Berry about modern technical information services (documentation services) in the U.S.A.: 'Apparently, in most cases, the transition has been direct from the classical form of card index to mechanized documentation, whereas manual punch-card systems have seldom been adopted, their most frequent purpose being that of auxiliary card sets within self-contained branches of a subject.' His analysis of documentation services in 25 large firms and institutions in the U.S.A. shows clearly that in nearly all these cases the collections contain over 10000 punch-cards. This goes to confirm the general experience that in documentation centers of medium scope, where (by contrast with the card files of individual scientists) an order of magnitude exceeding 10000 cards is usual, machine punch-cards are the choice most often to be recommended.

It may also be of advantage to use, for purposes of documentation, punch-card machines which already are available for other purposes. This, however, is not necessarily an ideal solution, for all too often it may happen that the demands of documentation are made to take second place behind those of other users, such as the commercial staff for whom the machines were originally installed by the firm concerned. This may lead into a vicious circle, since obviously the output of documentation work will suffer and the conclusion which may be drawn is that machine punch-cards are not a rational or economic solution for that purpose.

The most effective use occurs, therefore, in large documentation centers possessing their own installations of machines for their exclusive use. (Here see page 150.)

It is not yet known whether visual punch-cards would continue to work well over a long period in a documentation center of medium scope; the author does not think so.

Small scope (under 10000 cards)—Needle punch-cards, visual punch-cards in exceptional cases, machine punch-cards (using ordinary punch-card machines) may be indicated.

According to some authors, the scope for applying needle punch-cards in documentation has a still lower limit, somewhere around 5000 or even 3000 cards. Others, however, place the limit higher at, say, 50000 cards. As a general indication, 10000 would still appear to be about the right limit, but it should be noted that this refers to a unified and closed collection of cards. When a user is concerned with several readily separable fields of subject matter he can, of course, set up a corresponding multiplicity of separate card collections.

The author, from his own experience and his general impressions, concludes that needle punch-cards and visual punch-cards are the ideal tools for the *individual* intellectual worker or for the accomplishment of some specific task, and that in these fields of application they will become more and more popular.   Apart from the fact that here the limit of 10000 cards will nearly always be high enough, needle punch-cards allow for a very individualistic arrangement, corresponding closely to what the person concerned wishes.   Further, they are 'desk methods' which call for no expenditure on machinery but which nevertheless secure the important advantages of punch-card technique.   On the other hand, it is only in very exceptional situations that machine punch-cards will be suitable for use in small numbers where reference documentation is concerned.

Evaluation Cards and Result Cards
(*1*) Scope large to very large (exceeding 500000 cards).   Machine punch-cards in ordinary machines, or electronic computers
(*2*) Medium scope (10000 to 500000 cards).   Machine punch-cards using normal machines, or in exceptional cases needle punch-cards with suitable auxiliary apparatus
(*3*) Small scope.   Machine punch-cards using normal machines, needle punch-cards, visual punch-cards.

Needle punch-cards in particular, but also machine punch-cards and visual punch-cards, have successfully been used for biological keys in the form of card collections instead of tables of limited extent.   (Here see page 259.)

As regards the possible requirements in staff and finance, the following summary may be made:

It is important to distinguish between cost and profitability.   An expensive method may be more rational or more profitable than a cheaper one if its output is larger and more varied.   Be this as it may, the best output is obviously of no interest if one is unable to pay what it costs.   Quite apart from electronic computers, ordinary punch-card machines are commonly assumed to be very expensive, but this is not always a valid generalization. It is true, indeed, that to buy a complete set of machines may be very expensive, but most often, whether for statistical research work or for well-planned documentation, it is possible to make do with only a few machines. Often, indeed, all that is needed is a simple sorting machine, such as is nowadays to be found in not a few medical clinics and other scientific institutes.   To hire this costs less than the salary of even the cheapest clerical staff.   Any additional work requiring the use of other machines can be carried out by the contractor services of the punch-card firms which exist in all the larger cities.

In this latter connection the 'mark-sensing' process, which makes it possible for the necessary arrangements to be made very rationally and cheaply, is of special interest.

Having regard primarily to what have been designated at (*a*) and (*b*) page 13 as on main considerations, the following spheres of application for the various methods can in general be recommended:

Where the principal activity will be that of automatic counting, calculating or writing (that is, tabulation): the machine punch-card method.

Where, frequently, all or some of the cards in which a given reference content has been punched will need to be duplicated: the machine punch-card method.

Where more or less extensive texts will have to be recorded on the cards, or where abstracts, illustrations or the like will need to be pasted or otherwise attached to them: the needle punch-card method.

Where a publisher decides to bring out a work of reference, or the like, in card instead of book form so as to be able to combine the advantages of book printing with those of the punch-card method (even for large editions): the needle punch-card method.

Where it is desired to avoid having to develop a classification and coding system, or where the main purpose is to be able to pick out those references which have features in common: the visual punch-card method.

Where it is desired, without great expense, to code the contents of a card file or of some existing linear arrangement (as, for instance, a collection of answers to a questionnaire) multidimensionally—that is to say, to code from the point of view of many aspects or features of interest at once, either originally or by a subsequent operation: the visual punch-card method.

Comparisons of working time and cost—It is a matter for congratulation that Herr Soeken, manager of the Deutsche Gesellschaft für Dokumentation (German Documentation Society), has set up a Committee for Basic Costs, through which it is proposed to collect experiences bearing upon those.

It is unfortunate, however, that up to the present only relatively few such comparisons of working time and cost for the punch-card method have been carried out. Doubtless the reason for this, as other authors have rightly stressed, is the cost of undertaking such investigations. Furthermore, it is intrinsically difficult to find a common denominator capable of lending any significance at all to the exceptionally numerous and varied possibilities that exist for using and applying the punch-card method. For instance, an appreciable change in the layout of the punching pattern (as by substituting a pattern which can be seen at a glance for one which lacks this quality) may be enough in itself to account for quite different working times in punching and checking. Impalpable factors such as this, which elude any quantitative evaluation, are very numerous, and they make it impossible for machine punch-card firms to give any general indications of cost or working time, either in their catalogs or in answer to personal enquiries. If any indications of this kind were to be given, they would in fact be very suspect and open to doubt.

Various writers, however, have provided calculations and comparisons as to working time and cost in reference to particular working procedures, clearly defined, like those which will now be quoted:

Woitschach (1954) has given output tables for the IBM machines, from which it is very easy to read off the machine output corresponding to different quantities of cards, taking other factors into account also.

Scherpenhuijsen (1957) has given us the following important general indications as regards documentation:

> Assume a collection of 1 000 reports whose sequence is quite arbitrary. If, now, a question is presented which has to be answered by reference to these reports, the whole thousand will have to be gone through according to the nature of the question. How long does that take? For a rough sorting by title we can allow two seconds per report, which means 33 minutes for the thousand reports. At the end of that time we shall have, say, twenty reports which are the most likely to contain the answer to the question. These now have to be looked through somewhat more carefully. How much time that process will take depends on how detailed the question is; let us assume three minutes each, or another hour altogether. In other words, we have needed an hour and a half per question to sort out the whole heap.

> If, on the other hand, we decided to make a catalog of the reports, we should need, say, ten minutes for classifying each of them (leaving out of account the time required for establishing and maintaining the classification system) and perhaps half as long again for writing the catalog cards. That makes fifteen minutes for each report plus the time for arranging the cards in the file and other administrative work; let us say twenty minutes altogether.

> Thus 330 hours will have been needed to dispose of the 1 000 reports, and 220 questions will have had to be answered before the cost of the cataloging work will have been paid off.

> Here the time needed for searching the catalog has not been counted. On the other hand, no account has been taken of the fact that the existence of a catalog will have made it possible to refer to those reports which happened to be out on loan at the times the questions were dealt with, nor of the necessity that may exist for being able to answer any question quickly—within, say, one hour. It follows that, to take a rational view of the matter, one must decide beforehand the extent that heavy overhead costs are acceptable as the price of a catalog.

Thorne calculates the efficiency of a documentation system as follows

$$\eta = A/100 - (PN + RQ)/SCQ$$

wherein η is the efficiency defined as cost of a given system divided by the cost of obtaining the same results without having any system.

In this formula, A denotes the percentage of questions answered successfully, P the cost per document for establishing the catalog, N the annual number of documents received, R the cost of answering one question, Q the number of questions answered, S the average cost of each hand-sorted document and C the total number of documents.

Since A is the percentage of questions that could be answered from the catalog, failure occurs in $(100 - A)$ questions and the answers to these must be found by hand sorting, the cost of which is

$$SC\,(100 - A)$$

so that the cost of answering the whole hundred questions is

$$100\,R + SC\,(100 - A)$$

This corresponds annually to

$$RQ + SCQ\,(100 - A)/100$$

and the total annual costs, including the establishment of the catalog, amount to

$$PN + RQ + SCQ\,(100 - A)/100$$

From the definition of η it follows that

$$\eta = \{SCQ - PN - RQ - SCQ\,(100 - A)/100\}/SCQ$$
$$= A/100 - (PN + RQ)/SCQ$$

In the case here assumed, the question arises how big Q has to be in order to make the cost SCQ of hand sorting and the cost of establishing and searching in the catalog equal to $PC + RQ$. Then

$$SCQ = PC + RQ$$
$$1{\cdot}5\,Q = 330 + RQ$$
or
$$Q = 330/(1{\cdot}5 - R)$$

Q therefore is a minimum when R is a minimum, meaning when the cost of searching the catalog is lowest. For $R = 0$ we have $Q = 220$. If, now, it is desired to keep the catalog cost $PC + RQ$ low in comparison with the hand-sorting cost SCQ, then P and R must be kept low. Moreover, with a large number of questions Q, the left side of the equation increases more quickly than the right side.

The value of a much-used catalog is therefore obvious, but if this condition cannot be counted upon it is well to think twice before establishing a catalog.

For a large, long-established collection, $N < C$; hence the fraction N/C will be of low value and the work of keeping up the catalog will have a high efficiency.

What has been said here on the subject of catalogs in general applies, of course, still more to the introduction of punch-cards. In the author's opinion, however, there is an aspect of the matter which has not been considered. Is it really possible to say beforehand whether a documentation system will be sufficiently used or not? Is it not the case, rather, that the fact of having assimilated the literature will provide incentive to make more use of it?

For a comparative time study of different methods applied to the documentation of patents we are indebted to Danilof (1957) from whose work the following table is reproduced.

C

Table 1. Comparison of methods for the documentation of 10 000 patents relating to synthetic materials.

	Subjects noted per hour	Hours of preparatory work	Hours of searching		
			One subject	Two subjects	Three or more subjects
Ordinary DIN A 6 (4⅛ in × 5¾ in.) index cards	4	25 000	26	35	Up to 70
DIN A 5 (5⅞ in. × 8¼ in.) edge-notched cards with two rows of holes, using needles or a simple selecting device	20	23 500	14	12	Under 10
DIN A 5 (5⅞ in. × 8¼ in.) punched slitted cards with ten rows of holes, using electrically vibrated selecting device	22	26 000	10	9	Under 7·5.
80-column machine punch-cards, using old (1952) type of card sorter	40	17 000	2·3	5·1	Up to 19·8
80-column machine punch-cards, using newer type of card sorter	40	17 000	0·5	1·1	Up to 5·6
80-column machine punch-cards	40	17 000	0·5	1·2	Up to 6·2
Electronic statistical machine IBM 101	(30)	(14 000)	(0·25)	(0·5)	(Up to 2·9)
80-column machine punch-cards with electronic computer IBM 650	40	17 000	0·25	0·25	0·25

Jans (1956) has given accurate indications as to the profitability of the mark-sensing method:

The question of cost is by no means unimportant when deciding in favor of the mark-sensing method, and in support of this statement a few details may be of interest. In this context the overhead cost and the time involved in establishing the punching layout or "counting sheets" can be disregarded, seeing that an electrotype for printing the mark-sensing cards (even with the code pre-printed, as in our own case) costs no more than one for printing any other individually designed layout of a punch-card—namely about 100 German Marks—and this is a once-only cost for the electrotype, which saves any cost for printing the punched cards.

The data can then be set out as follows:

Hourly output of a girl punching in 54 columns . . . . . . 125 cards

Hence in 8 hours she will punch a total of . 1 000 cards

The same amount of time will be required for checking.

For the mark-sensing of 27 columns, the hourly output of the machine (Type 513 or 519) is . . . . . . 6 000 card passes

Which, having to be repeated for the marks
made on the reverse side of the cards in
order to cover the 54 columns, is reduced to   3 000 card passes
Whereas manual punching of 54 columns in
1 000 cards would cost .   .   .   .   70.80 DM*
To which must be added the same allowance
of time for checking   .   .   .   .   70.80 DM

                                             141.60

     The same output from a mark-sensing
machine in one hour, whereby 27 of the mark-
sensing columns are sensed from the pencil
marks and are automatically punched, together with checking for double punchings
and empty columns, would cost .   .   .   12 DM
this amount being derived from the fact that the machine can sense the
marks on both sides of the cards and punch and check them at the rate
of 3 000 an hour.

     It follows therefore, that these procedures alone secure the con-
siderable reduction in cost from 141.60 to 12 DM per 1 000 cards.

     These calculations, and also the practicability of so using double-
sided mark-sensing cards, are based on personal information received
from Arnhold of the Urological Hospital in Munich. He found, in
evaluating 5 000 cards, only 20 rejects and these were the result of
faulty marking by the hospital physicians (for instance, double
marking).

     In this connection it may be remarked further that the Statistische
Landesamt (Government Statistical Office) in Munich has, since 1950,
been computing its migration statistics very satisfactorily by means of
the mark-sensing process. In some large industrial undertakings (such
as, for instance, the Volkswagen automobile works) even the accounting
(e.g. of the payroll) is carried out by the mark-sensing process. Since
meticulous accuracy is a fundamental requirement in accounting work
it should be clear that any doubts entertained as to the accurate
working of the mark-sensing process must be purely theoretical.

     What, now, are the costs for hand punching and checking if hired
machines are used on one's own premises?

Monthly hire of type 011 punching machine   31 DM
Monthly hire of type 210 checking machine   33   ,,
Staff costs (not including overheads) .   .   300   ,,

                                     364   ,,

Assuming a monthly output of 10 000 cards in
20 working days, the total costs for processing
1 000 cards corresponds to   .   .   .   36.40 ,,
which still is 24.40 German Marks more expensive than IBM mark-
sensing work for the same number of cards.

* DM (German Mark) = 24 U.S. cents = 1s. 8d.

Hörnicke (1956) has given the following comparison between the use of ordinary index cards and edge-notched cards:

(*i*) *Bulk*—Measurements of the old and the new card collections show that the edge-notched cards take up, in the trays, about half as much space again as compared with ordinary index cards. It is true that immediately after the conversion the set of cards becomes nearly three times as deep as it originally was, because the existing collection is incorporated in the new one and the edge-notched cards take up about 55 per cent more space through having the others pasted on to them. Later, however, when only unpasted cards are taken in, this increase is cancelled out.

The format of the cards being twice as large—as may usually be assumed in order to provide space for writing and coding—the volume of the card collection is multiplied by three.

The biggest increase is in weight. Two hundred ordinary index cards weigh 190 grammes, whereas 200 edge-notched cards weigh 1 260 grammes, which is 6·6 times as much. Deducting, however, the weight of the index which is no longer required, the set of edge-notched cards weighs 5·7 times as much as the ordinary cards. This proportion holds good even with large numbers of cards, because when ordinary cards are used the index has to grow concurrently.

(*ii*) *Costs*—The basic establishment costs of the two systems, in German Marks, may be compared as follows:

Ordinary card file	DM	Edge-notched cards	DM	Ratio
2 trays for the visible		Edge-notched cards		
index . .	31.00	edge-punch .	22.50	
		2 sorting needles .	2.00	
	31.00		24.50	1 : 0.8

The edge-notched cards are, however, considerably more expensive than paper slips plus guide cards:

1 000 slips . .	10.00	1 000 edge-notched	63.00	1 : 6.3
100 guide cards .	4.25			
	14.25		63.00	1 : 4.7

Thus the total cost weighs more heavily against the edge-notched cards in proportion as the collection grows in size.

(*iii*) *Working time.*—The procedures described above involve ten operations in the case of the ordinary cards as against nine in the case of the edge-notched cards. Preparing and coding the indications must, in either case, be done by the scientific worker himself but the remaining operations can, if so desired, be carried out by clerical helpers.

The comparative working times required with the two kinds of card sets are contrasted below, these being averages for between 250 and 500 slips or cards. As they depend on the task in hand, they cannot be taken as generally valid. Each card requires the following amount of time:

Operation	Ordinary card file	Edge-notched cards	Ratio
Coding	26·2 sec.	27 sec. ⎫	
Notching	—	19 sec. ⎭	0·6 : 1
Alphabetical pre-arrangement	6·25 sec.	1·32 sec.	4·7 : 1
Filing	30·2 sec.	1·24 sec.	24·4 : 1
Total	62·65 sec.	48·56 sec.	1·3 : 1

It will be seen that, as regards establishing the collection, the edge-notched cards save only a little time as compared with an ordinary card index. This saving becomes quite insignificant when it is remembered that the varying amount of time needed for writing out the title and reference does not depend on which system is used. The only saving is due to the edge-notched cards not needing detailed alphabetical arrangement. On the other hand, the edge-notched cards prove far more advantageous for searching. Hitherto, when searching in an ordinary card index, it has been necessary after having found the wanted keyword to examine every one of the author cards so marked, in order to find out whether any of them contained it in the required combination with others. Because of its limited capacity for combination, an ordinary index file leads to more misses than hits, whereas a set of edge-notched cards delivers automatically whichever of them correspond to any desired combination of keywords; few unwanted cards come out and these can quickly be put back.

(*iv*) *Output and adaptability*—The real criterion consists of qualitative differences between the systems. These are difficult to express numerically but the following points deserve particular mention:

(1) The possibility, which edge-notched cards provide, for searching out combinations of keywords which had not been and could not have been thought of at the time of coding. Because of this, searching problems can be solved which would be impossible using an ordinary card file. Such a system, allowing the keywords to be combined in the desired way for the first time during the actual searching operation, approximates more closely to the associative capacity of the human brain than any two-dimensional, hierarchical system can do. Thereby it makes the work easier.

(2) Immunity of the edge-notched card collection from becoming disorganized. An ordinary card file only works on condition that strict order is maintained within it, which calls for unremitting care and attention. Misfiling can never be completely prevented and the only safeguard against this lies in regular inspection of the whole set, for which experience shows there is never enough time to spare. On the other hand, edge-notched cards can be in any order, yet each of them remains findable. Of course the efficiency of a card file can be considerably increased by numerous aids such as tabs and steps, signals, colored markings, etc.; but all this involves further care and attention in

arrangement and handling. Consequently, the card file no longer meets the purpose it is intended to serve as an aid to scientific work; for what the worker is entitled to expect from such an aid is that it should relieve him of secondary jobs and allow him to concentrate on his scientific task. The set of edge-notched cards does meet this requirement, for it produces the same result without calling for attentiveness and additional labor to arrange and maintain the cards in a particular sequence.

Indications of the working times using visual punched cards have been given in a paper by Knappe (1956):

In order to consider the economy of the visual punched card method, data are needed as to the amount of work involved in recording a document, taking into account only work connected with the punching

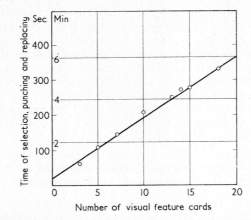

FIG. 2. Time taken to pick out, punch and replace visual or feature-punched cards (from Knappe, 1956).

operation. The time required for this increases approximately in direct proportion to the number of features of interest that are to be recorded. Fig. 2 is a diagram showing the time taken to punch the same position in several visual punched-cards, related to the number of such cards, these being taken from an alphabetically arranged file covering some 1 300 features. The working operations involved are those of selecting the required cards, superimposing those selected, punching them in a single operation and then putting them back at their places in the file. It can be concluded that when the number of features is large this method is economical in labor, as compared with filing multiple copies of literature cards under different headings in an ordinary card file. On the other hand, it must not be forgotten that this last makes possible the most efficient searching if only a single feature is being sought, which is not the case using any other punched card method.

should not be stored in a damp or hot room or close to heating apparatus. If unfavorable conditions have caused the cards to take up an excess of humidity they must be stored for some weeks in a dry room with a temperature of 17° to 23° C so as to regain their normal properties. Punch-cards for which the manufacturers require various delivery times should always be ordered long enough in advance to avoid their having to be used whilst fresh from printing. A preliminary storage of six to eight weeks in the place where they will be used is recommended.

Punch-cards are delivered in cardboard boxes containing 2000. The boxes should be stored standing on end so that the punch-cards will lie in contact over their whole surfaces and their own weight will reduce their warping to a minimum. The upper and lower edges of every card require particular care because it is here that the very accurately adjusted grips of the punch-card machines have to catch hold of them; consequently any damage to these edges must be avoided at all costs. Practical experience has shown that such damage may occur particularly if finger rings are worn by staff handling the punch-cards or when large packs of the cards are being shaken or knocked down to bring them into coverage of one another. Also it is not advisable to bind small or large packs of punch-cards with rubber bands, or in any other way as this is particularly liable to damage the long edges (Scheele, 1958 a).

It may be inferred from these considerations, and is shown by practical experience, that it would be quite impossible to overstress the fact that a punch-card is something relatively sensitive. Simple as it may appear, the card is fundamental to the whole technique. Therefore a strong warning should be uttered against doing anything to this delicate mechanical element which might produce any kind of mechanical change in the cards. This warning applies, for instance, to the introduction of film windows in the cards or to sensitizing them for the purpose of contact reproduction. Such treatments impair the proper function of the cards, rendering them appreciably more liable to derangements than others. Whenever, as a result of this, particularly in a sorting machine, a 'card salad' is produced, at least ten to twenty cards are rendered unusable. Normally this may not be very serious, as they can either be replaced by means of a card copier or can quickly be re-punched; but if the cards in question carry film windows or other additional unpunched indications, their replacement becomes considerably more difficult and troublesome. Finally, and most important, it should not be forgotten that a normal machine punch-card is extraordinarily cheap (0.7 to 0.8 of a Pfennig; or under one cent). Sensitized cards or those provided with film windows cost several times as much as others, and since it usually is not economic to introduce the punch-card method unless large numbers of cards are involved, these questions of cost play an important part. For such reasons it is best to proceed on the principle, when using machine punch-cards, that all indications to be recorded on them should be punched. This makes it always possible for damaged cards to be automatically duplicated, so that there is never any risk of the cards having to be worked upon by hand instead of put through the machines.   The only exception that should ever be made to this rule is when a duplicate set of cards is mainly or entirely withdrawn from machine working, for use as an ordinary card file.   When this is done, any desired notes or indications may of course be written by hand or with a typewriter on the duplicate cards, and under those conditions sensitizing them for reproduction might be a practical proposition.

Punch-Card Machines

All punch-card machines, quite regardless of their particular manufacturers, can be divided into a few large groups if the criterion adopted is that of the functions they perform, for often in that case the machines produced by different firms differ only in the ways that the various functions are combined with one another.

Punching and verifying machines—This is a heading under which all those machines may be grouped in which any kind of punching operation is either performed or checked.   It comprises, first of all, various kinds of punch—numerical, alphabetical, etc.—and devices for ascertaining that the punching has been done correctly, but the same group includes duplicating machines and automatic mark-sensing machines as well as auxiliary devices such as the adding punch.

Classifying machines—A second group is formed by classifying machines. These play a specially important part in the method as a whole.   The group may be made to include both straightforward sorting machines and their auxiliary devices as well as machines which compare the indications on the cards such as the collator; the function of these machines, in all cases, being that of arranging the punched cards in a sequence.

Printing machines—Another category is that of printing machines, which includes tabulators and punch-to-print 'interpreters'.   The machines in question perform either (like the last-mentioned) a purely printing function or they form part of assemblies (like the first-mentioned) whereby arithmetical problems can be solved, but they have no sorting function (Scheele, 1958).   Printing machines, whatever the system, can print only Arabic numerals and capital letters with a few additional signs.   It is possible indeed to change the type bars or type wheels so as to provide special symbols, but the total number of symbols which can be provided is limited so those which have been replaced are no longer available, which is a fact needing to be borne in mind as regards notation.

In reference to these printing machines, it is further to be remarked that one should not fall into the error of using them to record long passages of running text.   Punch-cards are not suitable for this and tabulating machines are too expensive for the purpose.   In using punch-card machines, the possibility of printing letters is obviously to be looked upon only as an auxiliary function and never as the main purpose.   Names, terms and other short indications which have some relation to the other contents of the cards can, for instance, be printed on them, but even to print titles of publications for purposes of documentation may be a matter of some considerable difficulty because the wording usually is too long to be accommodated on a single card (here see also page 240).   In fact I am inclined to regard any proposal to print long texts on punch-cards, with a view perhaps to reproducing them by that means, as a distortion of the proper purpose of these cards.

Calculating machines—This is the last group. They merge directly into modern types of large-scale computers which, as is well known, have evolved in the main from the punch-card method.   It is a common feature of all computing machines that they have to be 'fed' with punch-cards, from which they 'read off' the data to be used in computation.   Often, too, a punching function is combined with the computing function, and the values computed are then additionally punched in the original cards.

Here it may perhaps be pertinent to say a word as to why punch-cards have by no means lost their significance in large-scale computers ('electronic brains') and, as far as one can see, are unlikely to lose it in the future.   A machine, however complicated, ultimately has to be served by a human being, and even in computer installations there are certain problems which have, in one way or another, to be put into the machines by people.   That is to say, there is needed some kind of connecting medium between man and machine; and this intermediary role is one which the punch-card, for the following reasons, is especially suited to fulfil:

(*a*) Because, using the mark-sensing method, the card can be prepared by a person at his desk without the need for any special mechanical aid, and later can also be incorporated into an ordinary card file.

(*b*) Because, on the other hand, the punch-card can be used as an inexpensive 'external memory' serving as the input-output unit for a large computer working quickly and effectively.

(*c*) Because, finally, it makes possible a transition and connection between normal punch-card machines and large computers.

The four groups mentioned above suffice to represent the fundamental functions of all punch-card machines, namely: *punching and verifying*, *arranging in order*, *printing* and *calculating*.   But, as already explained, each machine need not necessarily be confined to only one of these functions. Often several different functions may be combined.   Obviously no attempt can be made in the following remarks to comprehend all kinds of punch-card machines and all the tasks to which they can be applied, for that would amount to copying out numerous manufacturers' catalogs.   Only the fundamental types in each group can be dealt with here, and readers especially interested in details of the various special types can most easily satisfy this interest by referring to the catalogs and leaflets which the firms concerned will gladly supply free of charge.

(B) The IBM System

The firm concerned is the International Business Machine Corporation. The machines may be either hired or bought.   They work on the electrical or electronic sensing principle as the case may be.

IBM punch-cards are divided into 80 vertical columns and 12 horizontal lines. Each intersection between these coordinates corresponds to one punching position, meaning a place in the card where one hole can be punched, so that the IBM punch-card has 960 punching positions. The holes used are rectangular (see Fig. 5). For normal uses, such as accounting and the like, particular numbers and letters are associated with particular punching positions or combinations of these. This statement applies to all punch-card machines. Apart from numbers and letters, other attributions or combinations of holes can be made to correspond with particular signs such as an asterisk, comma, etc., but these cannot be applied in all the

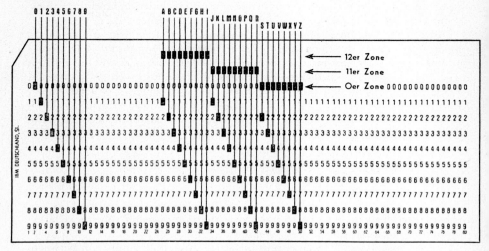

Fig. 5. Explanation of punching numbers and letters in the IBM card by using an 'internal code.' (IBM.)

machines, although special signs can be introduced, for instance in tabulating machines, to meet requirements in certain cases.

The attribution of numerals is determined in such a way that every column, beginning from the top, will record any of the numbers 0 to 9, each hole in a punching position within any given column corresponding to one numeral, so that normally only one hole has to be punched in each column to indicate a number. Each of the 26 letters of the alphabet can be punched by utilizing a combination of two holes in one column, for which purpose there are two additional punching positions in the line above the '0'. These additional holes do not—as might mistakenly be supposed from the fact that they are marked 11 and 12—have any numerical significance of their own, but either of them and also the '0' can be punched in combination with one of the holes numbered 1–9 in the same column, for the purpose of indicating a letter of the alphabet. The punching combinations adopted in the IBM system to cover the various letters of the alphabet are shown in Fig. 5. (*Umlaute* as used in German on certain letters cannot be independently represented, but must be indicated by combinations of separate letters).

'Mark sensing' has a special significance. The mark-sensing cards, specially overprinted, can be marked by hand at a desk for later automatic punching. The front and back of such cards, as in Fig. 6a and 6b, have small cells printed on them askew to serve for making pencil or special ink marks. In some designs of card these cells are horizontal but that arrangement has not been found so advantageous for quick work. The cards are so printed as to avoid any risk of the marks made between the punching lines running into one another in adjacent columns. In the automatic mark-sensing punches these marks can be sensed electrically, a weak current being made to flow through the graphite or special electrographic ink which was used for marking and this current being picked up by the sensing brushes, electronically amplified and used to actuate the required punching operation. Thereby all those working operations which otherwise would have to be done by hand punch and proving machine can be omitted, for the automatic mark-sensing machine can also be made to check the punching (subject, however, to there being no multiple punching in any one column). As appears in Fig. 6, the marks must be made of a certain length if undefective sensing is to be ensured, this length corresponding to the width of three columns so that each marking column corresponds to three punching columns. For this reason there is room for only 27 marking columns on one side of a punch-card. If the back of the card is used as well as the front there is room for a maximum of 54 marking columns and in this case the cards must be passed through the automatic mark-sensing machine twice over, once for the front and once for the back. Hence at most 54 of the 80 punching columns provided on a punch-card can be subjected to the mark-sensing process and the remaining 26 columns can be punched only by the use of a hand punch.

As shown in the illustrations, the additional holes 11 and 12 can, however, be marked on the mark-sensing cards and, by combinations of holes 0, 11 or 12 with any of the holes 1 to 9, letters too can be thus expressed (each column corresponding to one letter). From the illustration it may be seen, in the first mark-sensing column, which combinations of holes correspond to which of the letters. Above hole 12 is printed 'links' (left), above hole 11 'mitte' (middle) and above hole 0 'rechts' (right). Next to hole 1 are the letters A and J and next to each of the holes 2 to 9 are three of the remaining letters of the alphabet. In order to obtain a 'left' letter the corresponding punch mark must be combined with one in position 12; in order to obtain a 'middle' letter it must be combined with one in position 11, and for a 'right' letter with position 0. In any given column the letter A, for instance, is marked in positions 1 and 12, J in positions 1 and 11, B in positions 2 and 12, K in positions 2 and 11, S in positions 2 and 0 and so on. (For technical reasons, the additional punching position 12 *must not* be marked in the first column on the front or back of the card; that is to say, in columns 1 and 28 the only additional punching position that can be used is 11.)

The automatic mark-sensing punch includes a changeable plugboard

(6a = front of card)

34

(6b = back of card)

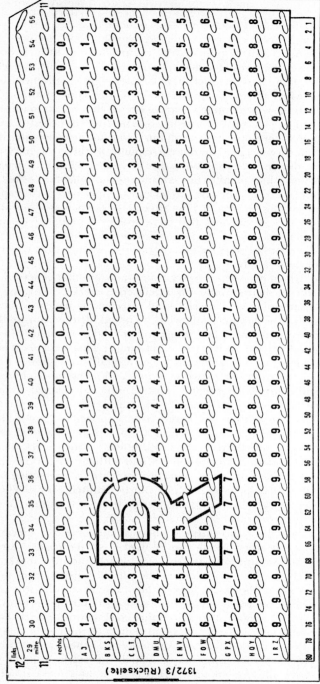

Fig. 6. IBM marking card for use with all mark-sensing applications. For certain reasons the numbers of the marking columns as here designed by the author range from 2 to 55.

which makes it possible to transfer the punching as marked in any given column of the cards to any other column instead.   For instance, the marks made in column 5 can be punched by the machine in any of the columns 1 to 80.   This is the basis of a checking procedure tried out by Steidle (and described by him orally) which can be used—provided there is enough room—even when there are several holes in the same column.   For this purpose, the mark-sensing punch is so connected that marks made in column 1 are punched in column 2; those in column 2 are punched in column 5; those in column 3 are punched in column 8 and so on, following the scheme $3 . n - 1$.   Since a marking column corresponds to three ordinary punching columns, this device brings the holes directly underneath the corresponding pencil marks, enabling them to be very simply and quickly checked.

There is on record a large body of technical experience in the application of the mark-sensing process.   This process is particularly suitable when several holes have to be punched in a single column, or when various unrelated punchings have to be distributed over the whole card as described in Part III here for the purpose of a literature reference card collection (the 'punching pattern' method).

One detail which has been learned from practice is that generally speaking it is better to use electrographic ink than pencil marks.   This ink requires, however, the adoption of a special kind of reservoir pen and the working instructions must be carefully followed.   The ink dries very rapidly, so the reservoir pen must not as with ordinary ink be held continuously in the hand when not actually in use for writing or marking.   This being so, it is essential to use a stand for the pen, having as its base a small damp sponge to keep the pen damp in the intervals between writing.   Furthermore, both the pen and the stand must be thoroughly washed out and cleaned from time to time.   Some of these special instructions may seem slightly pedantic and ridiculous, but the author has found from experience that if this bit of pedantry and the small inconveniences are accepted very good results can be obtained using the electrographic ink holder.   Such work, however, is only rational if undertaken continuously and without long interruptions.

In case a mistake is made in marking the cards a correcting varnish is available with which the wrong marks can be painted over.   The ink and all accessories can be obtained from the firm of Günther Wagner in Hannover.

In using a pencil for this purpose—here again there is a special electro-graphic pencil, but other pencils can be used if not too hard—care must be taken to have a hard and smooth base over which to do the marking.   The most suitable base is a glass plate.   The author's experience in marking with a pencil has not, however, been as favorable as in using the ink.   The pencil marks must always be made firmly enough and the cards in question should be used to operate the automatic mark-sensing punch as soon as possible after marking in order to avoid fading of the pencil marks in the meantime.   Pencil marks offer the advantage that they can be rubbed out.

In every case, whether using ink or pencil, the marks must be firm and thick and, above all, long enough.   It is better that a mark should extend somewhat beyond the intended field than the contrary, for marks which are too short cannot be correctly punched. Experience has shown that it is not expedient to make more than five mark-sensing holes close to one another on the same line—a case which is most likely to arise when for nstance the absence of any indication is always to be punched 0—for it has been found that the automatic mark-sensing punch does not always respond perfectly to a series of marks if they are closely aligned.

Several experienced users of the punch-card method, such as Hosemann, have preferred generally not to utilize the mark-sensing system to its full extent in marking all possible indications, but to use it only for supplementary indications added to the cards later. Likewise the 'punching pattern' system, developed by the present author for the purposes of documentation, never involves using the whole range of mark-sensing possibilities at the same time. Here, as in other aspects of punch-card work, it is a good rule that the full theoretical possibilities of the method should not be exploited to the utmost limit.

The principle of dual cards has given good results in conjunction both with ordinary punch-cards and particularly with mark-sensing cards. In this case the indications to be punched are entered in the writing field on the cards themselves, which makes it possible for the punching clerk to read them off directly during the punching operation. In the mark-sensing card which appears in Fig. 6 all the writing fields along the lower edge are printed as numbered cells, these cells corresponding to the columns 55 to 80 which cannot be used for automatic mark-sensing. In them are entered the numerals or letters which the punching clerk should punch using an ordinary punching machine. The latter is so constructed that the indications in the cells can be read off and directly punched even after the cards have been otherwise processed.

IBM Punches

Description—See Fig. 7 a, b. Numerals and letters are struck on a keyboard similar to that of a typewriter which causes the corresponding holes to be punched. Each time a key is struck and a hole is punched the carriage holding the card moves automatically one column sideways. There are numerical punches which can only punch numerals and alphabetical punches which can punch both numerals and letters.

A great variety of punching machines exists, ranging from the simple magnetic or 'key punch', as it is called, into which the cards are fed by hand, to complicated account-balancing key punches or book-keeping machines which are combined with various other devices. One possibility provided by the more complicated types of punch which calls for special mention is that of skipping certain of the columns automatically. Another important unit available is a reproducing device, with the help of which the contents of one punched card can be transferred to another card in whole or in part. Cards which have accidentally run together, or have otherwise been damaged, can quickly be duplicated in such a punch if no card duplicator is available.

Finally, mention should be made also of what is called the printing punch, which prints the indications in ordinary lettering along the top edge of the card at the same time as punching them in the body of the card. In some cases this may save having to instal a punch-card translator. Apart from

FIG. 7a.   IBM magnetic punch for numerals.

that, it simplifies checking the cards. There also exist punches which provide for transition from punched paper tapes to punch-cards or vice versa. One of the newest developments is the telepunch, which corresponds to the teleprinter.

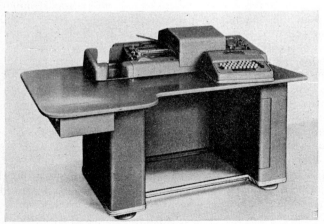

FIG. 7b.   IBM alphabetical punch for numerals and letters.

Rate of output—As punches are the only machines used in the punch-card method which are not entirely automatic their output depends on the rate at which the punching clerk can work. Data for this vary between 60 and 90 cards an hour for the punching of all 80 columns. Automatic duplication is done at the rate of 17 columns a second.

IBM Verifiers

These machines serve to check the finished punched card for correct punching. Their construction and working is similar to that of the punches. The punched indications read off from the punching plan are once again gone over on a keyboard and in the case of an error the machine stops so that the operator is made aware of it.

IBM Summary Punches

This term is applied to ancillary machines which can be electrically connected to a tabulating machine. They serve to punch the results given by the tabulating machine automatically in what are called dual cards which take the place of many separate cards in the later processing.

IBM Reproducers

Description—These are a form of duplicating machine whereby the indications punched in a group of cards can be wholly or partially transferred to another group of cards. An electrical connecting panel makes it possible for any given column on the mother cards to be so connected with any given column in the daughter cards that the contents as a whole can be completely 'reconstructed' on any desired plan. In the same way, it is also possible to arrange for certain indications which are recorded on two different groups of cards to be brought together into a single group. All the operations described above are known as 'reproducing'.

Another working possibility is what is known as gang punching whereby all or part of the indications on a single card are transferred at one time to as many other cards as is desired, thereby producing a corresponding number of duplicates.

Reproducing and gang punching can also be combined. All operations performed by the machine can also be automatically checked, with the exception of multiple punching in one and the same column, and in this last case the checking portion of the machine can be switched out. The card copier can also be supplied so as to be able to operate as a mark-sensing machine on the principle already described in detail when discussing IBM punch-card equipment (see page 33).

A further possibility is the use of the summary punch in combination with a tabulating machine. Finally, there exist card copiers able to print numerals, which are specially advantageous when punched cards are later to be used as an ordinary card file. With this form of printing the numerals which have been punched are printed in large size crossways up the left-hand edge of the card.

The output is 6000 cards an hour regardless of the number of columns to be punched.

IBM Classifying Machines—Sorting

Description—The object of classifying machines is to arrange punched cards in a pre-determined sequence or to pick out wanted cards from a collection. In the chapter on terminology these two functions, which require to be sharply distinguished from one another, were designated respectively as classification and selecting.

In commercial and statistical work, which hitherto have predominated among the applications of punch-cards, classifying has been the main purpose almost exclusively, whereas in documentation it is selecting which becomes the more significant. There are certain accessories to classifying machines, such as number seekers and multiple column scanners, which meet this need. In all types of classifying machines, the cards pass one by one from a 'card bed' automatically under electrical sensing brushes and thence through electromechanical guides into different pockets. The operation is always column by column, which means that a separate passage of the cards through the classifier is needed for each column, whereas in the selecting operation the accessories make it possible for ten columns to be dealt with in one single pass. The column to be sensed is determined by setting a handle. Since every column contains 12 punching positions, the classifier has 12 numbered pockets arranged in the same sequence. Pocket 9, which corresponds to technically the highest number, is the one farthest away from where the cards are fed into the classifying machine and pocket 12 is the one nearest to this. Besides these numbered pockets the sorting machine must have also what is called a reject pocket immediately next to where the cards are fed in, which receives all those cards which have not been punched in the particular column that is being sorted. If the sorting is to be by letters instead of by numbers the cards having two holes punched in each column must be passed through the machine twice over. The fastest IBM sorting machine (Type 083) allows, however, the use of accessory devices whereby alphabetical sorting is simplified. As will already be clear from the description up to this point, punched cards to be sorted numerically must have only one hole in each column and cards for sorting by letter two holes in each column, corresponding to the combinations which represent the respective letters; this indeed is evident from the fact that every card being sorted can fall into only one pocket and not into two at the same time. If, however, a card has several holes in any given column it will fall into the pocket which corresponds to the highest numbered hole, number 9 being reckoned for this purpose as the highest whilst 0, 11 and 12 rank lowest. In other words, the card falls into whichever pocket is farthest away from where the cards are fed in. In special cases, the design of the machine can be technically altered so as to allow packs of cards to be inserted in the machine face downward, thereby reversing the sequence in which the columns will be sensed; but then the designations of the pockets no longer hold good. The present author does not advise this complication.

When, as in documentation work, multiple punchings in the same column are to be used, the function to be performed is that of selection only. The columns with multiple punchings can be dealt with only in a classifier and in no other kind of machine. Sorting machines give the possibility of handling columns with multiple punchings as well as carrying out related procedures and cutting out any desired numbers of sorting pockets. If it is

magnetic core storage, magnetic drums or magnetic plate storage. The input and output, as already explained above, is by way of ordinary punched cards. These and the other named types of storage can be combined with one another. Their contents, that is to say the data stored in them, can be transferred from the one to the other at will. For instance, the indications carried by a fully punched card with 80 columns can be transferred to 1 cm length of magnetic tape, the recoding necessary for this purpose being carried out by the machines automatically. A reel of magnetic tape about 750 m long can store 4·5 million characters. Allowing for the necessary spaces between these, the contents of some 60 000 fully punched 80-column punched cards can be carried on one such length of tape. In one second 15 000 characters can be sensed or extracted. The fastest of these machines complete each step in a computation in something of the order of one millionth of a second. Walther cites the following times for the sake of comparison, relating to a particular problem:

Human computer . . . . 30 days
Electromechanical punch-card installation 6 days
Electronic punch-card installation . . 3 hours
BESK automatic computer . . . 5 minutes

The decisive preliminary work, in starting to use a large computer, is what is called the programming. By this is meant establishing the instructions which the machine is automatically to carry out one after another. To give details of this would take us too far.

Large computers can also have certain types of ordinary punched card machines, such as tabulators and punches, connected to them.

(C) The Bull System

Suppliers

Exacta-Continental Büromaschinenwerke G.m.b.H., Pfälzischer Ring 100, Köln-Deutz. The Bull machines may be either hired or bought. They operate on the electrical or on the electronic sensing principle.

Bull Punched Cards

These cards have the same size and layout as the corresponding IBM cards. Like them, they have 80 columns with 12 lines, giving 960 punching positions. The holes are rectangular. The punching positions have numerals attributed to them in the same way as IBM cards, but the combinations of holes for letters is different. This is shown in Fig. 8.

The Bull system also provides for a mark-sensing method, but here this takes a somewhat different form. The Bull mark-sensing card has 20 marking columns in its right-hand half (Fig. 9). Each marking position is formed of a rectangular cell in which the appropriate numeral is printed in dots, whereby any of the digits from 0 to 9 and the supplementary punching position 11 can be marked in each column. The left-hand half of the Bull cards can also be printed with numerical columns, so that a 40-column mark-sensing card is available. As in the IBM system, these cards must, however, be passed through the mark-sensing automatic machine twice over, once for the 20 columns in the right-hand half and a second time for the 20 columns in the left-hand half of the cards. With the Bull mark-sensing system the maximum number of columns which can be used is, therefore, only 40 and the remaining 40 of the 80 columns on the punch-card have to be punched in the ordinary way.

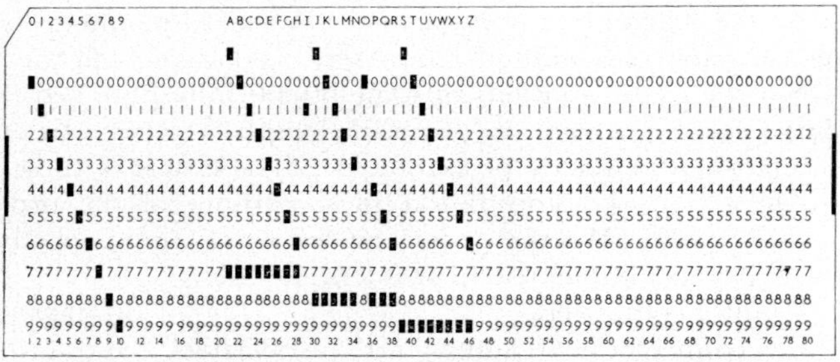

FIG. 8. Numerals and letters punched in accordance with the Bull 'internal code' procedure (Bull).

By contrast with the IBM system, the marking of these mark-sensing punch-cards can be done in various ways (see Fig. 9). Either the numerals to be punched can be formed in longhand by tracing over the pre-printed dots; or each desired numeral can be marked with an oblique stroke across the appropriate cell. In addition, there is the third possibility of stamping

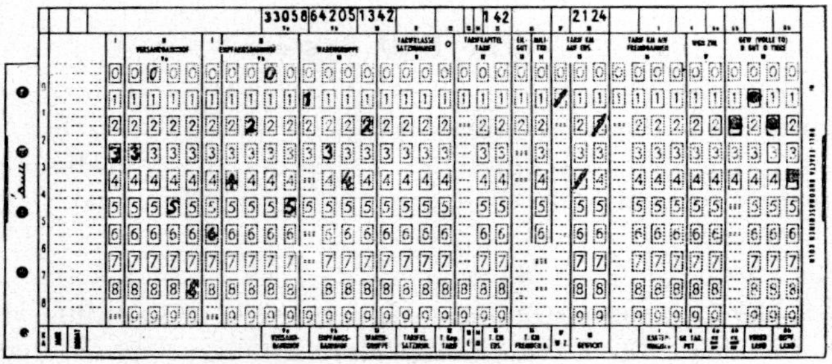

FIG. 9. Mark-sensing card of Bull system.

the desired cell with a circular stamp. This can be done very quickly and a special quick-drying stamping ink is used which gives a very intense black. The stamping process, therefore, is especially dependable when cards need to be stored for a long time before being punched.

Another difference between the IBM mark-sensing process and the Bull machine is that the latter does not work with electrical brushes to sense the marks, but by means of photocells. For this reason only the front side of the punched cards can be marked, the cards being exposed to light passing through each of them in turn. The photocells respond to the marks because these have a different degree of illumination as compared with the unmarked places.

Bull Punches and Verifiers

These Bull machines do not differ appreciably in the principles of their construction from the corresponding IBM machines. It need be mentioned only that the Bull punch-verifier marks each column that has been checked with a symbol, marks any columns which are wrong with a special symbol and automatically throws out any incorrectly punched cards.

The Bull Card Reproducer

Description—The Bull reproducer corresponds closely with that of IBM. It can be connected for photo-scanning. This method, which corresponds to the mark-sensing process of IBM, has already been described in reference to Bull punch-cards. Yet another method is, however, available—Bull magneto-scanning. This operates not with ordinary punch-cards but with sheets of paper three times their size. The marking is done with a ferrite pencil in the lower third of the form, both front and back. Altogether 60 marking positions are available.

Output—The reproducer processes 7 200 and the photo-scanner 3 600 cards an hour.

Bull Classifying Machines

Sorting machines—See Fig. 10. The Bull sorters work in a similar way to those of IBM but offer certain additional possibilities. For instance, it can be arranged by means of appropriate connections to direct the cards into any desired pockets of the 14 which are provided, such as pocket 1 for cards which are punched 1, 2 and 3 and pocket 2 for those which are punched 4, 5 and 6. In this way, particular groupings are made possible without upsetting the existing sequence. Further, the guide card can be sorted in accordance with the characteristics, which corresponds to multiposition numerical searching. Selection according to multiple punchings in the same column is also possible. All these operations are automatically checked. Thus the Bull sorting machines are very versatile.

Output—42 000 cards an hour.

The Bull Card Collator

Description—The Bull collator functions in a similar way to the IBM mixer.

Output—According to the type of work, 15 000 to 30 000 cards an hour.

Bull Printing and Tabulating Machines

Description—These do not differ notably from the IBM machines.

Output—9 000 cards an hour.

The Bull Punch-to-print Interpreter

Description—The Bull punch-to-print interpreter can print a maximum of four lines, each line containing 80 character spaces. The Bull accounting printer can print out 15 lines from the front and back of the cards.

Output—3 600 cards an hour.

Bull Computing Machines

The Bull company also has developed punching computers and large-scale computers, details of which need not be entered upon here.

FIG. 10.   Bull rapid sorter.

(D) The Powers System

Suppliers

Remington Rand G.m.b.H., Niddagaustrasse 33–35, Frankfurt-am-Main–Rödelheim.

Powers machines are both sold and loaned on hire. An especially useful facility is hire purchase, whereby a machine can first be hired and later bought, counting the rent already paid as part of the purchase price.

Powers machines mostly work on the mechanical sensing principle, but this does not exclude the adoption of electromechanical and electronic techniques.

Powers Punch-Cards

The format of these corresponds to that of the IBM and Bull punch-cards, but in contrast with those the Powers system uses circular holes (Fig. 11). As these circular holes take more space than rectangular holes, the Remington Rand Co. has adopted a different layout for its punch-cards in order to compensate for this disadvantage. The Powers card is divided into an upper and a lower half; as the whole card has 45 columns with 12 lines, this corresponds to 90 columns with five lines and a supplementary punching line in each half and gives 540 punching positions altogether.

In the Powers card numerals are represented either by a single hole or by a combination of two holes. As each half of the card has only six lines, combination coding is necessary even for numerals, and for the same reason letters have to be represented by the combined punching of two or three holes. Fig. 11 shows the code for numerals (punched in the upper half) and for letters (punched in the lower half).

The fact that the Powers system uses mechanical sensing of the cards in the punch-card machines excludes the possibility of an electronic or photo-electric mark-sensing method such as is supplied by the other two firms. This deficiency has, however, in one sense, been turned to a virtue. A method has been developed which allows Powers cards to be punched by hand using a portable device. Thereby one of the later operations which is necessary in the systems of the other firms, namely the automatic punching of the cards by machine, can be eliminated. The Powers cards intended for this manual punching can be supplied at a slightly higher price with small guide holes made beforehand in all desired punching positions (Fig. 12). The hand punching is done with what is called a pilot punching forceps fitted with a guide point so arranged as to prevent the forceps being closed unless it is able to enter one of the guide holes in the card. In this way, accurate register with the correct positions of the holes to be punched is ensured.

By this manual method it is possible, therefore, for any desired indications to be punched directly into the Powers cards at whatever place they are to be recorded.

Powers Punching and Verifying Machines

Description—The visual punch, as it is called, works on a somewhat different principle from the punches of the firms hitherto mentioned. All the indications which are to be recorded by the punch card are first 'types' on a keyboard and the actual punching is done afterwards in all the required positions simultaneously. Throughout the process the punch-card does not move and it is not ejected until the punching has been completed, whereupon another card moves into position. This method has the advantage that 'typing' errors can afterwards be corrected since no hole is punched at each touch of a key.

The Powers visual punch is so constructed that it can also be used as a verifier, merely by throwing over a lever. By contrast with the IBM and Bull methods already described, a regular check punching is then carried out which makes holes displaced 2 mm ($\frac{1}{12}$ in.) from those made previously and, in combination with them, produces oval holes. Consequently, when the verifying procedure has been completed, the card should contain only these oval holes, and the presence of any circular holes shows that the original and the proof punching do not coincide (Fig. 13). In a special machine, known as the oval checking automatic machine, all incorrectly

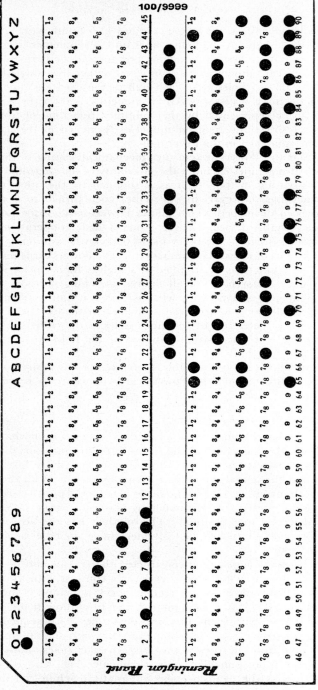

Fig. 11. Punching of numerals and letters in the Powers card (Remington Rand). (Internal code.)

50

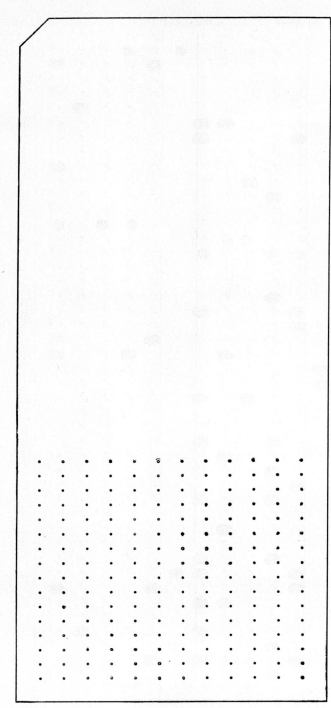

Fig. 12. Powers card showing a field of pilot holes. (The illustration represents the unprinted back of the card as this makes it easier to see the holes.)

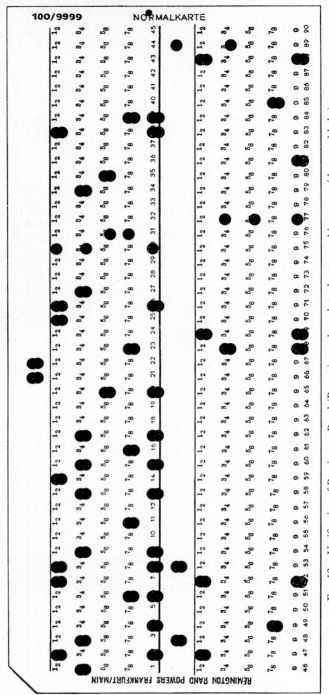

Fig. 13. Verification of Remington-Rand (Powers) punch-cards to detect punching errors (the round holes).

punched cards which anywhere contain circular holes are automatically sorted out or specially indicated.

Capacity of the automatic verifier—12000 cards an hour.

Powers Reproducing Machines

Description—The Remington Rand firm has also developed copying machines which correspond to those of the other systems, and what is called a mixing and duplicating automatic machine which combines punch-copying with sorting functions. This, then, is a combination of duplicator and mixer.

Output—6000 to 12000 cards an hour according to the job.

Fig. 14. Remington-Rand (Powers) tabulator with automatic punching of totals.

Powers Classifying Machines

Description—These machines and their accessories do not differ appreciably from those of the other firms. In the electronic classifier, photoelectrical sensing takes the place of mechanical sensing. At the same time, alphabetical sorting is improved.

Output—Ordinary machines: 24000 cards an hour. Electronic machine: 48000 cards an hour.

The Powers Collator:

See under mixing and duplicating automatic machine.

Powers Printing and Tabulating Machines

Description—See Fig. 14. Powers tabulators depend, like other Powers machines, on the mechanical sensing principle and perform, by what are called feelers, the same operational function as is secured in other systems by electrical connecting panels. This system although not so adaptable is very reliable.

Output: 6 000 lines an hour.

Description—According to the type of Powers punch-card printer, either 7 or 13 lines can be printed, each line containing 45 character spaces. Printing on following cards is also possible.

Output—5 400 cards an hour.

Powers Calculating Machines

Besides the Powers automatic computer, which corresponds to the computing punch mentioned above, the Remington Rand firm has developed a large electronic computer installation under the name UNIVAC.

(E) The Samas System

Suppliers

Samas Lochkartenmaschinen, Grabenstrasse 11 a, Düsseldorf.

These machines are either sold or loaned on hire. They work on the mechanical sensing principle.

Samas Punch-Cards

In order to meet as wide a range of requirements as possible, the Samas company provides punch-cards in various formats having respectively 21, 40, 80 and 160 usable columns. The system makes use of circular holes. Numerals and letters are represented in different ways according to the type of card. No mark-sensing process is possible with the Samas cards but in place of this a machine has been developed offering the advantage that the well known Adrema system, which cannot be further described here, may be combined with the punch-card method.

Samas Punches and Verifying Machines

Description—Punch-card machines are supplied which work either on the principle of IBM and Bull or on that of Powers, and the same is true as regards verifiers. On this system, the use of oval holes also is possible, and there is further an automatic verifying machine.

Output of the automatic machine—12 000 cards an hour.

The Samas Card Reproducer

This corresponds to the reproducer offered by the other firms.

Output—7 800 cards an hour.

Samas Classifying and Sorting Machines

The Samas sorting machine corresponds in its functions to the other makes of sorting machine.

Output—40 000 cards an hour.

The Samas Collator

This corresponds approximately to the IBM and Bull mixers.

Output—12 000 to 24 000 cards per hour.

The Samas Punch-to-Print Interpreter

Eleven lines can be printed. When printing on to following cards, both the front and reverse sides of the latter can be printed.

Output—4 500 cards per hour.

FIG. 15. Samas electronic computing punch.

Samas Calculating Machines

See Fig. 15. The Samas electronic computing punch processes 7 200 punch-cards an hour. Apart from this the Samas firm has concerned itself with the construction of large electronic computers, and has brought out what is known as the PCC equipment.

Samas Printing and Tabulating Machines

These correspond in their functions to those of the other tabulating machines.
Output—4800 to 6000 cards per hour.

(2) CODING FOR THE MACHINE PUNCH-CARD METHOD

Whenever possible the aim should always be to construct the code in such a way that only one card is necessary for each working unit. If this cannot be secured because of insufficient room on the punch-cards it becomes necessary to introduce what are called connecting numbers which serve to indicate those cards which appertain to the same working unit. It should be clearly understood that correlative research by means of punch-cards is made more difficult when two or more cards have to be provided for the same working unit. Often the establishment of correlation between two factors which are not recorded on the same punch-card necessitates the use of a card mixer and involves additional operations. Therefore, under conditions where each unit of the work has to be provided with several punch-cards, it is advisable that at least those factors in the problem which are expected to be related and whose dependence on one another is to be statistically investigated, or those factors which elsewhere occur associated with one another, should always be combined on one card.

Further it should be remembered, when preparing several cards for the same unit of work, that the card collection as a whole can be sorted only in respect of those indications which recur on cards that appertain to the same unit of work. As a general rule, this applies only to the connecting numbers. For instance, in a collection of documentation cards which are to indicate authors, sources and titles it is desirable to be able to sort according to authors alphabetically, even though this may necessitate having several punch-cards for the same publication (which here is the 'working unit'). Such sorting, however, is possible only if the author's name is punched into every single punch-card, which means a not inconsiderable waste of space. Here again, therefore, the advice needs to be stressed: if possible, arrange matters so as not to need more than one punch-card for each working unit.

The following coding possibilities are intended to show how this advice can be followed and the punch cards be utilized as rationally as possible.

Guiding Principles for all Machine Punch-Cards

(*a*) Technically, columns have priority over lines. This principle is to be respected in all codes and is to be observed when sub-dividing a code.

(*b*) Before beginning any special coding work for machine punch-cards, be clear about the following complications:

(*i*) All normally numbered cards are overprinted in such a way that reference can be made to individual punching positions or holes. (Here see also page 256.)

(*ii*) Each of the methods here described has an 'internal code' which is used in all the related machines, so devised that any arabic numeral or capital letter of the alphabet can be represented in any one column by a particular hole or combination of holes.

(*iii*) What appears in print on any normal numerical card for the purpose of indicating the holes or punching positions represents never more than a part of the potentialities inherent in the internal code (usually only the numerals).

(*iv*) In one's own coding work, there is *no need* to be limited by what is normally printed on the cards and by the normal designations of the holes. Any other desired overprint can be adopted instead, wherein the holes or punching positions can be marked with whatever designations or conceptual terms one may choose.

(*v*) Unless the punching field of the cards adopted for the time being is to be used solely for the purpose of employing sorting machines selectively, one is *always* bound to adopt the internal code of the chosen system and one's own coding must be related to this internal code as rationally as possible. Likewise one is obliged to use the same notation as has provided the basis for the internal code, consisting of Arabic numerals, capital letters and a few signs.

Simple Codes—(A) Direct Code

For simple punching in each column—(*i*) The simplest form of code is one founded on normal overprinting of the numerical cards as well as on the internal code of the appropriate system used.

In the IBM, Bull and (partly) the Samas systems, all numerals from 0 to 9 can be expressed by single punchings. On the Powers system only the 0 and the odd numbers can be so punched. The object of the code is to make it possible to transfer on to punch-cards either numerical values as such or numerical notations (that is, numerals serving as symbols for concepts or words). For this purpose, the supplementary holes need not be used. In this simplest form of code all ten possible indications, whether numbers or notational symbols, must be mutually exclusive of one another, so that never more than one hole is needed in any one column. This form of code—particularly when it is made into a compound code for multiple digit numbers—provides the basis for the performance of all computing work by the machines. By reason of its alternative character, it is less well adapted to the purposes of documentation.

(*ii*) The first of the complications which can be introduced is that of not limiting oneself to the use of only one column, but of disregarding the normal layout of the card and extending the use of the simple code into a second and any number of further columns, adopting for instance the arrangement on an IBM card shown overleaf.

Once again, using this form of coding, there must be only one hole in each column. The advantage is that as many indications can be punched as there are columns in use (in this example, four), whereas using a compound hierarchical code only a single indication could be carried (see page 65).

This code is suitable for computation work only on condition that 10 is added automatically to the values in column 2, 20 to the values in column

3 and so on.   This code is very well adapted to certain purposes of documentation.   It should be noted that from column 2 onwards a multi-digit
(here two-digit) number or numerical notation is coded by the use of only
a single hole.

Column 1	Column 2	Column 3	Column 4
0	10	20	30
1	11	21	31
2	12	22	32
3	13	23	33
4	14	24	34
5	15	25	35
6	16	26	36
7	17	27	37
8	18	28	38
9	19	29	39

With multiple punching in one column—The construction of the above-
mentioned code fully corresponds with the possibilities explained above,
but is subject to the limitation that all the indications contained in any one
column must be mutually exclusive.   In addition the supplementary holes
can be utilized, which gives a maximum possibility of 12 holes in one column.
Evidently there are other disadvantages which must be taken into account
also: punch-cards coded in this way, with the punching field here in question,
can be processed *only* in sorting machines.   Fortunately, it has been found
in practice that this disadvantage is mainly a theoretical one, because
several codes can be combined with one another on the same card, and the
one here described is used only for selection in the field of documentation.
In this field such methods have, in fact, proved the most effective from
every point of view (see also page 65).

The advantage of this code is that all indications can be recorded on the
same card or in the same punching field.   A disadvantage is its limited
capacity, in that only as many separate indications can be recorded as
there are holes used.   However, the punching pattern method (see page 66)
compensates for this disadvantage.   This code is not suitable for computing
work, but by using a machine which counts the cards sorted into each pocket
it is possible to ascertain how many punchings occur in each column and
thereby to evaluate them statistically.

Using whole columns—Orosz (1955), proceeding from the *incorrect* assumption that it is fundamentally impossible with machine punch-cards to use
multiple punching in one column, developed a method or a code for
documentation work which by reason of its originality ought not to be
omitted from mention here, even though, in the present author's opinion,
it takes away *a priori* a large part of the advantages of machine punch-cards.

Using this code, the columns alone are used and the numbers which they
bear are adopted as a notation.   If, for instance, the notation to be recorded
is 67, a hole is punched in some position within column 67.   There are,
then, at most only 80 punching possibilities.   Although Orosz does not use
a direct code, but only an abridged code, the unanswerable disadvantage

nevertheless remains that the capacity of the punch-cards is utilized to the extent of 10 per cent only. Such a code cannot be used at all for computing work and is not an acceptable solution for documentation work either.

Separate use of the supplementary holes—The IBM, Bull and Samas systems provide in addition to the ordinary punching field in their cards, a supplementary punching zone of two lines. These are known as the eleventh and twelfth lines, or alternatively the holes made in them may be described as x (11) and y (12). The Powers cards have an extra line of holes in each half. When an abridged code is being used these holes serve to represent letters, but independently of this they can be used for direct coding.

By a skilful use of the supplementary holes in conjunction with direct coding it is possible both to save punching columns and thereby considerably to increase the indicative possibilities of punch-cards. They can be used in the following ways:

(*i*) As guide holes in order to initiate particular functions in a particular machine.

(*ii*) For increasing up to 12 the range of numbers which can be recorded in a single column, in order to indicate for instance the 12 months of a year in a single column. It must, however, be noted that the 0 then has to be used as 10, and that the numbers 10, 11 and 12 if so recorded can neither be printed out nor used in calculations.

(*iii*) As directive holes for the purpose of giving a special and different significance to certain indications recorded in the same or in other columns, or for the purpose of creating a special punching field combination to express concepts.

Some further comment will now be made on the possibilities of application already set out.

One example of using indicative holes would be when punching temperatures in the appropriate column or group of columns, in order to indicate whether these are positive or negative values (degrees of heat or of frost), the negative values for instance being given also an indicative hole. Similarly, for indicating geographical data, the supplementary holes may be used to distinguish between north and south latitude and, on the other hand, between east and west longitude.

Another example of the applicability of indicative holes may be taken from research work. In certain investigations it is necessary to indicate depths of water which may range anywhere between 10 cm and 100 m. Here depths of less than 10 m need to be recorded to the nearest decimeter, but greater depths only to the nearest meter. Were it not for the additional possibility offered by an indicative hole, all depth values would have to be expressed in decimeters and three columns would be needed for the purpose, despite the fact that in excess of 10 m this degree of accuracy is not required so that two columns would suffice. In such a case, an expedient can be adopted whereby in fact only two columns are necessary for indicating depths but in one of these columns a supplementary hole serves to indicate the scale of measurement; in the example given, it can be laid down for instance that the presence of a supplementary hole means 'meter scale'. The two columns to which the meaning 'depth of water' is assigned will then always contain only two-figure values, relating to the 'decimeter' scale if the indicative hole has not been punched or to the 'meter' scale if it has been punched. For statistical processing, cards with the indicative hole in this position are first separated from those without the hole by the use of a sorting machine, after which further sorting and evaluation can be performed within each of the two groups. This principle can be adapted as desired to other similar examples, whereby in appropriate cases a great many punching columns can be saved without impairing the evaluative possibilities of the cards.

When one is not working with real numerical values but for instance in documentation and a particular concept is assigned to each individual hole in a column, a particularly neat application can be made of the possibilities which the indicative holes provide. This is to make use of them for indicating the fact that a concept recorded in that column is further referred to in another column which had been kept in reserve. The following kind of directive can be laid down: 'Indicative hole 11 means that the concept punched in that column is further developed in the reserve column n_1, and indicative hole 12 means that the concept is further developed in the reserve column n_2.'

(B) Abridged Code

With the punching combinations in one column only—(i) The simplest kind of abridged code consists of representing letters by having recourse only to the internal code of the system in use. As has already been explained when describing the forms of card used in the various systems, this internal code differs from one system to another, a fact which needs to be borne in mind when choosing which system to use.

Such a code serves for alphabetical sorting, alphabetical mixing, reprinting of a running text and for statistical purposes. It is suitable also for documentation, provided that a notation of capital letters is used. (On this point see the suggestions starting at page 234.)

(ii) The usual mode of punching letters, explained above, is based on an abridged code constructed in accordance with quite definite rules for each system. When this fact is considered, it will be apparent that numerous possibilities are opened up, particularly in the field of documentation, for using these rules to save space when different points of view have to be represented. As an example let us take the IBM internal code, which has the structure shown opposite:

Remark: The sign / (meaning the combination $0 + 1$) exists only in *some* of the printing machines and in electronic computers; χ means punching a supplementary hole.

In reference to this scheme it must first of all be stated that, using a direct code and abridged code in one column on the IBM system, the internal code enables ten figures (0 to 9) and 26 letters (A to Z) to be represented, with the addition in particular machines of a varying number of further signs. If only numbers and letters are in question this gives a total of 36 symbols which can be handled by practically all machines.

Line 12	χ		
Line 11		χ	
Line 0			χ
Line 1	A	J	/
Line 2	B	K	S
Line 3	C	L	T
Line 4	D	M	U
Line 5	E	N	V
Line 6	F	O	W
Line 7	G	P	X
Line 8	H	Q	Y
Line 9	I	R	Z

Besides this, the table above brings out possibilities for the construction of particular groups, by punching combinations of the abridged code for letters. For instance, letters A to I can be punched 12, J to R can be punched 11 and S to Z can be punched 0, thereby producing two 9-groups and one 8-group. In the direction at right angles to this the letters A to J are punched in position 1, the letters B, K and S in position 2 and so on, every three letters sharing one number of hole, so as to obtain eight 3-groups and one 2-group.

For the purposes of documentation or of systematics a corresponding notation of numbers and letters can be used and sequences can be chosen which correspond with these groupings. The following example is from botany:

Division, arrangement and marginal development of leaves

	I. Radical	II. Radical and cauline leaves		
Shape of leaf margins	leaves only	(a) Alternate leaves	(b) Opposite leaves	(c) Verticillate leaves
(1) Serrate	1	A	J	0 + 1
(2) Bi-serrate	2	B	K	S
(3) Incise	3	C	L	T
(4) Dentate	4	D	M	U
(5) Bi-dentate	5	E	N	V
(6) Crenate	6	F	O	W
(7) Repand	7	G	P	X
(8) Sinuate	8	H	Q	Y
(9) Entire	9	I	R	Z

Thus it becomes possible, using any machine, to distinguish two higher groups within the same column—'I. Radical leaves only' being denoted by numerals and 'II. Radical and cauline leaves' by letters—with the higher group II subdivided into three groups—namely '(a) Alternate leaves' denoted by the letters A to I, '(b) Opposite leaves' by the letters J to R and '(c) Verticillate leaves' by S to Z—and with the higher group I likewise subdivided into (1) to (9).

A further example may be taken from chemistry, in which the periodic system of the elements can with great advantage be referred to in four columns by using an abridged code of this type, the first of these columns being used as follows:

Periodic system of the elements
(from Hofmann: *Anorganische Chemie*)

Valence group	Incomplete period		Period 1		Period 2	
Group I	A	Hydrogen	J	Lithium	/	Sodium
Group II	B		K	Beryllium	S	Magnesium
Group III	C		L	Boron	T	Aluminium
Group IV	D		M	Carbon	U	Silicon
Group V	E		N	Nitrogen	V	Phosphorus
Group VI	F		O	Oxygen	W	Sulfur
Group VII	G		P	Fluorine	X	Chlorine
Group VIII	H		Q		Y	
Group 0	I	Helium	R	Neon	Z	Argon

It will be seen that it is possible in this way to assign every element to its period and its valence group at the same time. Each column accommodates three periods so that, if the rare earths are put together, the whole range of elements can be covered by four columns. If now, as an example, all the elements belonging to a particular period are wanted, these can be sorted or selected by reference only to the supplementary holes and 0, or if particular valence groups are wanted these can be sorted or selected in accordance with the numerals 0 to 9. The example also shows that with this kind of coding not all the punching spaces or combinations need to be taken up. Nevertheless, the code is a very rational one. The only stipulation that has to be made is not to do violence to the classification system but to transfer this correctly and appropriately on to the punch-cards in accordance with their coding possibilities.

Finally, an example of a code for countries may be given, using:

$$B = \text{Germany}$$
$$K = \text{Austria}$$
$$S = \text{Switzerland}$$

This triple group of countries belongs to the common collective concept 'German-speaking countries'. On sorting in the machine all the cards relating to such countries will fall into pocket 2. Similarly, the other triple groups contained in the same column can be used. In a second sorting operation, the individual countries or concepts within each triple group can be separated from one another.

It must be left to the imagination and ingenuity of the user to adapt these examples and suggestions to his own problems, and perhaps to develop them further.

(*iii*) If it is decided to disregard the internal codes of the various systems and to work entirely through the medium of sorting machines, it becomes possible to develop any form of abridged code that may be desired, making use of all 12 punching positions or holes in each column. The rules of combination allow the following possibilities:

$$\binom{12}{2} = 66 \quad \binom{12}{3} = 220 \quad \binom{12}{4} = 495$$

$$\binom{12}{5} = 792 \quad \binom{12}{6} = 924 \quad \binom{12}{7} = 792, \text{ etc.}$$

In this way, any of 4095 different indications can be given in one column. However, calculations of this kind are only of theoretical value, for in practice it is not possible to work with codes based on combinations of more than three holes, since attempting to do so would take up too much time. (An exception to this statement is the use of a 'Special Multicolumn Searcher').

IBM have tried to develop an internal machine code for the scanning machine on the basis $\binom{12}{5}$, but it appears that this attempt has been given up.

Finally, it is perhaps hardly necessary to insist that all such abridged codes can be used only for purposes of documentation and not for computing.

Using punching combinations over several columns—Codes of this kind allow a great variety of possibilities. In the first place, the punching field (that is, the number of columns) can be freely chosen, its only limit being the total capacity of the type of card in question. Further, there is complete freedom to decide how many holes are to be utilized for combination punching. The only governing condition is that the holes used in any one combination must be punched in different columns. Finally, the relation of the punching combinations to the indications can be either arbitrary or in accordance with definite rules. The following example uses a punching field extending over columns 1 to 60 and represents each indication by a combination of two holes in arbitrary fashion:

Inland waters in general		9/8	38/11	Ponds	.	.	.	5/0	14/1
Ground water	. .	1/6	5/8	Marshes	.	.	.	43/9	21/12
Wells .	. . .	7/12	3/9	Very small waters	.		.	11/11	7/2
Streams	. . .	53/1	1/1	Ice .	.	.	.	42/6	44/5
Rivers	. . .	31/5	17/4	Snow	.	.	.	12/1	2/4
Estuaries	. . .	11/3	19/6	Other	.	.	.	3/7	58/3
Lakes .	. . .	4/9	13/7						

Remarks: The number in front of the stroke indicates the column and the number after the stroke the line.

With this code, the number of indications that can be given is very large. At the same time several indications can be given in the same punching field, by what is called superimposed coding.

There is, however, the disadvantage that if too many indications are superimposed on a large total number of cards a certain percentage of irrelevant cards will be selected. As an example, if 'Harvest' is coded as 21/2 14/7, 'Wages' as 13/5 5/12, 'Transformers' as 21/2 5/12, and if references to 'Wages in harvesting' are wanted, some unwanted cards referring to 'Transformers' will also be brought out.

A code of this kind can, however, be further improved by observing certain rules of relationship. Furthermore group formations are possible by making use of the coding principle of Luhn (1956) known as 'randomizing squares'.

This code is only suitable for documentation and as a rule it can only be worked by the use of sorting machines.

Using whole columns—The coding principle of Orosz, already mentioned on page 58, can also be adapted for use in abridged codes. (This was in fact the application of the principle which Orosz published in 1955.) Orosz uses quaternary punching combinations; that is to say he uses four holes for each unit of indication. The following is one of his examples:

Tuberculosis	.	.	14	30	46	70
Streptomycin	.	.	2	25	50	63
Therapy	.	.	6	18	39	57

Here each number corresponds to one column in which Orosz normally punches the 9. As there can be only one hole in each column the number of indications which can be recorded in a punching field of 60 columns is $\binom{60}{4} = 487635$. Such totals may seem impressive, but all calculations of this kind are deceptive as regards the true value of a coding system, that being governed by other criteria.

This code, too, is suitable only for documentation. Anyway, in the present author's opinion, it is not a practicable one, first because it exploits the potentialities of the punch-card method too little and consequently the proportion of irrelevant cards becomes greater than need be, secondly because on technical grounds the machines can handle it only in an unrational way. Whilst it is true that such a code can be worked either in sorting machines or in card mixers, it involves too many operations or takes up too much time for making the electrical connections.

Hierarchical Codes

Composed as a unit—The normal case is a code put together from direct codes for the purpose of expressing multi-digit numbers. For this purpose a punching field is adopted which contains sufficient columns to accommodate the number of digits expected to be needed. Each column is assigned a different position.

Example: If numbers of not more than six digits are expected, a punching field of six columns will suffice.

Column	21	22	23	24	25	26
Position value	Hundreds of thousands	Tens of thousands	Thousands	Hundreds	Tens	Units
	0	0	[0]	0	0	0
	1	[1]	1	(1)	1	1
	2	2	(2)	2	2	2
	(3)	3	3	3	3	[3]
Punching divisions	4	4	4	4	[4]	4
	[5]	5	5	5	5	(5)
	6	(6)	6	6	6	6
	7	7	7	[7]	7	7
	8	8	8	8	(8)	8
	9	9	9	9	9	9

Explanation: ( ) = normal punching; [ ] = additional punching.

Here each column corresponds to a direct code for one digit. The great disadvantage of this code is the blocking of all columns within the chosen punching field even when the number to be punched does not require so many columns. In our example, for instance, the number 12 would have to be punched 000012. Hence everything must be done to avoid the need for long multi-digit numbers, for even ten eight-column punching fields will take up the whole card and if a hierarchical code is being used only ten separate indications can be so reproduced.

Long numbers can be avoided if running numbers for unit operations are replaced by designations which are sufficient to identify these accurately and unequivocally and which, at the same time, indicate particular properties and points of view. An example of this may be taken from documentation. Publications might be cataloged, as is done in most libraries, under accession numbers in the same sequence as they happen to have been received. In this way each publication is accurately identified without risk of error; it is not possible, however, to foresee how many digits (columns) this running number may eventually reach, and *a priori* plenty of latitude must be allowed for it. The disadvantage of this uncertainty can be avoided by using the year of publication instead of the total accession number, followed by a number identifying the periodical (which of course will be limited) and by a running number to cover the publications appearing within each periodical each year (which never exceeds 100 in any periodical except abstract bulletins). This device carries with it the further advantage that the individual publications can also be sorted according to the year and the periodical in which they appeared.

This example illustrates the general principle of breaking up long numbers into smaller parts in order to serve the purpose of identification and at the same time to obtain larger indicative capacity.

It has already been pointed out that, using a hierarchical code spread over a given punching field, only one indication is possible on each card.

The example given on page 64 shows once again that no superimposition of a second or further indications in the same field is practicable. Subject to this, the hierarchical form of code in its ordinary form as here explained (using numbers or letters) may serve for arranging, calculating and printing in all machines. Many special developments and examples may be found in the IBM pamphlet entitled *The IBM Number Code* obtainable from that corporation.

Compound Codes

Remarks: Compound codes are always formed by putting simple codes together. Coding must not be confused with notation. A compound notation (as is exemplified in every multi-digit number) *can* be coded by means of a simple code, but a simple notation (for instance the letter A) cannot be expressed by a compound code.

Mixed codes—Here it must suffice to state once again that various simple codes can be combined with hierarchical codes as desired. The more skilfully codes of very varied kinds can be combined with one another on the same punch-card, the more rational will the punch-card method become. Particular combinations for particular purposes must, however, be left for each user to work out for himself.

Associative Codes

These codes may best be constructed on the basis of direct codes with multiple punching in each column. They serve only for documentation.

It was on this basis that the author developed what he has named the 'punching pattern' method (*Lochbildverfahren*). His fundamental idea in doing so was to transfer an *orderly system of basic concepts* on to punch-cards without the intermediary of a notation, thereby avoiding having to attribute a determined 'position value' to each concept, and leaving them all free to be combined with one another. The number of combinations that are possible cannot, however, be determined from mathematical laws as it depends also on the nature of the conceptual system and on the significance of the concepts. Any particular concept can be derived from the appropriate combination of fundamental concepts. The advantages of such a coding system are the following:

Optimum use is made of the punch-card.

The conceptual capacity is very large.

Many concepts can be pin-pointed at the same time.

Selection can never bring out cards which have no relation whatever to the question being searched.

Instead of giving detailed examples, reference may be made to the exposition beginning at page 212 in Part III of this book. This form of code has worked very well in the hands of various authors, some of whom have independently arrived at essentially the same development, and it may be regarded as the best solution hitherto attained for mechanical documentation. It presupposes, however, an exceptionally thorough grounding in classification theory.

3. NEEDLE PUNCH-CARD METHODS

(1) NATURE OF METHOD AND ITS TECHNICAL AIDS

(A) General

By contrast with machine punch-card methods, in reference to which it was remarked above that they have relatively a good deal in common with one another, needle punch-card methods are characterized above all by their great variety. No doubt this is connected with the fact that needle punch-cards constitute predominantly a manual method of working which needs no machines. Consequently, their adoption does not make it necessary to envisage extensive equipment beforehand. For the same reason it is easy to understand why all efforts in the direction of standardization for needle punch-cards have proved abortive.

The multiformity of this method and of the cards used applies to their dimensions, the numbers of rows of holes in them and of holes in each row, the spacing of the holes from one another and from the edge of the card, the size of the holes and their arrangement and subdivisions. Apart from all this, the material of the cards and the accessory aids may also vary. It is scarcely necessary to repeat that this variety cannot be gone into here; instead our object must be to uncover those principles which all needle punch-cards have in common and to take fuller account of those differences between edge-notched and slitted cards which have already been touched upon in regard to the terminology and classification of methods.

On the general question of manipulating needle punch-cards, what has already been said at page 28 in reference to machine punch-cards holds good. Here again, proper storage and careful handling of the cards is the pre-condition for satisfactory work. Another difference from machine punch-cards is that needle punch-cards can be subjected to a great variety of additional manipulations. For instance, they can have other pieces of paper such as clippings from newspapers or abstract journals pasted on them, or they may contain film windows. Experience shows, however, that care is needed always to do this on the same side of the cards, either front or back, for otherwise those cards which have had paper pasted on them may stick together. Generally speaking, such pasting is actually an advantage as it makes the cards heavier, with the result that they fall out more easily in the process of selection. Sensitizing needle punch-cards so that they can be reproduced by contact printing has given good results, too.

Finally, a word as to the accessories. The present author is in general agreement with others that one of the important advantages of needle punch-cards lies in the fact that they can be worked 'with a knitting needle' so that the whole system falls within the financial reach of a private individual, and for him it offers a rational solution. It is certain that many

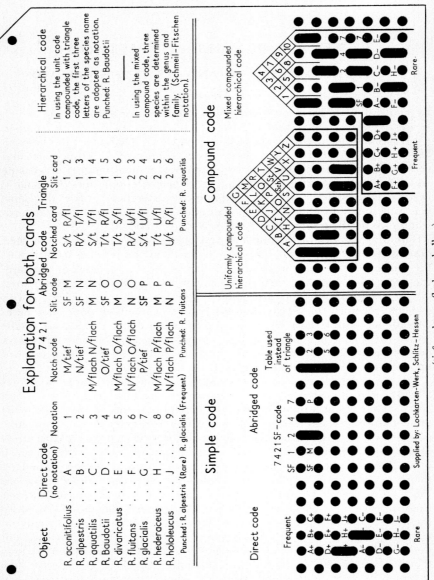

Explanation for both cards

Hierarchical code

In using the unit code compounded with triangle code, the first three letters of the species name are adopted as notation. Punched: R. Baudotii

In using the mixed compound code, three species are determined within the genus and family. (Schmeil–Fitschen notation).

Object	Direct code (no notation)	Notation	Notch code 7 4 2 1	Abridged code Slit code	Triangle Notched card	Slit card
R. aconitifolius	A	1	M/tief	SF M	S/t R/fl	1 2
R. alpestris	B	2	N/tief	SF N	R/t T/fl	1 3
R. aquatilis	C	3	M/flach N/flach	M N	S/t T/fl	1 4
R. Baudotii	D	4	O/tief	SF O	T/t R/fl	1 5
R. divaricatus	E	5	M/flach O/flach	M O	T/t S/fl	1 6
R. fluitans	F	6	N/flach O/flach	N O	R/t U/fl	2 3
R. glacialis	G	7	P/tief	SF P	S/t U/fl	2 4
R. hederaceus	H	8	M/flach P/flach	M P	T/t U/fl	2 5
R. hololeucus	J	9	N/flach P/flach	N P	U/t R/fl	2 6

Punched: R. alpestris (Rare)   R. glacialis (Frequent)   Punched: R. fluitans   Punched: R. aquatilis

Simple code

Direct code

Abridged code

7 4 2 1 SF – code

Table used instead of triangle

Compound code

Uniformly compounded hierarchical code

Mixed compounded hierarchical code

Supplied by: Lochkarten-Werk, Schlitz–Hessen

(tief = deep; flach = shallow)

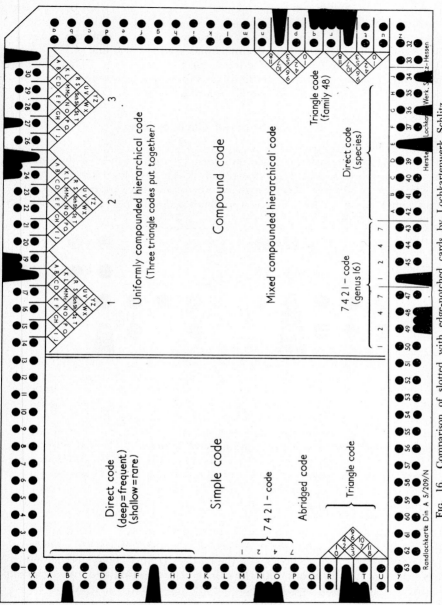

FIG. 16. Comparison of slotted with edge-notched cards by Lochkartenwerk Schlitz (Oberhessen) with examples of different codes.

users do appreciate it from this point of view.   In spite of this, a few manufacturers have developed some further accessories over and beyond the
selecting devices which doubtless are convenient and necessary.   Some of
these accessories are quite expensive, in some cases even expensive enough
to be comparable with the simpler machines used for machine punch-cards.
These, therefore, are mainly of interest for the large user.   Their special
uses cannot be discussed here, but insofar as they may be of interest the firms
concerned will gladly supply detailed information.

(B) Edge-Notched Card System

The Cards and Their Use

The following description is based on a form of edge-notched card produced
by Lochkartenwerk Schlitz in Oberhessen, Germany (Fig. 16).

This type of card is a sheet which may be of any size, around whose edge
(but sometimes not all around) is a single or a double row of holes.   Alter-

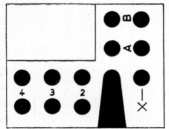 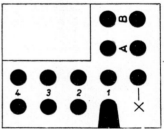

Fig. 17.   Portions of double-row edge-notched cards showing shallow and deep notching.

natively there may be three or even more such rows, but their number is
limited for the technical reason that additional rows of holes make the
notching progressively more difficult and the coding progressively less
rational; for this reason the edge-notched card system has been found to
work best with only a single or a double row of holes.   The central portion
of the card, on both sides, is left empty for writing in or attaching any
desired text.   Photographs, press cuttings, abstracts, etc., can be pasted
on it (see page 67).   The right or left top corner of each card is cut off
diagonally so that any card which happens to be standing upside down will
at once be noticed.

The indications to be recorded are associated with particular holes,
according to a coding system.   A card is prepared for use by converting
into notches, opening to the edge of the card, whichever holes correspond in
it to the desired indications.   In the case of a card having two rows of holes,
a distinction is made between shallow notches which reach only as far as
the outer row of holes and deep notches which extend through the outer
to the inner row (Fig. 17).

When, now, a long needle is inserted through the hole that corresponds
to any desired indication, running through a whole pack of cards, and the

pack is lifted on this needle, all those cards which have had that particular hole converted to an open notch fall off the needle. Thus, with the aid of gravity, all those cards are brought out which contain the desired information (Fig. 18). By using several needles at once, various different indications can be selected simultaneously in one operation.

From the nature of the system, it is impossible, however, to select desired punching combinations in one operation if the holes in question do not all occur on the same edge of the card. In the extreme case, therefore, searching out those cards which give the answer to a complex question may necessitate four operations, one for each edge of the card. However, it is possible by skilful coding so to arrange matters that those indications which

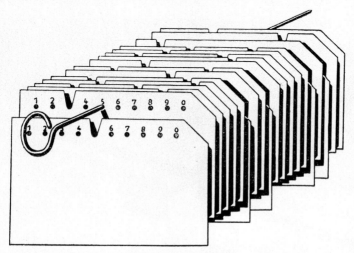

Fig. 18.   The searching operation with edge-notched cards.

are most frequently wanted in combination with one another are notched on the same edge of the card.

It can be regarded as an advantage of this method that, even without taking the cards out from the collection, one can see clearly what notches exist in any of them. This provides a general visual check and, at the same time, makes it possible for any particular card to be picked out without need to use the sorting needles.

Accessories and Aids

The only indispensable technical aids for using a set of edge-notched cards are notching clippers and sorting needles. These are supplied by the different firms in various forms. In the simplest cases from one to three needles can be used simultaneously, but if it is desired to use yet more needles in a single operation it is advisable to do so in a sorting device. These devices, too, are obtainable in different designs. Ruston (1952) has described a large sorting device of notably high capacity, remarking:

It is obvious that simple sorting needles are not an adequate means for handling large numbers of cards which may have numbers with as many as seven digits notched around their edges. It is theoretically possible to manage with one needle, but dependence on this would take far too much time and trouble. A simple sorting device is offered by the McBee Company, but the author has preferred to design one in a somewhat different form, as is shown in Fig. 19. This apparatus consists of a rectangular metallic frame A mounted on an axle B so that it can turn inside the support. At each end of the frame this can be clamped in either a vertical or a horizontal position by turning the knob C. The front side of the frame consists of two plates F, each

Fig. 19.   The sorting-out device in its open position (Ruston, 1952).

perforated with a double row of holes like those in the edges of the cards. By means of a guide bar E the front plate can be moved together with the frame and forms therewith a kind of drawer. The sorting needles G are inserted in accordance with the numbers or letters of the desired holes and are clamped into place. When the drawer is pulled out the points of the needles lie inside the holes of the fixed plate, and when it is pushed in they are guided by the groove H.

Sorting of the cards is effected by first of all setting the needles to correspond with the numbers or letter combinations wanted. Then, with the drawer open, a pack of up to about 250 cards is placed in the frame, with the edge to be sorted uppermost. The drawer is pushed in, and after loosening the knob C, the frame is turned over so that the cards are left hanging on the needles. Thereupon all those cards whose notches correspond with the required number or letter combinations fall off (Fig. 20). This method allows a large output, it being easily possible to sort through 30000 cards an hour.

Sorting devices of this or similar types are supplied by the firms concerned and there also are simple kinds of sorting frames which give very good value.

So as not to have to scrap a whole card because it has been wrongly notched in one place, 'card menders' have been developed (Fig. 21). These are gummed strips of stiff paper which have a fold along the middle, an appropriate length of which can be stuck over the edge of the card at the place where it has been wrongly notched.

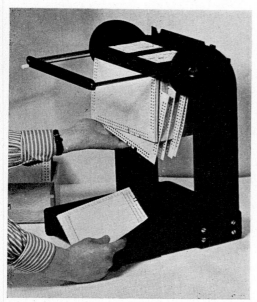

Fig. 20. The sorting-out operation. Here the selected cards are seen dropping from the pack (Ruston, 1952).

Fig. 21. Card patcher (Lochkartenwerk Schlitz).

Combination with Other Methods

Here will be mentioned only the possibilities that exist for combining this with other methods already discussed. In suitable cases, the notched card system can be combined with the various machine punch-card systems, those of them which use round holes (Powers and Samas) being particularly suitable. My own experience, however, does not lead me to recommend possible combinations of this kind save in exceptional cases, as they have not been found particularly rational.

(C) Slit Punch-Card Methods

The Cards and Their Use

The following description relates to the slit punched cards supplied by the firm of Allform in Berlin (Fig. 22).

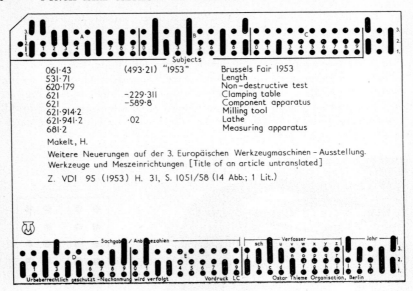

Subjects

061·43	(493·21) "1953"	Brussels Fair 1953
531·71		Length
620·179		Non-destructive test
621	-229·311	Clamping table
621	-589·8	Component apparatus
621·914·2		Milling tool
621·941·2	·02	Lathe
681·2		Measuring apparatus

Makelt, H.

Weitere Neuerungen auf der 3. Europäischen Werkzeugmaschinen – Ausstellung.
Werkzeuge und Meszeinrichtungen [Title of an article untranslated]

Z. VDI 95 (1953) H. 31, S. 1051/58 (14 Abb.; 1 Lit.)

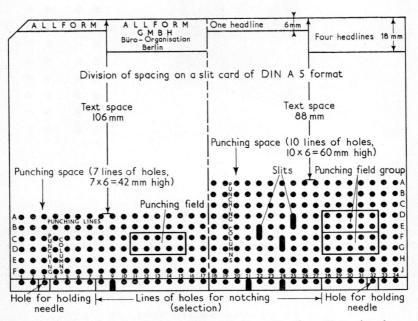

FIG. 22.   Slotted cards as supplied by Allform, Berlin.   The upper illustration shows an older type of card from this firm, slotted in accordance with the Universal Decimal Classification (which the author does not consider suitable).   The lower one shows a newer design, with the firm's own names for some of its features.

The slit punch-card may be of any format. Unlike the edge-notched card, it has rows of holes not only along the edge but in practically as many rows as desired, one under the other. Usually there are no rows of holes along one of the long sides of the card, so that along both of its short sides any unused space on the front and back can, as in the case of edge-notched cards, be used for writing or for pasting on other material. Here again, one corner of each card is cut off.

The assignment of indications to holes is in accordance with a suitable coding system. A card is made to record any desired indications by cutting away its material between whatever holes, vertically above one another, correspond to them (the manner of doing this being different in each system). Thereby slits are produced as seen in Fig. 22, wherefrom the method receives its name. As the edges of the cards are not affected they do not fall out when a pack of them is needled, so that a special kind of sorting or selecting apparatus is necessary, the underlying principle of which is similar to that described above by Ruston for edge-notched cards. Selecting is done by the insertion of needles into all the holes which correspond to the indications to be selected, whereupon, on the apparatus being turned over and the cards shaken, the wanted cards drop through a certain distance, corresponding as a rule to the vertical interval between two rows of holes. By inserting two additional needles through the unwanted cards which have not dropped these are held in place, whereupon the needles through the wanted cards can be withdrawn and these cards removed from the apparatus, if it is not sufficient merely to look at them as they are.

One advantage of this method is that all desired possible combinations of holes can be selected in a single operation, provided only that all the slits run in the same direction, as is now usual in most systems of this kind.

Accessories and Aids

For working with a collection of slit cards it is necessary to have a slitting tool or punch, as well as the sorting or selecting apparatus already described.

Combination with Other Methods

The slit card method can, without difficulty, be combined with the edge-notched card method using the same cards; but, generally speaking, better results appear to be obtained by separate applications of the two principles.

Theoretically, indeed, a combination with various kinds of machine punch-card methods is conceivable, but the author is not aware of this having been tried yet.

(2) **CODING FOR NEEDLE PUNCH-CARDS**

The same rule as before applies also to needle punch-cards, that whenever possible only one card should be necessary for each separate operating unit (see page 56).

(A) **Principles for Needle Punch-Cards**

(*a*) Unlike machine punch-cards, there is no technical reason with needle punch-cards for preferring one arrangement of holes to another. With these, the only rules that need be observed are those which have already been explained as differentiating the edge-notched card principle from that of slit punch-cards.

(*b*) As long as the reader keeps clear of the complicated additional apparatus which was excluded from consideration above there is no question, with needle punch-cards, of any internal code. The printed layout of these cards also is quite unrestricted, so that as regards the particular coding structure using these cards one is left considerably freer and more independent than when using machine punch-cards. Details of the coding procedure are subject to the following considerations:

type of method (whether for notching or slitting)
number of holes in each card
arrangement of holes
number of selecting operations
number of sorting needles that can be used simultaneously in one operation, or the type of sorting apparatus.

Simple Codes—(A) Direct Code

Using a direct code, each single hole in the chosen punching field has one indication attributed to it. When using edge-notched cards which have two or more rows of holes, care must be taken that those holes which belong to the same vertical columns represent indications that are mutually exclusive, seeing that the deeper notches incidentally open the outer holes also. Edge-notched cards with two rows of holes are the kind most often adopted, and in using these for purposes of documentation it is desirable that the shallower and the deeper notching of each card should correspond respectively to two variations of the same concept which are mutually exclusive, or should represent two alternative meanings of a certain concept. For example, if edge-notched cards are being used for records of biological specimens, one such card being provided for each specimen, a particular kind of organism is assigned to each pair of holes one under the other. Absence of notching in that position will then indicate that the organism in question is 'never' present in the specimen, shallow notching that is 'seldom' present, and deep notching that is 'often' present.

With slit punch-cards, any desired indication may be assigned to any of the holes; but on the other hand they have certain disadvantages. In very many cases, direct coding is best for needle punch-cards and in every case it is the simplest form of code. By its use, numerous indications can be recorded simultaneously, close to one another on the same card, and any indication can be searched for in one operation using only one needle. (An exception to this statement occurs when edge-notched cards are used; for in these, whenever the shallower notches are needled, any cards which have been deeply notched in the same positions fall out also, and have to be separated by performing a second operation which consists of needling the deeper notches.) Apart from this exception, the simultaneous use of several needles makes it possible to extract in a single operation all those cards which represent a combination of several (theoretically any) indications.

The disadvantage of this code is the limited total capacity of the card. Only so many indications can be recorded as there are holes in the card (or in the chosen punching field).

(B) Abridged Code

To use an abridged code, compound punchings must be made in a deter-mined punching field. Theoretically it would be possible to use the whole punch-card as one punching field, but in practice this is seldom done as several codes are combined on one card.

Additive codes—These are exemplified here in an edge-notched card with two rows of holes. The most advantageous additive code to use is

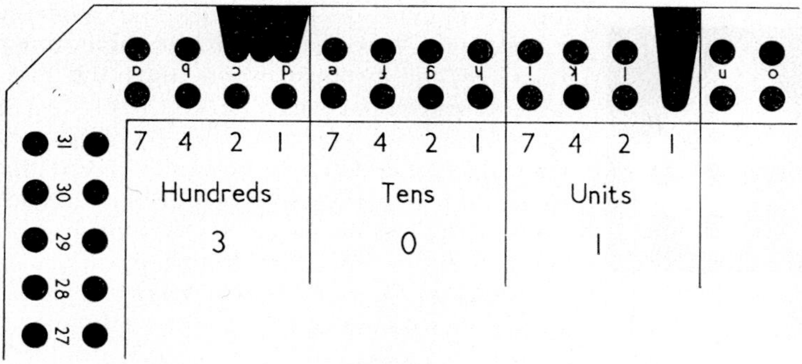

FIG. 23. Section of an edge-notched card with three-place 7, 4, 2, 1 code.

undoubtedly the 7, 4, 2, 1 code (Fig. 23), which necessitates a field of four pairs of holes and which accommodates the numbers 1 to 10 without risk of confusion. The numbers 1, 2, 4 and 7 are recorded by a single deep notching (which can be selected with one needle) whereas the numbers 3, 5, 6, 8 and 9 are recorded additively by the shallow-notching of two numbers which add up to them (which can be selected with two needles). The 10 is denoted by notching 4 + 7. When using several 7, 4, 2, 1 groups for fixing multi-digit numbers (by a combined code) it should be borne in mind that there is no zero but that in every position the numbers 1 to 10 are represented; hence the 10 needs only a simple coding (one 7, 4, 2, 1 group). Any following thus will then be put together from two digits; thus 20 is composed of 10 (7 + 4) in the units group plus 1 in the tens group. Like-wise 30 is to be coded as 10 × 2 and so on. The same thing applies to the hundreds and above, but if a zero occurs between two other digits—as for instance in 301—the zero is not notched at all (see Fig. 23). These rules are necessary because of sequential sorting (see page 83). It is also possible to use an abridged code 4, 2, 1 which allows six alternative indications to be expressed.

On the other hand, the 7, 4, 2, 1 code can, of course, be further extended. As an example of this, the months of the year can be coded by using an 11, 7, 4, 2, 1 code:

	Notching		Notching
January . . .	1/deep	July . . .	7/deep
February . .	2/deep	August . .	1 and 7/shallow
March . . .	1 and 2/shallow	September . .	2 and 7/shallow
April . . .	4/deep	October . .	4 and 7/shallow
May . . .	1 and 4/shallow	November . .	11/deep
June . . .	2 and 4/shallow	December . .	1 and 11/shallow

Using edge-notched cards with only one row of holes, or using slitted cards, the additive codes which have been explained require no pairs of holes but they necessitate one more hole in the chosen line of holes.   Thus, when using the 7, 4, 2, 1 code, five holes are needed in all.   This fifth hole is notched in every case where, in the example explained above, the notching would have been 'deep'.   When selecting this hole (denoted in the Anglo-American literature by S F meaning 'single figure') it must always be needled at the same time as the other; as, for instance, when using the 7, 4, 2, 1 code to search for any one of these four figures which otherwise would fall out by deep notching. The effect, therefore, is the same, except that one always has to search using two needles at once.

Fig. 24.   Numerical triangular code notched for the numeral 7 (Ruston, 1952).

From the classificational standpoint, it is possible to use additive codes for forming particular groups according to the type of card, either by using pairs of holes or columns or by using the S F hole.

Additive codes are widely applicable, both for the recording of purely numerical values and for other indications.   They are economical in space and simple to handle. Their disadvatange is that they enable only *one* indication to be punched at one time.

Triangular codes—The device of printing auxiliary triangles on needle punch-cards makes it possible, quickly and simply, to select combinations of two holes each.   Consequently this type of coding has been widely applied.

Example 1.   A triangular code for edge-notched cards, based on a punching field which contains four pairs of holes with numbers printed against them, is shown in Fig. 24.   The triangle is divided into square cells each containing two numbers.   On following along the sides of any such square from the right and left downwards a pair of holes is encountered. The rule which then applies is to make a deep notch in the upper number of the square on the right hand side (that is to say, in the right hand pair of holes) and a shallow notch in the left hand pair of holes.   For the lower number within the square, the procedure is the opposite to this; that is to say, this number has to be notched shallow on the right and deep on the left.   In the example here illustrated, the number 7 has been notched,

A triangular combination of n double holes allows $(n^2 - n)$ alternative recording possibilities.

Example 2. A triangular code for slit punch-cards, based on a punching field of nine ternary groups of holes with an imprint of letters: see under 'compound code', page 68.

Notching tables and coding instructions—It is not essential that coding combinations for abridged codes should be developed on the basis of auxiliary triangles; other solutions also exist, which often are more satisfactory. One of these is to use the notching tables published by Lochkartenwerk Schlitz for application to edge-notched cards (Fig. 25). The tables show combinations of notches, fully worked out, to which any desired letters, numerals or other indications can be assigned. For practical use it is desirable that the numbers assigned to the pairs of holes in the punching fields of needle punch-cards should be printed against them. In using the notching tables for notching they are read 'right way up', and in using them for needling 'upside down'. A specially notable feature is the provision of a notching table for sorting with three needles at once, which requires only five pairs of holes and provides 30 different possibilities (Fig. 25), thereby accommodating for instance the whole of the alphabet (including letters with the German *Umlauten*). From the notching table reproduced in Fig. 25 it will be seen that six of the notching combinations share a certain position of deep notching. From the point of view of classification, this means that there are five higher groups each comprising six single indications. Each of these higher groups in our example can be selected by means of a single needle inserted in the appropriate deep notch position. Little tricks of coding such as this—see also under the heading of additive codes—can in practice be very valuable. The experienced coder will be especially attentive to exploiting these possibilities which are inherent in the nature of systematically constructed codes.

Not even coding tables need necessarily be thought of as the last word. For many purposes, using needle punch-cards is simplest if the coding instructions can be directly implicit in the designation of the holes so as to make it evident at once how any given indication has to be notched or slitted. Coding instructions of this kind, for indicating the initial letters in authors' names, are shown overleaf (this example relating to edge-notched cards).

Notching tables can either be used directly or, as shown in our examples, they can serve as a basis for developing abridged codes to meet requirements, and can then be applied using more than two needles at one time in a single selecting operation. In practice, however, it is only in exceptional cases that codes for using more than three needles at a time are likely to prove satisfactory. All these codes serve primarily for general indexing and documentation. Their advantage lies in the increased capacity they furnish when used as alternatives.

The double pair code—The abridged codes mentioned up to this point are conceived with the aim that, wherever possible, only a single working operation shall be necessary for the selection of a simple indication. Where,

Authors' names: first letters

sh = shallow notch. dp = deep notch.

a, b, c, d, e are designations of pairs of holes in the card (as for instance, in Fig. 16).

A	=	c/sh,	d/sh,	e/dp		O	=	b/sh,	c/dp,	d/sh
A	=	b/sh,	d/sh,	e/dp		Ö	=	a/sh,	c/dp,	d/sh
B	=	a/sh,	d/sh,	e/dp		P	=	a/sh,	b/sh,	c/dp
C	=	b/sh,	c/sh,	e/dp		Q	=	b/dp,	d/sh,	e/sh
D	=	a/sh,	c/sh,	e/dp		R	=	b/dp,	c/sh,	e/sh
E	=	a/sh,	b/sh,	e/dp		S	=	a/sh,	b/dp,	e/sh
F	=	c/sh,	d/dp,	e/sh		Sch	=	b/dp,	c/sh,	d/sh
G	=	b/sh,	d/dp,	e/sh		St	=	a/sh,	b/dp,	d/sh
H	=	a/sh,	d/dp,	e/sh		T	=	a/sh,	b/dp,	c/sh
I	=	b/sh,	c/sh,	d/dp		U	=	a/dp,	d/sh,	e/sh
J	=	a/sh,	c/sh,	d/dp		V	=	a/dp,	c/sh,	e/sh
K	=	a/sh,	b/sh,	d/dp		W	=	a/dp,	b/sh,	e/sh
L	=	c/dp,	d/sh,	e/sh		X	=	a/dp,	c/sh,	d/sh
M	=	b/sh,	c/dp,	e/sh		Y	=	a/dp,	b/sh,	d/sh
N	=	a/sh,	c/dp,	e/sh		Z	=	a/dp,	b/sh,	c/sh

however, edge-notched cards are concerned, it also is possible to abandon this principle and thereby to devise a form of code which is very economical in space, namely the 'double pair' code (see Fig. 26).

As its name implies, two pairs of holes are here combined to make a double pair. Disregarding the case where this double pair is not notched at all, this gives eight possibilities of combination, as shown in Fig. 26. The line of thought which underlies this coding system is the following. If the pair of holes B is shallow-needled (sorting operation 1) the possibilities or concepts 1 to 6 will fall out whilst the possibilities or concepts 7 and 8 as well as all unwanted cards (not notched in this double pair) will remain hanging. The outcome of this operation then is two packs of cards which need to be further handled. Let us denote those cards which have fallen out by *I* and those which have remained hanging by *II*. In the next sorting operation (2), pack *I* is taken and the pair of holes B is deep-needled, causing the possibilities or concepts 1 to 3 to fall out whilst concepts 4 to 6 still remain hanging, so that pack *I* in its turn has been divided into two new packs of cards. Let us denote the cards which have fallen out by *I/a*, and those which have remained hanging by *I/b*. The third sorting operation now follows, which is performed upon pack *I/a* by shallow-needling the pair of holes *A*, thereby causing concepts 2 and 3 to fall out whilst concept 1 remains hanging. Let us call the cards which have fallen out last *I/a/a*. The same procedure, namely the shallow-needling of the pair of holes A, is carried out on pack *I/b*, causing concepts 5 and 6 to fall out whilst concept 4 remains hanging. Let us call concepts 5 and 6 together by the designation *I/b/a*. The pack *I/a/a* is then taken, and by deep-needling in the pair of holes A the concepts 2 and 3 are separated from one another (2 falling out whilst 3 remains hanging). The same procedure is performed upon pack *I/b/a*, causing concept 5 to fall out whilst concept 6 remains hanging. Now, finally, the pack of remaining cards, *II*, is shallow-needled in the pair of holes A, causing all the unwanted

the uppermost code 1, the middle code 2 and the lowest code 3. In this way they are combined to make a hierarchical code.

For instance, the first 'simple indication' in the name Schumann consists of the letter group 'Sch'. The appropriate combination of holes for this (the first simple code) in the uppermost line of holes is fixed by the straight lines running parallel to both the sides of both triangles, starting directly from the indication being sought, in this case 'Sch'. Both of the holes so arrived at are slit upwards. The next simple indication is 'u' and the

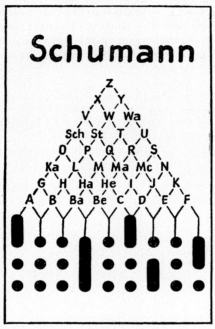

Fig. 27. Compound hierarchical triangular code, slotted for 'Sch', 'U' and 'Ma' (Draheim and Gdaniek, 1954).

third is 'ma': these are punched correspondingly in the second and third rows of holes within the triangular pattern.

Example 2 (a code devised by Grobe on the basis of the Universal Decimal Classification). Grobe, referring to the use of slit cards developed by himself, has published a numerical notation for applying the Universal Decimal Classification as a compound hierarchical code put together from direct codes. This is specially mentioned here because Grobe superimposes several UDC numbers in a single punching field which normally contains three direct codes, and this appears to have worked well. Other authors, however, do not favor such a procedure. Their opinion is that, although it works when the UDC is used because this is not a continuous numerical notation but consists of numbers with gaps between them, it would not be possible in application to a continuous sequence of numbers without interruptions, for in that case too many wrong cards would be selected.

Mixed compound codes—As already remarked at the beginning of this discussion, the user of needle punch-cards enjoys complete freedom to adopt combinations of simple codes of the most varied kinds in accordance with whatever may suit his own purposes and wishes. Here be it added that this freedom includes the possibility of using certain holes as indicators, as in the case of machine punch-cards, to confer a different significance on certain codes or on certain portions of the punch-card as a whole. Those who are interested in special coding possibilities applicable to needle punch-cards may be recommended the work by Draheim and Gdaniec (1954). Apart from this, the manufacturing firms concerned are very willing to supply customers with the benefit of their experience and advice.

Associative Codes

These codes can be constructed on exactly the same principle here as for machine punch-cards (see page 66).

4. VISUAL PUNCH-CARD METHODS *

(1) GENERAL

In the first edition of this book the author felt obliged to remark that the visual punch-card method (then known as the Cordonnier system) tended at that time to be undervalued and disregarded in comparison with machine punch-card and needle punch-card methods. In the intervening five years this position has notably changed. Many writers, both in Germany and in other countries, have recognized the importance of the visual punch-card method both quite generally and as being one which is particularly well suited for use by the individual intellectual worker. In consequence it can be stated that this group of methods, like that of needle punch-cards, now assumes quite a variety of forms. The various writers and suppliers of equipment have been at pains to adapt the principle for application in an ever growing number of fields; also to increase the number of holes in the cards, and to arrive at formats for the cards, and sizes and distributions of the holes, which will increase their range of suitability.

(2) THE CARDS AND THEIR USE

The following description is based on visual cards provided by the German company Checker G.m.b.H. at Frankfurt-am-Main (see Fig. 28). The visual punch-card may be a sheet of any dimensions, with punching positions over the whole of its area. In each special system these punching positions (defined on page 9 as being spaces where holes may later be punched) are differently arranged and differently marked. The total number of punching positions in a card depends, of course, on the format and on the size and arrangement of the holes; in those visual punch-cards which up to now have been described in the literature the smallest number of punching positions is 600 and the highest is 18000; the smallest diameter of hole used is less than 1 mm and the largest is more than 3 mm.

In many layouts of these cards the punching positions are not arranged in groups but take the form of a large grid of coordinates covering the whole card. Other manufacturers divide the cards into blocks each containing, as a rule, not more than 100 punching positions, and this form of layout makes them considerably easier to read (see Fig. 28). The Delta card designed by Loosjes (1957 a) is of interest in that the maximum possible number of punching positions in a minimum of card space is obtained by

---

* Unfortunately there is no English name for this system as unequivocal and self-explanatory as the German *Sichtlochkarten*. In America, where until recently it has been relatively little known, it is often called Peek-a-boo. In Britain the system has been described, in an attempt to be explanatory, as 'superimposable coincidentally punched-cards' and more conveniently (by J. L. Jolley) as 'feature cards', but more often, as in France, the cards are called by the names of inventors such as Batten, Borgeaud or Cordonnier, or by trade names.—Translator.

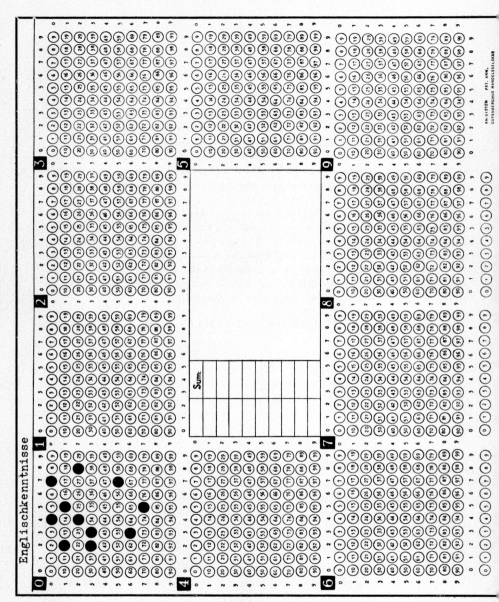

FIG. 28.   Visual feature-punched card of Deutsche Checker, Frankfurt am Main (Postfach 3621), used in this example to indicate knowledge of English.

the adoption of a triangular principle of layout, giving 10 000 punching positions (for holes of 2 mm diameter) in an area of 23 cm × 26 cm (about 9 in. × 10¼ in.).

The punching positions are identifiable either by making them readable as coordinates or by the direct printing of serial numbers as in the card here illustrated. In the author's opinion this direct numbering is the more satisfactory.

Either along the top or along the bottom edge of the cards, and also some-times in the middle, more or less extensive writing areas are provided.

Using this punch-card method, no coding system in the proper sense of the word is needed. As already explained in reference to the terminology on page 7 the visual punch-card method works on a principle which is in a sense the opposite of that which underlies the use of machine and needle punch-cards.

As an example, let us take a collection of personnel cards. Using any method in the other two groups, one machine or needle punch-card is provided *for each operating unit*—that is, for each individual person in this present example—and in every machine or needle punch-card a particular punching position or hole is assigned to each possible indication. But using visual punch-cards it is the other way round: one card is provided *for each possible indication*, and punching positions are provided on all the cards to correspond with the various working units numbered in serial order.

For the purpose of our example, let us make a list of the indications which might arise:

Under 20 years old
Between 20 and 30 years old
Between 30 and 40 years old
Between 40 and 50 years old
Salary rates other than those mentioned below
Salary rates I–III
Salary rates IV–VI
Salary rates VII–VIII
Salary rates IX–X
Wage rates
Knowledge of English
Knowledge of French
Knowledge of Spanish
Knowledge of other languages
Qualified in typewriting
Qualified in stenography, etc.

For each of these indications a single visual punch-card is provided and that indication is written on the card, preferably along the top edge. The cards are filed either alphabetically or in groups such as, in this example, the groups 'Age', 'Payment', 'Language knowledge' and 'Other qualifica-tions'. Every employee of the undertaking is given a personal serial number, which may conveniently correspond to his or her number in an alphabetical list of names or in some existing personnel card file. Newly engaged employees must not be given the numbers of persons who have ceased to be employed but must receive new numbers in a continuing series.

The next step in the operation is that of punching the visual cards. Beginning with personal number 1, and taking in hand a list of the indications which are applicable to that person, a hole is made in punching space No. 1 on each of those visual cards which correspond to the indications which are applicable to that person. If, for instance, employee No. 1 in our example is 27 years old, is paid a salary in class III, knows English and is qualified in typewriting the visual cards marked respectively 'between 20 and 30 years old', 'payment classes I–III', 'knowledge of English' and 'qualified in typewriting' are taken out from the file and, by means of a punch or forceps, each of these cards is punched in the position which corresponds to No. 1. A similar procedure is followed in the case of each of the other personal numbers. The punching apparatus may be such as to allow of several cards being punched simultaneously.

A collection of visual punch-cards prepared in this way makes it possible rapidly to examine the situation of all the employees from any desired point of view, and also to answer combined questions. If, for instance, it is desired to identify all staff members between 20 and 30 years old, nothing more need be done than take out the visual punch-card which records this particular feature and read off the serial numbers of the individuals in question from the punching positions which have in fact been punched. These numbers make it possible to refer back to a personal card file in which the names and other indications of the persons concerned have been entered. If, however, only the *total number* of employees between 20 and 30 years old is wanted there is no need to refer back to this personal card file, but merely to count the holes which have been punched in the appropriate visual card.

The main advantage of this method, however, does not become apparent until a combined question has to be answered. Should it for some reason be desired to find out which of the employees between 20 and 30 years old know English and also are qualified in typewriting, the visual cards that correspond to all three of these features are taken out, superimposed on one another and held up to the light, or (examined on a glass plate illuminated from below). Thereupon any holes through which the light is seen to pass indicate that the corresponding serial numbers have been punched in all three cards, which means that the employees who bear the numbers of those holes combine all three of the desired features. Thus the question is answered in the quickest and simplest possible way.

Here the example of a personnel card collection has been taken because it is one of general application and is easy to understand. By analogy it can be transferred to any other field of application. (For further examples see Part III, pages 248 and 260.)

It seems important to make one further remark. If, after having recorded let us say the 143rd working unit (in our example the 143rd employee), it is perceived that yet another feature ought to be taken into account, for which no visual card has yet been provided, such an additional card can be added later. If one does not wish to go to the trouble of re-examining all the existing numbered cases (in this case employees) to see which of them ought to be punched for this new feature, the newly added visual card which records this new feature should be marked with the fact that it has been taken into account only from No. 143 onward. In some other fields of application, for instance in literature searching, this procedure has a still more important function to fulfil.

When a set of visual cards is full, that is to say when all the punching positions have been used up, a second set must be begun. If necessary a different color of card can be used, or a special notching in the case of notched visual cards. If the second set of cards is to contain numbers which continue the series on the first set it is desirable (according to Knappe, 1956) to stamp the final number (total capacity) of the first set clearly upon all the cards in the second set. This stamped number then has to be added to the running numbers in the second set, in order to arrive at the running numbers which actually apply.

The numbers punched in this type of card may also be such as to carry further expressive possibilities; they may for instance correspond with the numbers of the pages in publications. The present author does not, however, feel any urge to advocate this special device, as too many gaps in the numbering may ensue and this may give rise to a risk of errors. The matter is different when existing *serial* numbers are recorded by punching in the visual cards.

Braband (1957) has suggested and tried out an interesting further development of the visual punch-card system. His suggestions, once again, may most easily be explained by taking a personnel card index as an example. It is obvious that nearly all the enquiries handled with the aid of a visual punch-card collection thus applied relate to staff members who are still actively employed, rather than to those who have already left their employment at the time of the enquiry. It is, however, inherent in the nature of the method that the punching positions assigned on the cards to staff members who have ceased to be employed cannot simply be cancelled, as the records can be cancelled when an ordinary card index or machine-punched or edge-notched cards are used. Cancellation would be possible only by pasting over the holes made in the visual punch-cards, which is not a practical proposition. Braband, therefore, introduces among his other visual cards one which is of a different color from the others—in his example, light green—which he calls a 'leaving card', and also a black underlay card of the same size. In the leaving card the serial numbers of staff who have left or are leaving the employment are punched. When, now, the visual cards are being consulted, the green leaving card with the black underlay underneath it is placed behind any cards corresponding to the features sought for. Consequently any holes in these cards which are in alinement and would normally be seen through, their numbers corresponding to those of the staff members sought for, will now reveal either the green leaving card (if this *has not been* punched in that position) or the black underlay (if the leaving card *has been* punched in that position). This device provides the additional possibility of showing whether the individual in question is still in employment (green background) or has already left it (black background). Instead of using two cards—the green leaving card and a black underlay—it may be preferred to use a single leaving card which is not punched but which is blackened at the punching positions that correspond to the former employees who have left (as, for instance, by using a soft black pencil). This development of the system can also be applied in other directions.

Apart from this, Braband has also described other possibilities, based on various different ways of marking the punching positions. The present author, however, feels some misgivings about complications of this kind, impairing as they do the masterly simplicity of the visual punch-card method as normally applied.

The principle underlying visual punch-cards can also be carried out with machine punch-cards. For instance, the owner of an IBM or Powers punch can make use of it to produce visual cards, though subject to the limitation that the range of serial numbers which can be accommodated in IBM or Powers cards is relatively small (960 in the former and 540 in the latter). The Powers cards are specially well adapted to this use, as Remington Rand has produced a simple kind of punching forceps which make it possible to punch the cards by hand. (See the description of this on page 49.)

Lastly, mention may be made of Carlé's (1955) adoption of the visual punch-card principle for a 'Synoptic method of recording and studying the propagation of epidemics in time and space by reference to a file of punched maps'. This represents a transfer of the same principle from cards to geographical maps or plans, which is yet another direction in which manifold other possibilities may be envisaged.

(3) **EQUIPMENT AND AIDS**

The equipment needed for use of the visual punch-card method is extremely simple, involving nothing more elaborate than some sort of device for punching the holes. In the 'Sphinxo' system, for instance, two holed templates, a baseboard and a punching rod are provided; the visual card is inserted between the templates over the baseboard, and the rod is pushed through to punch the required hole. Several cards can be so punched at the same time. Other manufacturers provide punching forceps. Yet others have developed more complicated punching devices, whereby the punching positions are set to coordinates (Fig. 29). Generally speaking these punching devices with coordinate setting are necessary for positioning the holes accurately when they are very small, whereas with larger holes the forceps work well enough. It would be useful if the firms which produce equipment using large holes would exploit the principle, developed by Remington Rand (Powers) and described on page 49, of pre-punching a small guide hole in every potential punching position, for this would enable the large holes to be quickly and accurately punched as required by closing the forceps over the pilot holes; but experience alone can show whether this improvement would in fact be worth its cost.

The possibilities of the visual punch-card method also could be amplified by various little technical and organizational aids such as the use of interlaid

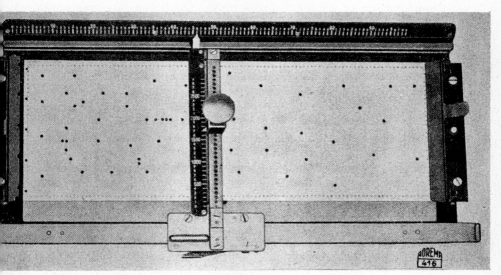

FIG. 29.   Gang punching device for visual feature-punched cards (Kistermann, 1957–58).

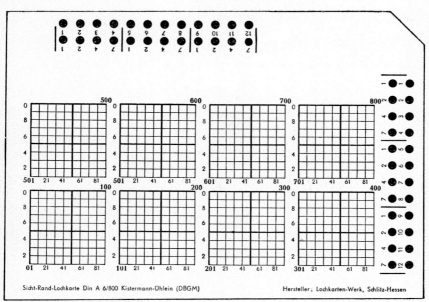

FIG. 30.   Combined visual feature-punched and edge-notched card from Lochkartenwerk Schlitz.

transparent plates and other special tricks.   According to a bibliographical reference, a mechanical method of using visual cards has also been developed, but the author has not followed this up as he is of opinion that visual cards, like edge-notched cards, represent a typical hand method and that it is precisely here that their great advantage lies, so that mechanization does not appear profitable.   Whoever wishes to use machines should adopt machine punch-card methods which have been proved reliable.

(4) COMBINATION WITH OTHER METHODS

The principle of the visual punch-card method can be combined with that of the machine punch-card method on the same cards and, quite apart from this, machine punch-cards can themselves be used as visual punch-cards. A combination of the visual punch-card principle with that of edge-notched cards has been worked out, and applied in practice, by Kistermann and Ühlein (Fig. 30).   A similar combination with slitted cards is conceivable also, though less practical.

PART II

GENERAL RULES AND EXPERIENCE FOR
APPLYING PUNCH-CARD METHODS IN RESEARCH
AND DOCUMENTATION

words as hunger, thirst, storm, rain, dog, tree, light—we may either, like Sigwart, regard the associative process as being the consummation of natural imagery or, on the other hand, we may regard it as consisting in discernment of a logical object: that is, of a *concept*.   Thus *conceptualization consists always in objectivizing the contents of consciousness*. (Translated from Elsenhans, 1936.)

As it is not possible in science (or in ordinary life) to build on a loose foundation composed merely of propositions held in common, these have to be consolidated into definitions as accurate as possible so as to convert them into the more determinate form which we call a 'concept', and have then to be designated by symbols.   The most widely usable symbols for this purpose are those provided for us in spoken and written language.   These, however, are merely *aids* towards explaining the *significance* of concepts.   The word associated with a concept is no more than a help towards re-awakening in us a common proposition.   Indeed, we think primarily in the words of our language and only secondarily in concepts.   What matters, however, is not what is said, but what is meant; that is, the significance of the words used. For every general proposition, that is for every datum, only a single concept exists; but in each language there is *at least* one word for it, contributing to a total of many words.

To summarize, it may be said that each general image is subjective and belongs to the domain of psychology, whereas concepts are objective and belong to logic.   Finally, words are no more than symbols for concepts, and they belong to the field of linguistics.

The situation being so represented, we are concerned, then, first of all with the field of logic.   In this context it has been found that logic and logical theory as a whole are not important for application to the punch-card method in research and documentation; hence only those terms and rules of logic which are necessary for us will here be stated and discussed.

What are important are the logical properties of concepts, as will be explained in close accordance with Elsenhans (1936).   In reference to each concept we can name:

(*a*) the features which identify it
(*b*) the facts related to it.

From these two possibilities, there arises the differentiation between:

(*a*) the intension (content) of the concept, and
(*b*) the extension of the concept.

The greater the number of features inherent in a concept, the greater is its content.   The greater the number of data it covers, the greater is its extension.   Intension and extension tend to be in a reciprocal relationship to one another: the greater the content of the concept, the smaller is its extension, the greater its extension, the smaller is its content.

Example: The concept 'living habit' has a small intension as it can be identified by reference to relatively few features; at the same time it has a large extension for it covers many data (appertaining to the lives of all plants, animals and people).   The concept 'dachshund' has a large intension as it requires very many features to identify it, but has only a small extension as only a small number of living habits come under it. A concept is *clear* when its extension is clearly delimited from the extensions of other concepts. A concept is *intelligible* when all the characteristics it contains are clear in themselves.

(A) The Intension of a Concept

The characteristics which determine the content of a concept are divisible into:

(*a*) Essential characteristics
(*b*) Accidental characteristics.

The essential characteristics are those without which the concept in question could not be thought, and which therefore necessarily appertain to it. This is the same as saying that the essential characteristics must always necessarily appertain to all of the instances which fall under the concept in question.

Accidental characteristics are those which do not have to belong to the concept, which is to say that they may be missing from particular facts which fall under the concept in question.

Example: Essential characteristics of the concept 'camomile' (*Matricaria chamomilla*) include, among many others, the white color and the shape of its flowers, the shape of its leaves and the camomile scent. Accidental characteristics of the camomile are the number of its leaves and the number of its flowers.

The essential characteristics of a concept can further be divided into:

(*a*) individual characteristics (*notae propriae*)
(*b*) common characteristics (*notae communes*)

Individual characteristics belong exclusively to the one set whereas common characteristics also appertain to others.

Example: The scent of the lily of the valley is one of its individual characteristics. On the other hand, the parallelism of its leaves is a common characteristic which it shares with the majority of monocotyledonous plants.

According to the number of characteristics, a distinction can be drawn between simple concepts and compound concepts. Simple concepts have only one characteristic. (Examples: something, to be, space) whereas compound concepts have several (plant, animal, triangle).

(B) The Extension of a Concept

According to the extension, a distinction can be drawn between:

Individual concepts
Concepts of kind
Concepts of class.

Something which occurs only once and momentarily cannot be grasped as a concept. We have no difficulty, however, in forming a general impression and concept of a single individual person when we have met that individual at different times and he has on each occasion appeared to us the same.   It is in this way that an individual concept is formed.   Concepts of kind follow directly from individual concepts, but concepts of class derive from a plurality of concepts of kind and are therefore *higher* and *wider* concepts by contrast with concepts of kind which are described as narrow.   The higher and wider a concept the larger is its extension.

It is a regrettable fact that our words 'kind' (species) and 'class' (genus) have ambiguous meanings.   On the one hand they are connected with the logical definition given above, according to which the concepts or meanings associated with these words are very wide.   On the other hand, in biology these words have a much narrower meaning, being associated with a single, definite content; there 'kind' denotes the totality of all those individual modes of life that have the same original descent, form a community of propagation and agree as to their most essential observed characteristics, whilst 'class' denotes the next higher category of habit relationships.   It is very misleading when the logical and the biological meanings for the words 'kind' (species) and 'class' (genus) have to be used together.   In the present chapter only the logical meaning is intended.

According to the degree of their extension, a distinction is drawn between what will here be called:

Higher collective concepts

Collateral or coordinate concepts, and

Lower specific concepts.

Concepts of class always stand higher than concepts of kind.   Concepts of kind within a class are collateral.   Concepts of kind are always subordinate to concepts of class.

For a classification to be logically perfect, the collateral concepts within the same class must be mutually exclusive of one another (see also page 117 in the section on classification theory).

As was made clear above, all concepts derive from common impressions; that is to say, from something which is general.   The philosophical distinction drawn between what is meant by the 'individual' and the 'general' cannot and need not be gone into here, but von Weizsäcker (1948) has treated the problem of what is implied by 'general' in a way which is very useful for our present purpose.   He writes:

The 'general' means that which is common to many individual cases. In order to obtain our first notions of what is meant by 'general' we may remember that the logical distinction drawn between subject, predicate and a whole proposition makes it possible to divide everything which can be talked about at all into objects, properties and subject content. . . . We meet with 'the general' in all three of these forms.   There is no name for 'general' as a property to distinguish it from 'individual'.   The general as an object is called class, the general as a subject content is called a law.

Further examination will show that properties always appear in the form of the general *only*.   Since, however, concepts of properties also vary in extension, and can be divided into higher and lower categories, the logical designations 'kind' and 'class' ought also to be applied to these concepts of properties; or else other corresponding expressions should be found for them. In this book, an attempt will be made to introduce and define such designations, since their absence often leads to misunderstandings.

We shall call the category which corresponds to concepts of kind, when it is applied to concepts of properties, by the term '*characteristic*', and the category corresponding to that of a concept of class we shall here call '*characteristic dimension*'. We then have the following scheme, with examples:

The 'general'

As 'object'	As 'property'
Kind (red ball)	Characteristic (red)
Class (ball)	Characteristic dimension (color)

Further consideration shows that the distinction drawn between objects and properties provides us with the basis for making the distinction between nomenclature and terminology, which has already been mentioned and will later be discussed. For objects there exists mainly nomenclature, for properties there exists terminology.

(3) LANGUAGE AND WRITING

As we have already seen, language and writing—that is to say, spoken or recorded words—are the most usual way of symbolizing or referring to concepts.

Language is older than science and has developed separately within each of the various human communities, taking no account of logic or of general scientific needs. With the increasing development of science this circumstance has led to ever greater difficulties. Language as used in normal intercourse is indeed an extraordinarily versatile instrument, but for this very reason a very inaccurate one for science. Consequently, in the course of time, a special technical language for scientific purposes has been split off from ordinary language. Nowadays, however, even this special technical language labors under serious defects and often it is still cramped by primitive formations.

These problems, too, are of fundamental importance in the whole activity of publication as in the problems which remain to be treated here, for, since all publications are clad in language, ordinary and technical language are used together. In the course of scientific development the proportion between ordinary and technical language has shifted more and more in the direction of the latter—though of course to a different extent in the various disciplines, and leaving ordinary language still strongly predominant.

Here two contrary tendencies are manifest, one of these being founded in the nature of language itself whilst the other derives from science which looks upon language as a tool. As regards language itself, and those who handle it as poets and authors, the tendency is in the direction of liveliness and multiplicity of forms. Scientists, on the other hand, aim at the greatest possible definition, and this tends to make language insipid and colorless.

Thus synonyms, which as used by the poet contribute to liveliness and style, are for the scientists a sore encumbrance.

A distinction may therefore be drawn between the two extremes to which language can tend. On the one hand is the possibility of ministering to the esthetic taste in prose and poetry and also to some extent in daily use, and of cultivating language to this end. On the other hand is the possibility of using language exclusively as a vehicle of information. These two modes of using language have to exist side by side. Having regard, however, to the overwhelming flood of printed material it has become one of the most urgent of problems so to foster the development of language for use in the *purely scientific* publications as to make it as far as possible a tool of precision for the conveyance of information. In this connection, other solutions and systems of symbols for fixing and storing knowledge call for consideration also (see Chapter 7).

'Artificial' languages such as Esperanto and Interlingua have been developed. Other proposals have been made, either to revive Latin as the language of science or to recognize some living language such as English as serving that purpose, but up to the present none of them has been accepted universally.

American and British authors, in particular, have rightly urged that more attention should be paid to what is known as information theory in the field of publication and documentation (Heumann, 1955; Fairthorne, 1956). One of the questions which is being examined, within the scope of this theory, is that of the smallest number of symbols (including the letters and words of a language) necessary to reproduce unequivocally a particular item of information (knowledge, etc.). If we are to cope nowadays with the flood of knowledge some such rationalization of scientific information or records is becoming compulsory. Mastery of the problems of publication and documentation must, then, begin on the level of terminology and nomenclature.

Of course, the need for rationalization and standardization of scientific language does not imply that alongside of purely scientific information there should not appear general scientific publications in the more esthetic and circumstantial literary form. That, however, is another question which does not affect the core of the problem we are discussing here.

As has repeatedly been pointed out, concepts can be expressed only by the use of words or other symbols. Hence the delimitation or definition of concepts plays a decisive part in fixing the relationship between concepts and words in spoken and written language. It is in this way that the meaning of a word which designates a given concept is determined. This can occur either by stating the characteristics of a concept or by stating the next higher collective (*genus proximum*) to which it belongs and its differences of kind (*differentia specifica*).

Any definition is subject to the difficulty that it is impossible to cite all the characteristics of a concept. Definition is exposed, directly or indirectly, to a great variety of errors and ambiguities such as are encountered every day in scientific practice. A distinction may be drawn between:

(*a*) errors in the definition itself

(*b*) inadequacies lying outside the actual definition.

(A) Errors in Definition

(Adapted from Elsenhans, 1936)

(*1*) A definition is too wide when it omits to mention essential characteristics of the concept it seeks to define.

(*2*) A definition is too narrow when it includes too many characteristics.

(*3*) A definition should not include superfluous characteristics which are implicit in other characteristics already mentioned, or are necessarily associated with those.

(*4*) The name of the concept which is being defined must not reappear within the terms of the definition either openly or in hidden form (tautology).

(*5*) Definitions must not run in circles, as happens when a concept is explained by reference to a second, third, etc., concept and the last in the chain is explained by reference to the initial concept.

(*6*) A definition must not make use of figurative expressions, as these are too uncertain.

(*7*) Only in exceptional cases, where positive statements do not suffice, should a definition depend on negative statements.

(*8*) A definition must not be confused with enumeration of the forms in which the concept occurs—that is to say, with establishing the extension of a concept—for these forms are inherent in the concept itself (as its *genus proximum*) so that a circle would be formed.

(B) Inadequacies Outside the Definition

(*1*) Several words may exist for expressing the same concept. Synonyms, as these are called, may exist within the same language (pansy, heartsease) or in different languages (*Mutter*, mother, *mère*). In technical language which is not yet international, such multilingual synonyms must necessarily occur for most concepts. On the other hand, there are many languages, particularly those of underdeveloped countries, in which no words exist for many concepts.

(*2*) The same word may designate several concepts although these may be clearly distinguishable from one another. Such homonyms often arise through figurative transfers of meaning.

(*3*) The same word may have provided a basis for differing conceptualizations, each correct in itself but relating to varying numbers of characteristics or to differing characteristics of the concept in question. Thus the meaning of the word changes like a play of colors: it ought properly to be unambiguous, but is understood and used differently by different people.

There can be no doubt that this very circumstance applies to large numbers of words and concepts so that the resulting problems are far more difficult than those which arise under points (*1*) and (*2*). When the multiplicity of languages is taken into account the whole problem, of course, becomes particularly complex. Here the first priority should be the establishment of order within one's own language; but fortunately, meanwhile, Unesco and the International Organization for Standardization are attending to these questions on the international plane too (see also page 113).

(*4*) Changes of concepts in time constitute a problem in themselves. Such changes occur when, at a given point in time, a concept has been correctly defined by reference to the knowledge then existing and a corresponding word has been assigned to it, but subsequently the advance of knowledge has altered the characteristics and extension. Thus the concept may have become wider or narrower, or it may have been found necessary to split it into two separate concepts. In most cases, however, the word originally chosen continues in use, confronting the student with the awkward task of tracing back the changes of meaning it has undergone in the course of scientific development. Often these changes are apparent in the word itself. In the medical field Hartung, especially, has given some very striking examples (for instance, 'tuberculosis').

(4) NOMENCLATURE AND TERMINOLOGY

The natural sciences, including for instance chemistry, all recognize fundamentally the same distinction. Nomenclature relates to the objects of research, to which 'names' are applied having as far as possible a validity which is independent of their verbal meanings and does not change. Terminology, on the other hand, relates to aids, processes and general concepts, also to technical expressions which from time to time are newly matched with the changing requirements. The difference is sharply observed in botany and also in zoology. Thus terminology establishes those technical expressions [terms— Author] which designate properties, whilst nomenclature deals with names. Terms occurring in morphology are coelum, oesophagus, delthyrium. Terms in physiology are secretion, breathing, homothermy. Terms in taxonomy include those denoting hierarchical steps such as species, genus, family, order. On the other hand, names are applied only to the actual living units, such as felis leo, felidae, carnivora, mammalia. Nomenclature is pertinent only to names in the true sense. Nevertheless, nomenclature has within itself a terminology of its own, including such terms as nomen nudum, binary, lectogenotypus, monotypy, objective and subjective homonomy, regularity and validity.   (Translated from R. Richter, 1943.)

(A) Nomenclature

A more or less self-contained nomenclature, following its own rules, is to be seen principally in chemistry, mineralogy, botany, zoology (including anthropology) and astronomy.   These are the sciences in which a multitude of concrete natural objects occur such as elements, compounds, minerals, rocks, plants, animals, people and stars.   For this reason those disciplines can also be characterized as object-controlled sciences.   It is a characteristic of nomenclatural usage that the initial process of conferring a name raised relatively small problems; thus 'atoms' and 'individuals' were perceived as self-contained 'indivisible' units, upon which it was merely necessary to confer the name without its being immediately necessary to agree upon a complete and unequivocal definition.   One merely had to say 'I shall call this object X and that object Y'.   The circumstance that it is easy to bestow a name explains the possibility of securing almost unchangeable validity for a name, regardless of the meaning associated with that name as a word.   In zoological and botanical practice, for instance, the procedure followed has been to lay down what are called 'types' of the individual species of organism.   Such types are single individuals, preserved for instance in a certain museum, to which the specific name in question is related.   Such exhibits are accepted once and for all as being bearers of the name conferred upon them and as objects with which to compare other individuals of the same species.   Here, therefore, it is possible to indicate concretely what one means, without the need for a long definition.   In chemistry the conditions are considerably easier still, because all atoms forming part of the same isotope of an element and all molecules in a given compound are absolutely equal in their nature.

Obviously, man bestowed names upon natural objects in his environment long before the scientific age.   Generally these are known as 'trivial' names and most of them are looked upon in the scientific world with disfavor because they are synonyms.   The trivial names exist side by side with the scientific names deliberately created for the purpose of scientific understanding, most of which are international in character.   There are two kinds of scientific names, those which make the structure or properties of the object in question immediately apparent and those which do not.

The best developed nomenclature is that of chemistry.   F. Richter (1955) has published a good account of this.   Among other things, he stresses the importance of taking a historical view of nomenclatural questions:

> It may perhaps be said that a knowledge of history is nowhere so necessary as in matters of nomenclature.   At any rate, many characteristic facts may be learned from it.   The foundations of the modern nomenclature we owe to Lavoisier, who made some notable remarks about it in the introduction to his treatise published in 1789.   He said, 'When I undertook this work it was merely my intention to carry further what I had said in my lecture delivered in April 1787 about the need to improve chemical nomenclature, . . . but whilst I thought I was concerning myself only with nomenclature, there took shape unnoticed in my hands, without my being able to stop it, the present textbook on chemistry'.   In these words the inevitable connection between the state of knowledge and the nomenclature associated with it is very strikingly expressed.

The governing consideration in chemical nomenclature is the fact that the names of the compounds allow their structure to be directly inferred. This, in turn, connects with the possibility of recognizing the place which each substance occupies in the system of compounds, or in other words to perceive from the name its affiliation to particular classes of substances. Of course this high level of nomenclature is made possible only because the present state of chemical science allows the structure of each compound to be definitely determined, so that a completely unequivocal connection between substances and their names can be established.

In botany and zoology the situation is much less favorable. It is, indeed, a fact that organisms do mostly appear in the form of individuals, but they have an infinitely more complex structure than chemical compounds and instead of being mainly static they are units which have to be regarded as dynamic, so that they offer no basis for nomenclature such as can be compared even approximately with that of chemistry. In botany and zoology scientific nomenclature is scarcely 200 years old, deriving as it does from the famous systematic work of the Swedish naturalist Carl Linnaeus (Linné) *Systema Naturae* (10th edition, 1758).

It is mainly a 'binary nomenclature', according to which each species of organism is denoted by two internationally understood Latin (or Latinized) or Greek names or often by names which are a mixture of these two languages. The first of the two names is that of the genus and the second that of the species, as for instance in *Viola odorata* (violet) and *Canis lupus* (wolf).   There exist complete, though unfortunately separate, rules of nomenclature for botany and zoology designed to make internationally uniform names possible and to eliminate double naming as well as other causes of misunderstanding (Mansfeld, 1942 a, 1942 b; R. Richter, 1943).   By reason, however, of the separate treatment of botany and zoology there unfortunately exist various names of genera which appear both in botany and in zoology, such as *Balanus, Fritillaria, Lunaria*.   Most botanical and zoological names do not, in principle, relate to the properties of the mode of life in question, and do not make it possible to recognize the systematic place occupied by the organisms in question further than the genus, the name of which is always included.   The fact that many specific names, and also some genetic names, derive from conspicuous characteristics of the organisms to which they are applied—*Viola* **odorata,** sweet scented violet; **Cardium** *edule,* (heart-shaped) cockle—in no wise alters the fundamental fact that these names are 'unsystematic' and provide only a slight mnemonic aid.

The binary nomenclature of botany and zoology, which so to speak is nowadays part of the flesh and blood of every biologist, has another disadvantage, one which is important from the point of view that mainly interests us here of being able to apply the punch-card method.   It is the general and unchallenged use of this nomenclature that makes it a help from force of habit.   A binary name (disregarding here for simplicity ternary and quaternary names which are the result of a later development) relates always to some definite biological category, the genus or the species, and that particular category has won itself a recognized central position in biological systematics.   The central position, however, can be justified only from certain quite definite aspects which will be further considered in Chapter 6.   Such names occupy a privileged position of 'monopoly' which

has led to the neglect of other lines of thought. Too often it has been forgotten or not sufficiently considered that the 'species' category does not in
any sense constitute a primary unit corresponding roughly to that of a
compound in chemistry. In biology, the primary units are property as
exemplified not in the species of 'moth' but rather in the egg, the cater-
pillar at each of its various stages of development, the chrysalis and finally
the butterfly (*imago*) itself. Likewise, also, for the two sexes and the castes
(workers, soldiers, etc.) among bees and ants.

Recently, Hennig (1950) has considered these questions in a detailed
work from which the following is an extract:

> It is often assumed, as will here be explained, that the final and
> simplest element in biological systematics . . . is the form of life (the
> 'individuum'), if indeed it is not the species or individuum which is
> bound to recur identically in all possible systems. However, it is one of
> the simplest and oldest of known facts in biology that individual forms of
> life, with their attendant properties and characteristics, are not constant
> values, but undergo changes within short intervals of time. Very
> recently this fact has again been brought prominently into the fore-
> ground and an extreme dynamic view has been put forward, not only
> as regards processes of life but as regards living forms 'No describable
> form is more than an arbitrary extract, determined by the point in time
> at which it is taken' (Torrey as cited by von Dabelow).

And further:

> It follows from these considerations that the ultimate element in bio-
> logical systematics cannot be the mode of life or the individual (to say
> nothing of the species) but can only be the mode of life of the individual
> at a particular point of time, or better still during a particular interval
> of time. This we designate here as being the characterizing element for
> all biological systematics: the bearer of characteristics, or semaphoront
> for the sake of brevity. No generally valid indication can be given as
> to how long, in practice, the interval of time has to be measured so as to
> ensure that the semaphoront may exist as a constant systematically
> usable magnitude (Hennig, 1950).

Thus species, as the basis for the binary nomenclature, is not an elementary
concept but a group concept. But there exist neither an international and
general nomenclature, nor any corresponding rules, for the semaphorontes
which we must now prefer as the logical elementary units when applying
the punch-card method to biology.

The present book cannot, of course, be concerned with details of these
questions. Like all other problems of biological systematics, they must be
left for a separate publication.

(B) Terminology

By contrast with nomenclature, we find a terminology existing in all branches
of science. Recalling from page 104 the distinction drawn between 'objects',

'properties' and 'subjects', it now becomes possible to see clearly the boundaries between terminology and nomenclature, for it can be laid down that terminology relates always to properties and not to objects.   Here, however, the qualification must be stressed that 'objects', as already pointed out in reference to nomenclature, must be taken to include only such data as we possess in the form of separate and self-contained units.   Portions of self-contained data which are not themselves self-contained must not, therefore, be included under the concept 'objects'.   This applies, for instance, to the cells, tissues and organs of organisms, which ought to be regarded rather as properties of the mode of life in question (not constituting self-contained data and therefore an 'object'), so that their naming belongs to the sphere of terminology, not to that of nomenclature.

Evidently it is necessary to decide exactly what is to be regarded as an object and what as a property.   In other disciplines, such as technology. this question is still more difficult.   Later, in classification theory, there will arise the problems of categorization which are made clear for instance in the proposals of Ranganathan (1957), Vickery (1957) and others.   From the fact that terminology always relates to properties, there follows a circumstance which is especially pertinent to our discussion, namely that properties always appear as something general.   It is inherent in their nature that they are more general than objects, because they always appear the same in more than one object.   According to our definition, this necessarily implies that terms must tend to have a more general character than names.   Logically, then, terms as a rule have a wider extension than names.   The more general a science, the more will terms take precedence over names.   Thus physics, which is the most general of the natural sciences and which is concerned mainly with properties, possesses only a terminology and no nomenclature.   Within the framework of biology there are branches such as morphology, physiology, genetics and (in the narrower sense) ecology which share this 'cross sectional' character, in that they cut straight across the object-determined disciplines such as bacteriology, botany, zoology, anthropology, palaeontology.   The former may be described, therefore, as being disciplines which are concerned with properties (the structure of bodies, life functions, phenomena of heredity, conditions of environment) that appear in all objects (organisms).   Consequently a uniform terminology would here be very desirable, but unfortunately it is not available (see below).

The process of assigning terms is often much more problematical than the process of conferring names.   By reference to what principle, for instance, should the organs in organisms be uniformly designated?   A more detailed examination of this question shows up an almost impenetrable tangle of conflicting requirements.   Let us take for example the heart.   Superficially this word suggests a definite form or shape, which figuratively can be transferred for application to the shapes of the leaves on plants for instance, and likewise in daily speech we use the description 'heart-shaped'.   But in most organisms the heart itself is not in fact heart-shaped.   When we talk of the heart in insects or snails we no longer mean a particular shape, an object in the form of a heart, but a particular part of the organism which performs a certain *function*. By contrast with this consideration the shape or structure falls into the background, so the same word is applied both to a morphological and to a physiological concept. The very word 'organ', which after all means no more than 'tool', inclines us to look upon and to define terminologically the structures of organisms, particularly their organs, as when we say that the heart is the central organ of circulation, the kidney is the organ of excretion, and so forth. It is easy to see that it would indeed be impossible to proceed in any other way. In other sciences, too, and in the everyday use of language, most things are determined and named from their functions. Thus what primarily interests us about a chair is not its structure or the history of its manufacture but the fact that one can sit on it.

In biology the procedure should be, therefore, to define those terms which relate to organs according to the functions of the latter. Having fixed the technical expressions in this way, it will then be possible to make progress in classification theory and to arrange the organs in accordance with the requirements of various systems, that is to compare them as objects (species or organisms, and semaphorontes) from various morphological, physiological, evolutionary and other points of view.

On the question of terminology in the chemical sphere, F. Richter (1955) has written as follows:

> For many problems in the field of documentation, linguistics, that is to say the coining and delimitation of words and concepts, is the essential substratum either directly or indirectly. Experimentally determined data, and reasoning based upon them, are given expression in words; and in the opposite direction it is words which lead back to subject content, as for instance via an index. Most of the words we have to do with in chemistry are of a double nature. They relate partly to terminology, partly to nomenclature. When, today, we consult the index of a chemical abstract journal we may notice that the number of general concepts falls far below the number of names of substances; and seeing how many substances are known this is not surprising. Nevertheless, it shows that neither the arrangement of our science in accordance with subject concepts [terms—Author] nor the subsidiary arrangement of known material under these concepts has developed as far as it properly should if the needs of current research are to be satisfied.

The unsatisfactory status attained in what concerns terminology is easily understood from what has been said earlier here. Since properties always have a 'cross sectional' character, they may crop up in the most varied regions of knowledge and it is much more difficult to reach agreement as to naming them in a uniform way than it is in clearly delimitable and scientifically self-contained fields of nomenclature such as, for instance, botany and zoology. The farther specialization proceeds in science, the more do disciplines become separated and separately developed, and the more often will it happen that properties which in principle are the same throughout will be known under different terms according to the things (objects) where they are observed to occur.   For instance, not even designations of symmetry —such as disymmetrical, bilaterally symmetrical, dorsiventral, actino-morphic—are the same in the descriptions of fundamental shapes in botany and in zoology.   Sometimes they are even contradictory.

Scientific terminology, then, has hitherto been very incompletely developed by contrast with nomenclature.   With a few exceptions (for instance, some systems of measurement in physics and technology and notes in music) there are practically no internationally established terminologies and it is only very recently that Unesco has concerned itself with the matter by assisting the production of multilingual technical dictionaries, whereby at least an equivalence of the terms in various languages may be attained.   Other national and international organizations, too, are begin-ning to feel compelled by the circumstances to concern themselves more and more with the problems of terminology.

At the time when Latin still was in universal use as the language of learning, terminology was in a far more favorable position than now when more and more of the national languages are gaining an entrance into the sciences, so that standardization of terms becomes increasingly difficult. (On this matter see Holmstrom, 1957.)   Nevertheless the author is of opinion—and the endeavors mentioned above go to confirm this—that it ought to be possible to secure unchangeable international recognition for at least the most important expressions not only in nomenclature (as F. Richter considered: see page 108) but also in terminology.   Thereby human thought would be freed from a very heavy load of unnecessary ballast, the result not of complication in the data and concepts which are in fact available but solely of that chaos of languages and words which man has created for himself and can himself redeem.

6. SIGNIFICANCE AND PROBLEMS OF THE THEORY OF ORDER

(1) GENERAL

(A) Definition

In accordance with the successive steps we are following here, the nature of technical language has been approached not from the standpoint of the facts and concepts themselves but from that of the symbols for them, whereof spoken and written language is composed—symbols which, as we have seen, consist partly of names and partly of terms. In order consistently to follow up this line of thought, the names and terms were first considered quite apart from the question of any order existing among them. That having been done, the present chapter will deal with the arrangement of concepts and their symbols.

This problem of arrangement is encountered not only in science but in all fields of human life. Without such arrangement, it is quite impossible for us to contend with our environment and to lead our lives at all—on this point see Frank, 1957. However, the scope of this book is limited to scientific questions of order, in the sense that a physicist (Madelung) has described knowledge as being nothing more than ordered experience.

Here it must at once be stressed that a system of orderly arrangement is not necessarily bound up with a system of notation assigning its individual categories and technical expressions new and different symbols (such as letters, numerals or other symbols) as exemplified in the Universal Decimal Classification (UDC). The systems of order and of notation are rather to be looked upon as twofold. Of course a system of order can be expressed in letters or numerals throughout, with a view to easier apprehension, but a system of order should not be forced into conformity with any *a priori* sequence either of numerals (as on the decimal principle) or of letters (as when the alphabet of 26 letters is used).

(B) Possibilities of Subdivision

The various ways that things can be arranged in orderly patterns can themselves be classified on the basis of what was said in the previous chapter. In accordance with the distinction drawn there between concepts on the one hand and the symbols allotted to them on the other, a system of orderly arrangement may be governed either by the symbols or by the actual concepts themselves which are the meaningful content of the symbols. If the symbols alone are used for the purpose, the result is a *formal arrangement*, depending on the outer form of the symbols. The best known example of this is the arrangement of words in alphabetical order. As a further example the American 'Uniterm' system may be mentioned, which likewise operates only upon symbols (words) and not on their significance; for this reason it is bound to the use of a particular language. If, on the other hand, it is the concepts themselves—the substantial significance of the symbols—which forms a pattern the result is a *systematic arrangement*.

Likewise, corresponding to the distinction drawn in the preceding chapter between nomenclature and terminology, systems of order can be subdivided according as they relate to names (of objects) or to terms (denoting properties). Thus, within the scope of the theory of order, we may distinguish between *object systems* and *property systems*. A third and independent division may be made in the scope of the theory of order, on the basis of the purpose which a particular order is designed to serve. This leads to a distinction which must be expressly defined in the context of this book because elsewhere it is not a usual one or has not been consistently thought out, namely the distinction between '*system theory*' and '*classification theory*'.

By system theory is to be understood systematics in the ordinary sense, defined by Hennig (1950) as follows:

> We must lay it down that 'systematics' means rationalization, and therefore the arrangement of phenomena to form a pattern. 'Systematics always has to do with the conceptual arrangement of experiences; that is its general meaning (Naef, 1919).' Hence conceptual, logical character of order appertains only to its formal structure. What orderly arrangement expresses in conformity with the principles of logic is not purely formal logical, transcendental relationships, but such relationships as exist in nature independently of human contemplation and in this sense are real relationships between natural things and events (not considering these last two concepts as in straight opposition to one another). 'Systematics'—in biology too—means therefore the orderly, rational patterning of the phenomenal world in this sense, and its scope extends over the discernment of the laws of nature throughout the whole range of scientific activity.

The aim of scientific systematics—which we describe here as 'system theory' with a view to unambiguity of the concept—is not therefore to *introduce* any kind of order among the multitude of separate phenomena that occur, but to recognize and display an order *inherent* among them. A true system, in the sense of 'system theory', is the periodic system of the chemical elements.

On the other hand we shall designate under the heading of 'classifications' those systems of orderly arrangement whose sole purpose is to provide a bird's eye view over the existing multitude of data, with their main interest attaching to the disposal and retrieval of data. As regards classifications, in the sense here defined by contrast with system theory, it will be legitimate to envisage occasional deviations from the logical principles of division so long as these do not impair the aim. Typical examples of classifications are the Decimal Classification and practically all the systems of arrangement applied in librarianship and documentation which here, of course, are what interests us more particularly.

I

(C) General Problems and Rules

(*1*) The basis for any classification is the procedure which is known in logic as 'subdivision'.

(*2*) Subdivision is a complete statement of the parts which together make up the extension of a concept.   By this means a logical concept of class is split into the specific concepts which it embraces, or a dimension of characteristics into the separate characteristics.

(*3*) The pre-requisite for subdivision is that the concept to be so treated shall be indeterminate in at least one of its characteristic dimensions.   The characteristic dimension according to which subdivision is made is called the basis of subdivision (*fundamentum divisionis*).

Example: The higher collective concept 'bloom'.   According to our definition, this concept is one which may occur in a hierarchical system of properties (see below), either as a characteristic or as a characteristic dimension, according to the mode of subdivision.   If the classification is carried further, the color or for instance the shape of a flower may be adopted as a characteristic dimension.   If the further subdivision is made according to color, then the characteristic dimension 'color' becomes the basis for subdividing according to particular characteristics such as 'purple', 'blue', 'green', etc.

(*4*) The subdivision of a concept may be effected either on the basis of characteristic dimensions already implicit in its definition or on the basis of newly adopted characteristic dimensions.

Example: In the definition of 'plants' it is not implicit that all plants must have the property of being able to bear flowers.   Therefore it is possible to subdivide plants according to the characteristic dimension 'flowering', giving rise to the alternative characteristics 'with flowers' and 'without flowers'.   Thus even the absence of a property may be usable as a characteristic.   The concept of flowering—or perhaps the concept of a leaf—does, however, necessarily imply such a characteristic dimension as shape, since there are no flowers or leaves which have no shape.   Hence, to give an example, if a system for classifying the properties of plants is established with 'shape of flower' as the characteristic dimension, it must be expressly stated for the purpose of applying this system to plants as objects, that the characteristic 'no shape' (which in its literal sense is illogical, and therefore is better indicated by the notation 0) is used for expressing the fact that there are *no flowers*.

In this example, all difficulties can, however, be eliminated from the start by introducing as a characteristic dimension for all plants (and therefore for all organisms of any kind) not 'flower-bearing' but 'organs of reproduction'.   The example may serve to show the kind of problems that arise when the underlying theory of systems is consistently explored.

(*5*) According to the number of subheadings (which correspond to kinds or characteristics), the mode of subdivision is called dichotomy, trichotomy, tetrachotomy, or polytomy.   Often the subdivisions in such a case fade away into an endless series.   Thus 'shape', as a characteristic dimension, leads to an infinite number of possible characteristics.

(*6*) The subdivision may be made according either to the *logical* or the *empirical* extension of the concept.   Subdivisions according to the characteristic dimension 'length' will, for instance, embrace as their logical extension a practically infinite number of length characteristics (measurements of length).   If, however, organisms are grouped according to their 'length', only those empirical orders of magnitude which in fact occur among living organisms are used.   Considering the logical as against the empirical extension of a concept leads us to enquire into the reasons for the incongruity between them.   In the example of 'length', the question arises why organisms in fact are limited to certain orders of magnitude.   Especially as regards system theory, it may be useful and important to consider the logical extension of the characteristic dimensions, so as to establish and mark their boundaries by comparison with the empirical boundaries.

(*7*) The following errors may occur in subdivision:

(*a*) A subdivision is too wide if it contains too many headings, or too narrow if it contains too few.

(*b*) The headings within a subdivision may not be mutually exclusive (see page 103).

(*c*) Since often the number of subdivisions cannot be fixed *a priori* at the time when a pattern of arrangement is adopted—particularly if this is intended to serve a practical purpose of classification—it is absolutely necessary that every such system should include a separate category bearing the often ridiculed label 'other'.   It is better to possess a 'dump' of this kind for uncertain cases than to overload the remaining clear-cut categories (concepts) with compromises and thereby to take away their value.   Independently of the heading 'other', every system should also include the group category 'general', to which everything should be assigned that relates to the system in question as a whole.   (On this matter, see also (*6*) on page 244).

(*d*) Different principles of subdivision should not be mixed with one another, or the classification will become disorderly.   This is the mistake which most often occurs, for often a good deal of thoughtful labor is entailed in arriving at really clear principles of subdivision and in finding clear-cut concepts for them.   In the classifications themselves this mistake can, if necessary, be accepted and compensated for the sake of simplicity but in system theory that does not apply.

Example: In the Universal Decimal Classification we find the following subdivisions under class number 577·47:

Life environments

Life environment of the atmosphere and of empty space
Life environment and life groups in water
Fixed forms
Freely movable forms in general
Plankton
Life environment on land.

This mode of subdivision is confused in that three different principles are combined with one another.   For the sake of orderly arrangement free from defects they must be placed independently side by side, appearing some-what as follows:

Life medium	Life space	Mobility type
Gaseous	Free atmosphere	Fixed
Liquid	Free hydrosphere	Free, but without own locomotion
Solid	Land under atmosphere	Free, with own locomotion
	Ground under hydrosphere	
	Air/water boundary surface	
	Air/land boundary surface	
	Water/land boundary surface	
	Living organisms	
	Dead organisms or products	
	from organisms	

(8) According to the amount of material to be subdivided, there exist systems having few layers and few subdivisions or having many layers and many subdivisions. It has always been the endeavor of science to create one great uniform system, whereby as far as possible all data may be incor-porated and interconnected within a single general picture of the universe of satisfactory size. This endeavor is served also by the philosophical studies of categories, those of Aristotle and Kant being the best known, purporting to be general systems of *thought*. In various modern classifica-tions the endeavor to create a single, all-embracing general system of science has again been taken up. If, however, it is directed not to the creation of philosophical thought-patterns but to the establishment of general categories useful for specific practical purposes (in documentation), quite formidable difficulties are encountered. Consequently it is not surprising that the number of different classifications existing has risen, especially in the most recent times, to about 350 (according to Vickery, 1955). These questions were exhaustively discussed at an international meeting in Dorking in England, whereof de Grolier (1957 a) has published a summary account.

To give one example, Ranganathan (1957) has created in his Colon Classification a system which uses as its fundamental categories 'personality', 'matter', 'energy', 'space' and 'time'. Other authors (for instance de Grolier, Haldenwanger, Vickery) have arrived at different or additional categories. The distinction drawn in this book between 'objects' and 'properties' represents yet another particular kind of categorization, from which the author has derived and made use of the following fundamental concepts:

Structure (derived from 'space')	Study of data
Procedure (derived from 'time')	Ontogenetics
General laws	Phylogenetics

It is true that here the words 'ontogenetics' and 'phylogenetics' are borrowed indeed from biology, but they are transferable to other fields where appropriate.

In practical terms, the following is the situation now reached. If only a few very general categories are taken, these do not suffice to make a usable classification (Scheele). If, on the other hand, a larger number of categories is taken, they will not always cover all of the data without doing violence to some (see the arguments of de Grolier, 1957 b). So far as can be seen, this situation leaves no other course open, at least for the present, than to abandon the idea of a single general system of classification for the whole of the sciences under common collective concepts (fundamental categories). At any rate, the author sees no possibilitiy of progress except in the direction of systematizing first of all some limited region of science, of greater or lesser extent, which can be regarded as inherently self-contained.

In attempting this, it is best to follow the usual division between moral and natural sciences. As regards the former I am not qualified to appreciate the special situation. As regards the latter, my own experiences up to now have been such as lead me to advocate drawing a sharp line between, on the one hand, the pure theoretical natural sciences which address themselves to enquiring into nature uninfluenced by man and, on the other hand, the applied disciplines such as agriculture, technology, medicine, etc. It has been found that the elementary categories or concepts differ too much as between these groups (pure natural science on the one hand and applied natural science on the other) to allow them to be combined into a single usable system. Historically regarded, this has long been known, though perhaps forgotten. It dates back to Aristotle who consigned all man-made data to a separate and subordinate position under the heading of 'artefacts'.

However, the two great divisions of pure and applied natural science are still too wide in themselves. If we disregard those applied disciplines which must be left for cultivation by the appropriate technical specialists, the kind of classification which remains for the pure natural sciences is that shown in Fig. 31.

FIG. 31. The systematics of the natural sciences. Object of investigation: the (physical) world of bodies. Scientific discipline: Natural science.

General properties and objects of nature (Essence of the physical world) I. *Sciences relating to fundamentals*			Directly empirical natural data (Existence in the physical world) II. *Sciences relating to reality*		
Quantitative properties *Mathematics*	Qualitative properties *Physics*	Basic components (objects) *Chemistry*	The heavenly bodies *Astronomy*	The Earth *Earth sciences*	Life *Biology*

If, now, we enquire which disciplines are suited for inclusion in a single system from the nature of the concepts they embrace, we arrive at the following picture:

Mathematics	(remains by itself)
Physics and chemistry	(together make one system)
Astronomy	(remains by itself)
Earth sciences and biology	(together make one system)

The proposal to combine the earth sciences and biology in one system is repeated in Part III (page 212). This illustrates the need not to be governed by the historical boundaries between disciplines but to try to work out those which actually correspond with the pattern of modern knowledge.   The same thing ought to be true in other departments of science (and de Grolier too agrees with this).   But no criticism of the way that science has in fact been organized is here implied, for in that context Hennig's words (1950) as follows apply quite generally:

> The rivalries between the various separate departments of science . . . are of great practical importance, in that they influence the representation and recognition of those departments in the universities and other public scientific institutions, and thereby ultimately they influence the economic bases of progress.

These points of view are mentioned here in order explicitly to stress that theoretical scientific systematics must not be allowed to intervene when these realistic technical questions are being weighed.   We are confronted here with two separate issues which, for the sake of either, must not be confused.

(2) SYSTEM THEORY

In system theory, the differentiation between a system of objects and a system of properties plays an important part although, so far as the author knows, this differentiation has hitherto scarcely been noticed or had any stress laid on it.   No doubt the omission stems from the fact that, when it is sought to classify objects systematically instead of formally, they can in fact be classified only by reference to their properties.   That is to say, we are not able to apprehend a 'thing in itself' absolutely, but only through its properties.   Thus a system of objects is built up from the names of the objects which it covers or is intended to cover; that is to say in biology from the names of the semaphorontes, in chemistry from those of the elements and compounds.   In biology we have for instance a system of objects made up of semaphorontes whose total number falls within the range of magnitude 10^7 to 10^8.

A system of properties is built up from terms and by consideration of the points of view from which the objects ('bearers of characteristics') are viewed.   For didactic reasons, we will first discuss systems of properties, then systems of objects.

(A) Systems of Properties

Every characteristic-bearer (object) has associated with it a number of properties (characteristics) which determine the object.   For the purposes of system theory, only those characteristics are significant which are not shared by all of the characteristic-bearers within the same system of objects (see page 116).   Those single characteristics which are possible must be grouped together under 'characteristic dimensions'.   An example of a single characteristic is 'red flowers', which belongs to the characteristic dimension 'color of flowers'.   This illustrates that the characteristic dimension implies, at the same time, the criterion by reference to which objects are to be divided into different classes of resemblance: plants bearing red flowers, blue flowers, yellow flowers, etc.

The following are two circumstances which may render the problem of system theory particularly difficult.   An object may have not one but very many characteristic dimensions (or points of view from which subdivisions can be made), and secondly the terminology for characteristics and characteristic dimensions is inaccurate, lacking in uniformity and altogether in a very unsatisfactory state.   (See page 112.)

The 'multidimensionality' of objects has hitherto received insufficient attention in classification theory.   Generally speaking, consideration has been devoted only to a single or to a few dimensions or—with that liking for compromise which in system theory ought to be avoided—several dimensions have been jumbled together, which results in confused subdivisions.

What seems to me more important than anything as the objective of 'classification' (or of 'systematics ', which means the same thing) is to conceive each individual as being a specific case of some higher collective whole.   Now it is an established fact, clearly pointed out for instance by O. Spann, that no individual case can exist as the sole member of a single higher collective whole and only of that.   This statement applies also to the objects of biological systematics.   'Living natural forms' constitute, in their totality, a 'multidimensional manifold' if we agree with Ziehen (for instance in 1939, II, page 20) in regarding as 'dimensions' the main directions of the differences between them which also are the main directions of the different positions they occupy in 'proprietory space'.   And it may equally well be said that the 'difference in situation' of living natural things is determined by the variety of the relations that exist between them.

Thus, living natural things can be incorporated into many different systems according to which one of these varied relationships is to be considered, the differences being those determined by the choice of relationships expressed.   In themselves, however, all these different systems have fundamentally equal justification, provided that each system correctly specifies the position of the natural thing in the universe as a whole as measured along whichever dimension has been adopted as a basis for the system.   On the other hand, it must be clearly stressed that every system is quite definitely governed by the nature of the relationships within the multidimensional manifold which the system is designed to represent—or, in other words, by the construction of that whole to which the individual cases are conceived as subordinate.   It follows that, in building up a system, no arbitrariness can be allowed.

The individual systems for specifying the positions in which identical concrete units are ranked under different 'wholes' do not, however, stand side by side irrelevantly to one another.   Rather is it true to say that their relevance to one another, determined by the way in which the various dimensions of the individual things in the multidimensional manifold are inter-related, is susceptible to scientific and systematic examination.   On the other hand it is fundamentally not a scientific task to combine several systems thus developed; for one and the same object occupying any given position cannot be conceived and represented as being a subordinate member of several wholes at the same time (Hennig, 1950).

As Hennig shows in this quotation, the characteristic dimensions by reference to which it is possible for the objects to be pinpointed in different systems are not unrelated.   Rather do these systems, in their turn, build up into what was described above as a 'system of properties'.   The establishment and elaboration of such systems belongs to the field of epistemology.   The system which, as a system of properties, prevails in the biological sciences is seen to be none other than a system of those systems of characteristic dimensions by reference to which it is possible to arrange organisms (semaphorontes).

Here be it remarked that a system of properties is not affected by those terminological difficulties which have been mentioned above, and which are due to terminology being neither so uniformly nor so well developed as is nomenclature.   Characteristic dimensions do, however, give rise to notable epistemological problems, the nature of which will now be briefly indicated.

These difficulties occur in deciding upon the characteristics.   It is possible to establish or recognize the characteristics of an object only through the existence of a subject, and in science this subject is man.   Therefore every establishment of a characteristic depends on the transmitter–receiver principle, the object being the transmitter and man the receiver.   No other means exists for us to apprehend the material world.   Consequently the establishment of characteristics depends not only on the nature of the object (the transmitter) but also on the construction and operation of the receiver (man).   The natural receiving instrument, possessed by every healthy human being, is his sense organs.   It is these that constitute his natural method of apprehension.   Over and beyond these, man has developed artificial instruments and methods which can, so to speak, be interposed as outpost listening devices between his natural sense organs and the objects to be apprehended.   By this means, quite new universes of characteristics are opened up.   But not only that.   Under the microscope, the pointed forms of plants appear blunt, invisible things become visible, smooth surfaces appear rough; with x-rays, opaque bodies become transparent; using slow motion films, dynamic phenomena are seen as if slowed down—and so on.   It follows from this, as regards framing a scientific system theory, not only that quite new characteristic dimensions are evolved but also that those individual characteristics which are already accessible become hopelessly tangled.   However, as soon as this problem is recognized (see Lecomte de Nouy, 1948) a solution to it becomes apparent, which consists of distinguishing between the different phases of observation. It is best to start with that phase of observation which is natural to man when he is working on the basis of his natural senses.   This may be followed by many artificial phases of observation, made possible by different methods which can be applied to the recognition of characteristics.   The results from all these phases are to be regarded as equally valid.   For system theory, this entails the requirement that the phases of observation—the methods whose use has governed the choice of characteristics or characteristic dimensions—should always be indicated.   It is clear that the methodological 'dimension', too, must be introduced and taken into account when the system of properties is under consideration.

It has already been emphasized above that in, for instance, the system of properties for earth sciences and life sciences we have a way of systematizing the possible systems of organisms (semaphorontes).   Consequently, the total system of properties presents a much ramified and very complicated picture.   An attempt to arrive at its 'highest collective' member is reproduced in Fig. 32 but, as Hennig points out, its further subdivision down to the level of individual dimensions has so far been achieved only in fragmentary fashion.   Furthermore, the total system continually increases its extension with the progress of the sciences.

Here are tasks for system theory which, in combination with the punch-card method, open up quite new possibilities.   Indeed, punch-cards make it possible, for the first time in the history of fixation methods, to pinpoint the positions of objects (here organisms or semaphorontes) not only along *one* dimension in the system of properties—which hitherto has mainly been the phylogenetic dimension—but along *as many* dimensions at the same time as may be desired, and make it possible to operate upon them without having to give precedence to any one dimension or having to choose any one dimension beforehand for the practical use of the system (here see Chapter 11).

(B) Systems of Objects

Systems of objects, as such, also have of course to be arranged in some sort of pattern.   Here a formal arrangement, consisting of an alphabetical sequence of names, is suitable, because this does not necessitate referring back to some particular dimension in the system of properties which would thereby be given precedence over the others.   But, in systematically arranging the biological system of objects (semaphorontes), one such dimension is always preferred and the system of objects is arranged accordingly, this being the dimension of genetic relationship (phylogeny).   The justification for this procedure, and all the questions which are connected with it, cannot, however, be discussed within the limits of this book.   (On this matter, see Hennig, 1950.)

Certain authors have addressed themselves to the problem of creating new names for organisms in accordance with a plan which would make it possible to read off accurately the position of each organism in a pattern arranged according to the dimension of 'genetic relationship' (called the phylogenetic or natural system).   Indeed the ultimate aim envisaged, following the chemical example described in the previous chapter, is that the name should express both the position of the organism in the system and its genetic composition, and therewith also indicate its properties (Schmalfuss, 1937).   These proposals of Schmalfuss aim at the assignment

FIG. 32. The systematics of general ecology. Object of investigation: the Earth as holocöon. Scientific discipline: General ecology.

A. Idiobiology

	'Semaphorentes' I. 'Gegebenheitslehre' Basic structure				'Cycles' II. Ontogenetics Genetic laws				'Genealogies' III. Phylogenetics Laws of specific change			
	(a) Biochemistry and biophysics				(b) Heredity				(a) Descent			
	(b) Morphology in reference to:		(c) Physiology in reference to:		(b) Study of formal phases, in reference to:		(c) Evolutionary physiology of:		(b) Genealogy of:		Genealogical physiology of:	
	Form	Action	Form	Action	Form	Action	Form	Action	Form	Action	Form	Action
1. Cells	Cells	Cells	Cells	Cells	Cells	Cells	Cells	Cells	Cells	Cells	Cells	Cells
2. Tissues	Tissues	Tissues	Tissues	Tissues	Tissues	Tissues	Tissues	Tissues	Tissues	Tissues	Tissues	Tissues
3. Organs	Organs	Organs	Organs	Organs	Organs	Organs	Organs	Organs	Organs	Organs	Organs	Organs
4. Habitus	Habitus	Performance	Habitus	Performance	Habitus	Performance	Habitus	Performance	Habitus	Performance	Habitus	Performance

B. Coenobiology

	'Semaphorentes' I. 'Gegebenheitslehre' Laws of environment		'Cycles' II. Ontogenetics Laws of succession		'Genealogies' III. Phylogenetics Laws of metamorphosis	
	(a) Study of environment		(a) Study of modification		(a) Study of metamorphosis	
	(b) Morphology:	(c) Study of activities:	(b) Study of succession:	(c) Study of activities:	(b) Genealogy:	(a) Study of activities:
	Form	Action	Form	Action	Form	Action
5. Study of environment	Study of environment	Aut-ecology	Study of environment	Aut-ecology	Study of environment	Aut-ecology
6. Symbiontics	Symbiontics	Sociology	Symbiontics	Sociology	Symbiontics	Sociology
7. Biocoenetics	Biocoenetics	Synecology	Biocoenetics	Synecology	Biocoenetics	Synecology
8. Chorology	Chorology	Biogeography	Chorology	Biogeography	Chorology	Biogeography

of 'planned' names in which each category of the 'natural' system would be represented by a certain letter, consonants alternating with vowels so as to render the names pronounceable. The following is an example carried as far as the family:

Section	Sub-section	Class	Sub-class	Order	Sub-order	Family
a	t	i	l	i	t	a

Family name: Atilita

The first section in the vegetable kingdom is assigned the letter a, the second is denoted by the next vowel in the alphabet, e, and so on. Likewise the various sub-sections are denoted by consonants, and so the scheme proceeds alternately. Apart from the other advantages already mentioned, this produces a concordance between formal (alphabetical) and systematic (phylogenetic) order within the scope of the system of objects applicable to organisms.

Considerations and proposals of this kind are of quite special interest with a view to applying the punch-card method, since they aim to use the smallest possible number of symbols (in this case letters) for obtaining the largest possible range of expressive possibilities and therefore of significant contents. It would be well, therefore, to follow up the suggestions of Schmalfuss.

(3) CLASSIFICATION

As can be inferred from the way they are respectively defined, system theory and classification are not quite independent of one another within any given field of science. In principle it would be more correct to say that classification must be built on the foundations laid by system theory and must take over parts of systems comprised in it. Of course this statement assumes that a system theory is already available for the branch of science in question, which unfortunately is true only to a limited extent.

What, then, are the principles which classification can borrow from system theory, and how must they be adapted for the purpose of classification? First of all, the principle of separating the system of objects from the system of properties applies, in all cases, to classification also. Subdivision of the system of objects must proceed in accordance with one or other of the possibilities described under the heading of system theory, but the construction of the system of properties is always quite different in classification and in system theory, since in classification the main consideration must be to adapt it to practical requirements.

As a general rule in most cases, it can be laid down that subdivision in classification is carried as far down only as the characteristic dimensions, not down to particular characteristics—for instance, down to the characteristic dimension 'color' but not down to the characteristics 'purple', 'blue', 'green', etc. It is never good practice to carry subdivision down into small ramifications, for not only does that make documentation needlessly complicated but often it separates publications which belong together. (On this question see Chapter 9.) Even in special cases where deep subdivision is desired it should stop at the level of categories that are the subject of controversy among experts, or in which the concepts are uncertain. Otherwise, the incorporation of material will be attended by difficulties. In this context, it should further be borne in mind that often varying degrees of attention have been devoted to the allocation of different data at the same level of categorization.

Finally there is a very important difference between the points of view from which systems of properties are seen in system theory and in classification, which calls for separate and further consideration. In system theory a small section of the system of properties in biology appears as follows:

Organ Morphology

Flowers		Leaves		Roots	
Flower size	Flower shape	Leaf size	Leaf shape	Root size	Root shape
	Flower color		Leaf color		Root color

(The same section might be arranged as follows):

Organ morphology

Size			Shape			Color		
Size of flowers	Size of leaves	Size of roots	Shape of flowers	Shape of leaves	Shape of roots	Color o flowers	Color of leaves	Color roots

It is at once apparent that the question of coordination and subordination cannot always be decided quite unequivocally. This again is due to the fact that the separate characteristic dimensions, and therefore the terms, have a 'cross sectional' character and intercalate with one another. The higher the category of the property concept, the greater is the extension of that concept according to the dimension considered and the more frequently does the property in question recur. (Example: Morphology. This is the science of the structural properties of organisms, and in all the concepts shown in our scheme above, the fundamental property 'structure' is implicit.)

To constitute, in system theory, a system of properties quite consistently—which ultimately means to describe fully all the characteristic dimensions of all objects—it is inevitable that sometimes the same concepts (like, for instance, size, shape, color) will recur at various places in the system despite their cross sectional character. But in classification, that is for taking cognizance of literature, it is well known that there cannot be any question of describing the objects under reference (such as organisms) in accordance with all of their characteristic dimensions (see page 165). Rather, it is a matter of limiting oneself to indicating under which characteristic dimension, among the many that are possible, there will in fact be found references to the objects described in the pertinent publications. Hence it follows that, for purposes of classification, it is possible to construct a system of properties on the principle that all the needed characteristic dimensions (like size, shape, color, temperature, chemical character) appear *only* once. In order to construct such a system, the field of science to be documented has to be examined along all its characteristic dimensions ('cross sectional' concepts) in order to put these together into a suitable form and subdivide them. Anyone who consistently carries out such a task will be surprised to find how few conceptual properties can be made to suffice for reference documentation. Be it further mentioned that in this way special concepts can be created which stand in predetermined relationships to other concepts. In Chapter 13 of this book a classification system of this kind for the earth sciences and life sciences is described in detail; hence no detailed examples are necessary here.

In fact, in most existing classification systems this principle has more or less been adopted, whether consciously or not.   In the Universal Decimal Classification it finds expression in what are called the 'common analytical subdivisions' but unfortunately it is not very consistently carried out there. In the author's opinion, however, anyone concerned in the elaboration of a classification system—especially if it is intended for applying the punch-card method—should endeavor to make the utmost possible use of the principle that objects should be separated from properties, as well as of the fundamental principle that the properties concept should only occur once.

It is very apparent how great are the advantages to be gained from observing these two principles, particularly in using the punch-card method. The reduced number of concepts is easier to record on a punch-card by direct coding.   At the same time, complicated subordination of concepts becomes unnecessary, as all concepts stand side by side on an equal footing and can freely be combined with one another in any desired way, as well as being searchable separately (see the example on page 242).

7. SIGNIFICANCE AND OBJECTS OF NOTATION

(1) GENERAL

(A) Definition

Notation is to be understood as including every mode of designation or symbolization in which the original words are replaced by other symbols. (Here the concept 'symbol' is *not* intended to include the holes made in punch-cards, the magnetized spots on magnetic tapes or other like forms of record.)

According to this definition, notation occupies a field to itself which can be clearly delimited and can be separately examined either in the theory of order or from the standpoint of punch-cards. Probably its frequent mention in the theory of order stems from the decimal and similar classifications, as these constitute at the same time a system of order and a system of notation. The connection with the punch-card method is to be explained by the habit of talking about 'coding' and 'keying' both in reference to notation and in connection with the allocation of indications to the holes in punch-cards (see page 10). Consequently a very disadvantageous confusion of concepts has arisen which might be avoided by general use of the expression 'notation'. When confusion is thus avoided, the term 'coding' can be confined exclusively and directly to the punch-card method as a system (see also page 6).

(B) Possible Subdivisions

A subdivision of this topic according to the kind of symbols in use shows that it is possible to draw a distinction between optical, acoustical and mechanical symbols. Here optical symbols include all kinds of written characters and marks, acoustical symbols the sounds made in speech and mechanical symbols for instance the touch-reading characters in braille for the blind. In this book it is exclusively the optical symbols that are of interest. These can be divided into:

Numerals
Letters
Other symbols
Combinations of above.

Each of these groups can be further subdivided as follows:

(*a*) Symbols having no connection with the properties of the data they indicate, or with the sequence of these data. (Example: serial numbers.)

(*b*) Symbols which at the same time show the structure or other properties of the data they indicate. Such properties may also secondarily constitute an order. (Example: chemical formulas.)

(*c*) Symbols which immediately indicate a certain order among the data in question; from this order it is possible secondarily also to see certain properties of the data. (Example: the proposals of Schmalfuss for a new biological nomenclature; numbers showing the sequence of the chemical elements in the periodic table.)

This mode of subdivision can also be applied separately along with the first mentioned.

After the possibilities of subdivision according to the kind of symbols and according to their expressive values have been studied, it is also possible to subdivide them according to their length and complications—for instance, into simple and compound notations—and it is conceivable that they might be arranged according to the purpose of application. These parallel arrangements will not, however, be considered here. There follows below an exposition of notational possibilities on the several bases explained above, with corresponding examples.

Numerical Notations

(a) *Without relation to the properties or to the sequence of data*—The simplest principle is that of serial numbers (*numerus currens*), meaning merely that the data are numbered in the order in which they happen to have been collected. Much use is made of this principle for applying the punch-card method, as in other applications. A serial number unrelated to any principle of arrangement has, however, no indicative value, so this system should be adopted only when there is no possibility of choosing any other.

A special role is played by what is called interrupted numbering. By this means serial numbers can be related to a classification system, the principle being to leave one or more digits free in the serial numbers so that, although these determine the sequence, related objects can be brought together under the same serial number. The disadvantage is of course the waste of numbered positions which this entails.

(b) *Coupling of numerals with properties of data*—This applies to many units of measurement in the physical, chemical and technical fields.

(c) *Coupling of numbers with a system of arrangement*—A wealth of very varied examples of this principle might be given. The best known is the Universal Decimal Classification. Towards the end of the last century the American librarian, Melvil Dewey, by combining a few simple basic ideas, created what has since developed into a masterly system—although controversial now as ever—with the help of which the whole of human knowledge can be classified and expressed in numerical symbols. The basic ideas are the following:

(*1*) By contrast with the letters and words of particular languages, numerals are everywhere known and internationally current.

(*2*) The decimal arrangement of the digits forming the numbers constitutes straightaway a usable system of order which likewise is internationally understood.

(*3*) When the decimal places are understood as following an imaginary initial decimal point (so as to represent tenths, hundredths, etc., in relation to ordinary numerals) the subclassification can be carried as far as is desired without affecting the higher categories.

In this way Dewey constructed a system for the arrangement of all branches of human knowledge, specially fashioned so as to fit in with the decimal numeral notation. Thereby he created the decimal classification. It is evident that what this really involves in the first place is a decimal *notation*, for the classification naturally inherent in the data of the material to be classified does not always follow the decimal principle of subdivision. The same of course is true of any other numerical arrangement. Because of its international significance, the Universal Decimal Classification is again separately discussed here from page 138 onward. Numerical notations, despite their disadvantages, are much liked and often used, since they provide the considerable advantages explained above, and are convenient to use.

A short remark may be made here on the manner of writing the numbers. Experience has shown that 0 (zero) when written fast is apt to be confused with a 6, or in mixed notations with the letter O as in Otto. For this reason, some authors replace the zero with a simple horizontal stroke (which, however, may lead to confusion with the indication 'not punched') or by Ø. Here it seems to the present author that standardization is urgently needed, especially since punched card operated printing machines do not enable the zero to be distinguished from upper-case letter O.

In view of the increasing use made of mixed notations in documentation, it will probably be impossible to carry on without giving the zero quite generally and compulsorily a new symbol all to itself.

Letter Notations

(a) *Not related to the properties or sequence of the data*—In chemistry, the letter symbols for the elements have given us a letter notation remarkable both for its internationality and its brevity, providing the basis for chemical formula language. In themselves, the symbols for the elements, have, however, no relation to either the properties or the sequence of the elements. Very recently some workers, especially in America [such as Luhn (1956, 1957) and Perry (1948, 1955a, b) with the latter's collaborators] have described letter systems in connection with their search for a solution to the problem of mechanical translation and mechanical selection, these being derived either from abbreviations of normal language in accordance with various rules or by the creation of a special notation intended for machine use.

(b) *Coupling of letters with properties of data*—Here the author knows of no actual example.

(c) *Coupling of letters with a system of arrangement*—Corresponding to the order which is inherent in numbers on the decimal system, wherein each numeral has a definite position value, it is possible also to construct letter systems in which letters are arranged in accordance with such position values or categories. It may, for instance, be laid down that the first letter of a compound notation shall represent always the highest category in the system of arrangement, the second letter the second category and so on. If vowels and consonants are made to alternate the result is pronounceable words, but otherwise it is merely sequences of letters which every now and then happen to form words. The proposal of Schmalfuss (see page 123) for a new biological nomenclature may serve as a practical example of a system using alternating vowels and consonants.

Hierarchical systems with varying numbers of ramifications can be constructed wherein each branching (or subdivision of a category) corresponds with the number of letters used for designating it—that is, up to 26 using our own alphabet, or more or less than this number if other alphabets are used.

There also are notations which use both upper- and lower-case letters, or which draw upon various alphabets (such as the Greek) in order to express the numbers of the various categorical steps in the classification system adopted. (On this point see also de Grolier.)

Other Symbols

(a) *Without relation between properties or sequence of the data*—Here the signs of punctuation (such as the comma, etc.) as well as various mathematical and logical symbols can be drawn upon. The well known Morse code also comes under this head.

(b) *Coupling with the properties of the data indicated*—A notation of this kind is formed by every true pictorial symbolism, since pictures can be used to reproduce certain properties (such as shape and perhaps also color) of the data directly. The same principle governs many of the conventional signs used in geographical maps to represent shapes of ground and other features of the landscape. It is possible to imagine the development of corresponding systems using colors and shapes for other scientific purposes, seeing that colors and shapes would reproduce these properties of the data directly without the need to interpose some other system of notation. An existing example of this is the flower diagrams used in botany.

(c) *Coupling with the system of order*—Here musical notes might be cited as an example.

Combinations of Numerals, Letters and Symbols

(a) *Without relation to the properties or sequence of the data*—The most usual is the combination of numerals with letters as a means of extending the possibilities of serial numbering.

(b) *Coupled with properties*—One of the best examples is given by the formulas for chemical compounds in which the letter symbols of the elements are joined with numerical indices. As is well known, these formulas make it possible to read off the structure of the compounds in order to adapt them for application to the punch-card method. Systems of notation have been developed at various places and by various authors which make it

K

possible to write all kinds of formulas occurring in inorganic and organic chemistry in linear fashion, and thereby to transfer them on to punched cards. It can, however, be shown that nothing very much has been gained by so doing (see page 255). A further example may be found in the flower formulas (not the diagrams) in botany which indicate the number and arrangements of the parts of each flower.

(c) *Coupling with systems of arrangement*—Under this head may be mentioned the indication of parts and chapters in a book such as the present.

(C) General Problems and Rules

(*1*) A notation should in no way alter, shorten or extend the indicative content of the original words.

(*2*) Farradane (1957), in his paper reviewing the subject of classification and mechanical selection, has stressed the necessity for treating notation as a separate question, one to be considered after that of pattern theory, thereby giving this precedence: 'Notation is, however, but a systematization of already ordered material; it cannot by itself, however ingenious it may be, contribute to the analysis or ordering of knowledge and can be of value only as a step for scanning a problem. Without previous formulation of accepted principles of order in knowledge, it remains sterile.'

One cannot but agree with this statement. Notation, indeed, serves only for designation and not for arranging in order. It cannot replace classification theory. All attention which is concentrated on notation cannot itself contribute anything decisive towards solving questions in documentation and other problems treated here. In this context it will later be shown that in applying the punch-card method the notation stage can, in certain cases, be jumped, whereby considerable simplification may be obtained.

(*3*) In his book *Auf den Pfaden des Lebens,* von Bertalanffy (1951) has made the following remark among others under the heading 'Science as a calculating machine':

All thinking is based on the substitution of signs or symbols for the things themselves. If I say to my wife, 'please give me a cigarette', the word cigarette is a sign for a particular thing, 'give' for a particular activity, and my wife gives me the cigarette—or does not. If I write down the problem '39 times 27', the numbers 39 and 27 are signs representing certain complexes of ideas and 'times' means a certain operation which I propose to perform. 'Thinking' and 'calculating' mean nothing more than connecting such signs together in accordance with certain rules; thus the operation 39×27 gives the number 1053. The ease with which a thinking operation can be performed depends very much on the system of signs employed: thus when writing was done with roman numerals even a simple multiplication was a very difficult problem. In fact XXXIX times XXVII looks forbidding enough, and in order to carry out this calculation an abacus had to be

used which had sections for units, tens, hundreds and thousands.   For
instance, $9 \times 7 = 63$ was represented by three balls in the units and
six in the tens section.   During the twelfth century these roman
numerals were replaced by what is called the Indian system of numerals,
wherein the position value of the last place corresponds to units, the last
but one to tens and third from the last to hundreds, and so on.   This
trick, so simple in itself, made the abacus unnecessary and we now learn
at our first school that units, tens, hundreds, etc., when written underneath one another can so easily be added together as to make child's
play of what was once a difficult problem.

What we have demonstrated by this simple example applies in
principle also to the most difficult regions of higher mathematics and
for all thinking of any kind.   In the final analysis thinking corresponds
to a huge calculating machine in which, so to speak, the problem is put
in at the top whereupon the machine works in accordance with pre-
determined rules and the answer drops out at the bottom.

In these remarks by a well known biologist two points emerge which are
especially important for us.   One of these is the point already discussed
in Chapter 5 here that man has substituted symbols in the place of the
real data, the most primitive symbols being those known to us as spoken
or written words.   Both the remarks of von Bertalanffy in the quotation
on page 132, and the whole tendency towards analogizing numbers and
words (or concepts), are notable in this respect.   If we confine ourselves to
the natural sciences and their methods it follows inescapably, as regards the
problems which interest us here, that anything which can be expressed in
words can also, in principle, be handled by machine.   How far in particular cases that may be expedient and can be realized in practice remains
merely as a question of procedure, to which an answer can be given.

The second important point is the statement that 'the ease with which
an operation can be performed depends very much on the system of signs
employed'.   Here it may at once be stated that our system of signs, consisting of verbal language even in its improved form as technical language,
provides only a very inadequate one.

Ultimately, as de Grolier has stressed, all this amounts to realizing the
great Leibniz's dream on a new plane by the creation of a general logically
constructed 'language' of science which shall be as efficient as possible and
be understood by all the world's scientists (see page 104).   That is to say,
the ordinary words and technical terms which have hitherto been in use
must be replaced by a notation which initially may stand alongside those
words, but which one day will completely replace them.

As to the nature of this new notation or kind of 'international language'
the opinions of specialists are very varied.   It seems fairly certain, however,
that it will have little in common with the verbal language now current
among us.

It is evident that Farradane, as represented in an earlier quotation here,
has a different aim in view from de Grolier's and does not contemplate such
wide objects as the latter.   The present author is of opinion that the new

notation ('the language of science') should be coupled with the properties of data indicated, or be *coupled with a system of orderly arrangement*. (Here see the example given under 'Possible subdivisions'.)

In this context the following note may be of interest as showing how widespread is the contemporary quest for a suitable notation:

In order to escape from this unsatisfactory situation, the Eighth International Congress on Agricultural Work held at Bad Kreuznach was made acquainted with a new system of communication, designed to improve the understanding of data relating to working time studies.

A first step had been taken in 1950 when accurate definitions were adopted and made binding upon all. It was attempted in this way to ensure that English speakers, Frenchmen and Germans using the same technical expressions would in fact mean the same things. Another experiment consisted of adopting Latin as the current and most accurate language for use by all the participants in describing certain procedures of work observation as well as for use in work studies and work experiments, as has long been the practice in other departments of knowledge. This system, too, was found to have only limited efficiency, and difficulties of understanding continued to occur through the use of non-roman characters in China, Russia and Japan. The search for a way out of these difficulties led finally to the solution of an internationally valid code of picture writing. This 'writing' is composed of pictorial elements each having only one meaning, to which are added a few of the Arabic numerals in international use. With the aid of these pictorial elements and numerals any question in work time studies is made understandable to everyone. Moreover, the pictorial writing makes it possible to indicate working procedures, and accurately to describe machines.

According to the information given by a German participant at this Congress, it takes less time to express information in the pictorial writing than to describe it in words.

By this new method it proved possible to keep all the participants intelligibly informed of the reports on visits to model agricultural undertakings arranged during the Congress. It is proposed to develop the pictorial language far enough for even abstract concepts to be expressible in that way. As an example, one possibility for its application will be to the headings in statistical tables. Instead of explanations in three or four languages there will need to be printed over each column of numerals only a single pictorial symbol [*Deutscher Forschungsdienst*, vol. 5, No. 5 (1958)].

This and the other examples of notations already given show that there already exist, of course, many well-proved systems of notation; and these will always be necessary to meet many special purposes. A new general form of notation usable as a 'language of science' can obviously not aim to render superfluous these existing and tried notations for special purposes.

(*4*) It seems desirable to link the promotion of a notation suitable for use as an 'international language' in the sense of Leibniz—a problem in notation which for the present can be regarded and considered quite independently—with the consideration and requirements of the modern punch-card method (or automatic selection in general), or to coordinate the two endeavors. These ideas have produced the expression 'machine language', which is not a very happy one because under that head various considerations which it would be better to handle separately run uncontrollably together.

Is this current activity in the direction of new notations and automatic methods of selection, especially by way of punch-cards, really sound and beneficial to the object sought? This critical question can be divided under the following heads:

(*a*) For using the punch-card method is a notation necessary at all?

(*b*) When such a notation is necessary, is it possible to reconcile the fundamental technical principles of machines with the principles underlying notations usable apart from machines?

(*5*) We shall now first consider the question of the necessity for a notation for using the punch-card method—a necessity which hitherto has nearly always been taken for granted. Then the question formulated above will arise, as to whether ordinary notation and machine language can be matched with one another.

If a new notation of the ordinary type is to be really capable of replacing technical language (see page 134), it must be easily pronounceable and easily learnable. Besides this there is the requirement already discussed above that it should be made possible to couple the notation with a system of classification or of specifying properties. On the other hand, a notation for use in machines needs neither to be pronounceable nor to be learnable by heart, since neither of these problems arises in machines. Instead of them, such a notation needs other qualities, above all brevity. According to the literature so far available to the author relating to the stage which investigations of this kind have reached, the question whether it is possible to reconcile the technical requirements of the machines with those of an ordinary notation must be answered in the negative. The only result visible so far is an unsatisfactory compromise.

(*6*) The fundamental question then arises whether endeavours have not hitherto been proceeding in the wrong direction because of an uncritical *a priori* assumption, and whether when using automatic methods (punch-cards, etc.) a notation in the sense here defined may not in fact be a redundant and unnecessary dead load. This conclusion, heretical as it may at first appear, had in fact been reached by the author on the basis of his own experiences. It rests on the following considerations.

It is evident that using punch-cards (and the same is true using magnetic tapes and other storage media) that the stress is continually laid on the mode of recording, on the way in which the dual principle ('yes' or 'no') is applied and on great capacity for storing numerals and letters; but another basic consideration, just as simple and important, is seldom brought out:

namely, that every single hole on the punch-card has its own definitely assigned position which distinguishes it from every other hole. If, now, we confine ourselves to the IBM punch-card this means nothing else than the fact that the cards themselves predetermine a certain arrangement of units, an arrangement which is imposed by the working method of the machines. If the IBM card is being used on the coordinate system (Fig. 33) the x values are represented by the numbers of the columns and the y values by the numbers of the lines. By reference to these two values, every punching position or every hole can be unequivocally described. This being so for all holes, it follows that very often (and especially when direct coding is used) the mere assignment of concepts to holes (that is, coding as distinct from notation) is all that is needed for applying the method. Then any additional notation is useless ballast. By consulting a keyword index to the subject field of the work, and by using a system of classification which has been designed to match the pattern of columns on the punch-card, the latter can be punched directly. This applies to all kinds of machine and needle punch-cards.

What does this mean in relation to our problem? It was established above that anything which (in the field of the natural sciences and their generalized method) can be expressed in words can also be handled by machines. Further it was pointed out that a symbolism for use in machines must be as concise as possible. It follows then that any kind of symbol (in the sense of a notation) can be dispensed with and that machines are capable of keeping concepts sorted out, and of operating upon the concepts with perfect logic, by reason of the fact that holes or tiny magnetized or electrically charged spots are localized at quite definite places in punch-cards or in magnetic tapes. The pre-requisite for using modern machines in this way is the development of a perfectly sound system of orderly arrangement, and the adaptation of that arrangement to the engineering of the machines.

Finally, the qualification must be stated that it is not always possible to dispense with a notation, and that it is of course possible to use codes with and without notation on the same punch-cards.

(7) Our consideration of the questions of notation that apply to the punch-card method can now be summarized as follows:

(a) Every kind of notation should always be based on and be linked with a good system of arrangement.

(b) The great independent aim of notation is the creation of a 'language of science' in the sense used by Leibniz. This development may best be pursued independently of the problems of automatic selection and those of the punch-card method, because the machines either need no notation at all or operate under notational requirements which cannot satisfactorily be reconciled with those of a 'language of science'.

(c) Thus, coding for punch-cards can be done either with or without a notation. The two possibilities may also be combined on the same card. Insofar as, in this respect, a notation is necessary at all, it should be developed

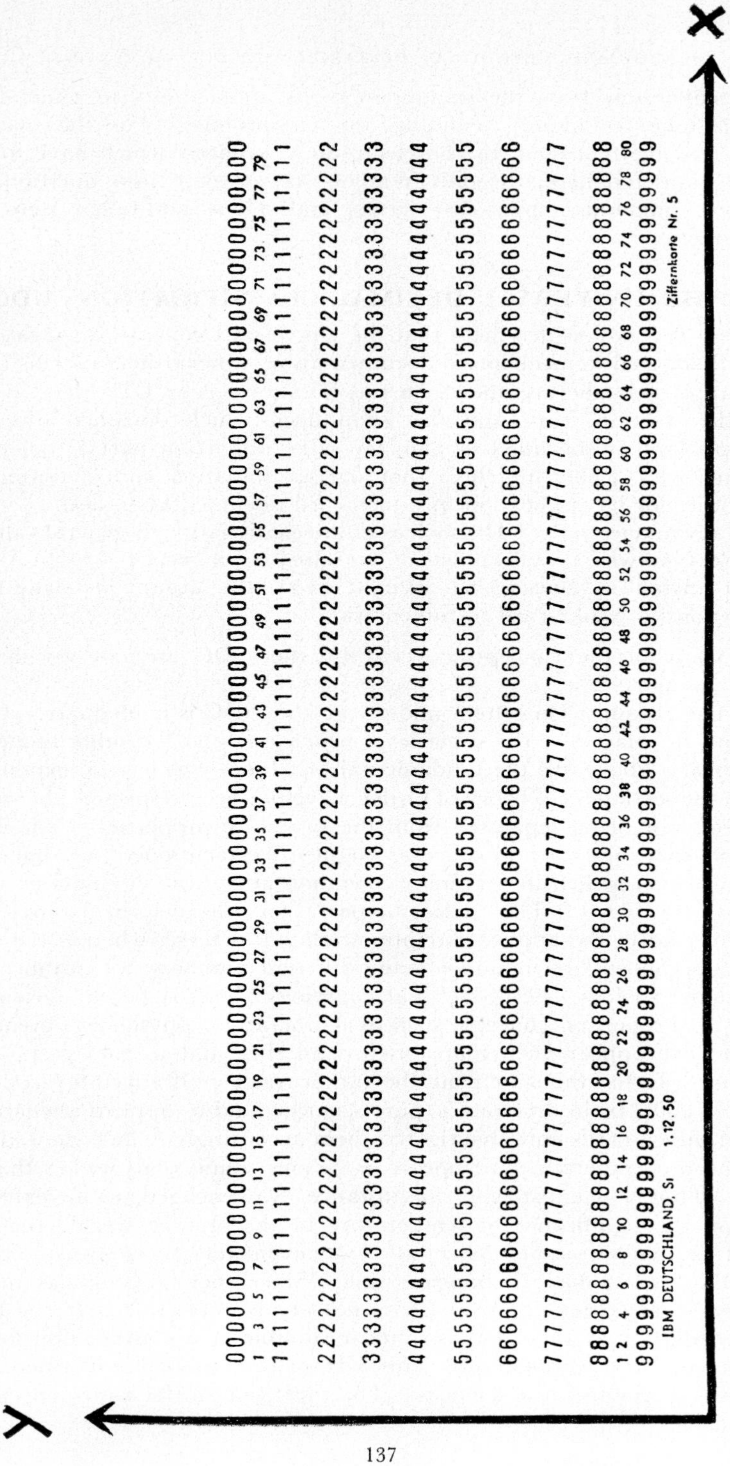

FIG. 33. The IBM card used as a coordinate system.

137

quite deliberately from the standpoint of its applicability to punch-cards and machine techniques, avoiding any compromise. For the machine punch-card method, and for the electronic computers which have mainly to be considered here, the only symbols which come into question are, therefore, numerals, upper-case letters and a few additional signs (see page 56).

(2) THE UNIVERSAL DECIMAL CLASSIFICATION (UDC)

Although it is now widely held that the Universal Decimal Classification is not well adapted to mechanized documentation, it nevertheless seems useful to assemble here the arguments on this question. The UDC has, in fact, been the starting point and the germ from which documentation has developed and it continues to play the same important part as before, so that one owes it the duty of a thorough examination and of testing the possibilities for its application in punch-card documentation also.

The advantages of the UDC such as its internationality, its general validity, etc., are everywhere well known or are already on record, so that I may confine myself to considering straight away the arguments against its application for punch-card documentation.

(a) Many of the concepts covered by the UDC are not yet defined clearly enough.

(b) The classification system underlying the UDC is inadequate. Often concepts are placed at the same level which ought to be subordinated or vice versa. Above all, the fundamental principles which were expounded here in the section on 'Theory of Order' have not been respected, the system of objects not being separated from the system of properties. Nor is the principle that fundamental concepts ought to be mentioned only once, the germ of which is seen in the use of 'common analytical subdivisions', consistently developed. This defect appears for instance in biology and medicine and in the applied disciplines related to these, wherein the same objects (organisms) recur under many different numbers: for instance pigs recur under zoology (599.731.1), palaeontology (569.731.1) and agriculture (636.4). 'Properties' concepts such as temperature, physiology, breathing and the like appear even more often than this, and in the most varied positions. To test this statement, the author transferred some 3 000 concepts from the UDC main divisions 5 (pure sciences) and 6 (applied sciences) on to IBM punch-cards and investigated them accordingly, which showed that the concept 'temperature' reappears in various connections no less than 44 times! Thus a scientist who, for instance, was engaged on an extensive work on the significance of temperature in the organic world, and who wished for this purpose to collect all the relevant references with the aid of the UDC, would have a hopeless task. Since such a book has in fact recently been written my example is not at all unrealistic. It has to be acknowledged that the UDC is quite unsuitable as a classification for use in attacking 'cross sectional' problems. It operates more as a fragmentation than as a synthesis of the sciences. The repetition of the same concepts in several places always constitutes an intolerable obstacle for using it with punch-cards.

(c) The UDC combines in itself a system of classification and a system of notation. So far as concerns the classical methods of documentation hitherto in use this is an advantage, since cards which have been marked with UDC numbers 'file themselves', as it has so neatly been expressed. But for the application to punch-cards this is an important disadvantage since in that application often no notation is necessary (see also page 136). Every hole in a punch-card is quite definitely located by its coordinates (x and y values) or generally by the topography of the card. Thus the notation system in the UDC unnecessarily complicates punch-card documentation by entailing an additional and redundant working process. At the same time, additional sources of error arise which are particularly important in long numerical notations wherein any one of the digits may be mistaken and wrongly written.

(d) When the numerical notation of the UDC is transferred to machine punch-cards, as many columns are taken up by each concept as there are digits in the UDC numbers that may occur. Since on the average at least eight-figure numbers must be allowed for, and since in general the first decimal places (representing higher collective concepts) cannot be left out because of the defect explained under (b), eight columns are blocked for every concept regardless of whether or not the UDC numbers actually used turn out to be as long as that. Thus, having regard to the other data which have to be punched in it, an 80-column punch-card can accommodate only about eight different concepts, which means that the installation of punch-cards is not economic.

Where nevertheless it is decided to proceed in this way and, for instance, eight UDC numbers each made up of eight digits are to be punched in corresponding punching fields of an IBM card, there are two possible arrangements: either it may be accepted that any punching field can be used for any of the numbers or each punching field may have assigned to it a particular range of numbers (that is, of concepts). Both these solutions present disadvantages. Using the first alternative any desired concept must be searched for in all eight punching fields. Using the second it is impossible to punch on the same card two concepts which belong to the same punching field.

For the first alternative, Heimerdinger (1955) has indeed developed a switching device for using the card mixer in documentation, but this makes it possible to search for a particular number in only three and not eight fields. Again from that point of view, therefore, the UDC is seen to be practically unusable in application to punch-cards. (The same thing applies to its use with needle punch-cards.)

The superimposition of different numbers in the same punching field is not advisable as it leads to too many wrong cards being selected which have nothing to do with the theme of the search. This applies both to machine and needle punch-cards. Calculations of selectivity or of the occurrence of unwanted cards, as carried out by Grobe (1952, 1954), must be regarded with caution.   Insofar as they relate to practical experience in using the UDC it is to be remembered that this classification operates with numbers which are very far from forming a continuous series; hence, the greater the extent to which the gaps in the numbers are filled in by the interpolation of new concepts the more favorable will appear the selectivity when several UDC numbers are superimposed.

The provision of several cards for the same publication is also to be avoided for the reasons given earlier, page 56.

There remains the possibility of shortening the UDC class numbers or of replacing certain groups of numerals by letters in order to obtain a shorter notation.   Suggestions and experiments in this direction also have been made.   However, they run counter to the fundamental rules of the UDC itself which, in the interests of general applicability, rightly discountenance any alterations to it being made on private authority.   These are only palliatives and of little value.

What has here been said of the Universal Decimal Classification applies also to any other numerical notation of similar kind.

8. SIGNIFICANCE AND PROBLEMS OF PRIMARY RECORDING AND OF RESEARCH USING PUNCH-CARDS

(A) Definition

By primary recording is meant the procedure whereby any piece of knowledge is recorded in any way for the first time. It is by this procedure that knowledge is rendered independent of the persons knowing it and able to be diffused and transmitted.

(B) Possible Subdivisions

Optical, acoustical and mechanical methods of record may be distinguished.

Optical methods of recording range from ordinary handwriting through typewriting, hectographic reproduction, photographic contact printing and letterpress to microfilm. Acoustical methods of recording include phonograph discs and magnetic tapes. Within the field of mechanical methods of recording punch-cards form a separate subdivision and may best be considered quite separately.

(C) General Problems and Rules

Hitherto optical methods of recording have occupied by far the greatest part of the scene. It is well known, however, that the output of print in the shape of scientific literature (and otherwise) has reached such overwhelming proportions as to create a real problem. If a solution is to be found to this problem imposed by the flood of literature, it will be best to begin by examining not its effects but its causes, and by trying to prevent so much being published! In other words, it may be said that the problems of primary record and of documentation, including those of secondary recording, are reciprocal. Any possible measures at the stage of primary record which may conduce to the rationalization of publishing will mean a relief of the load at the subsequent stages, particularly that of documentation.

What, then, are the sorts of measures that might be taken at the stage of primary recording? One of them consists of certain works being left in their original form of record (handwriting or typewriting) and being collected in a 'depository of unprinted manuscripts', a bibliographical list of such writings being published either separately or in a periodical. Proposals for this kind are now being considered by the Deutscher Forschungsgemeinschaft (the German Association for Research Interests). But fundamentally this amounts to no more than a makeshift as it does nothing to reduce the total amount of reading which the scientist has to do; the only resultant saving would be in printing costs.   Rothschuh (1955), however, has clearly proved and elaborated his thesis that what confronts us today is quite a different problem, namely that of the 'utilization' of the literature and of knowledge. This being so, a much more rational solution is offered by the punch-card system which is a mode of record having quite exceptional qualities: for *punch-cards combine in themselves the recording and the reproducibility of the knowledge and the possibility for processing and evaluating it statistically (that is, for doing research).   At the same time they render possible, without external aid, a very rapid and inexpensive mode of reproduction for editions which can be varied in size as desired.*

This statement holds good principally of machine punch-cards, but needle punch-cards also can play a part under certain conditions.   Visual punch-cards are excluded from this purpose.   The decisive advantage of the machine punch-card method, in particular, consists of the fact that the evaluative statistical research dovetails into the archivization which is necessary, or can be combined with this.   (In the first edition of this book, card collections of this kind were called 'working cards'.)

Unfortunately, however, the punch-card method has not yet taken sufficient root in science for its advantages to become well enough recognized. If this were otherwise, it might be a good idea for a depository of unprinted manuscripts to be started in association with a punch-card archive.   Such an archive would be able, in the field of the natural sciences, to accumulate all the numerous data, indications and tables which make up so large a proportion of publications.   If these data were not to be printed but instead were to be accumulated on punch-cards, and if the thing were properly organized, the advantages of the machine punch-card method for science would ensure its exploitation on a wide basis.   As soon as enough material had been so collected the contents of the punch-cards could be transferred to magnetic tapes and thus made amenable to further processing in electronic computers.

Today this is no longer any technical problem but only the problem of finding the most suitable code and proper external organization.   At the same time it should not be overlooked that the difficulties here are quite formidable.   With goodwill on the part of those concerned such problems could, however, be solved step by step, if only the initial decision were taken to make a beginning.   If, on the other hand, everyone were to wait until everything were ready to perfection nothing would take shape.   Hosemann (1951) and his school in particular, along with other medical workers, have shown that any pioneer work in this direction is rewarding (see page 184).

Unfortunately, starting with medicine, the recording and processing of scientific data (*Befunde*—case records) has given currency to the term *Befunddokumentation* ('Documentation of findings').   In my opinion this expression is a very unfortunate one.   Experience has shown, too, that it works to the detriment of something which is good in itself, for it attaches a false label to scientific evaluative work and whatever carries a false label is also falsely handled.

Primary recording is not documentation. Documentation means collecting documents systematically and making them accessible and useful. But people are not documents, nor are scientific data and facts recorded about people. The word *Befunddokumentation* is therefore meaningless and contradictory. It should if possible be eradicated. What is said here about medicine applies in the same sense to other branches of science, such as biology. Animals and plants, too, are not documents, and work which has to do with them is not documentation but research. Improper extensions of concepts such as this can only lead to confusion and cause corresponding harm.

Taking medicine as an objective prototype, the following plan can be followed for progressively carrying out primary fixation by the use of punch-cards and for the establishment of the corresponding archive:

First Step

Instead of, as hitherto, merely recording the results of their experiments in laboratory notebooks and the like, later working them up with the aid of check lists or some such means, individual researchers and specialists should start putting them straight on to punch-cards. Thereby they obtain not only a substitute for written records but, at the same time, a 'working card' collection which can be used as desired for selection or reproduction and for statistical analysis of the punched data. Circumstances may make it possible to incorporate data from pre-existing records (for instance, in medicine, from case records) or from the publications of other authors, so as to extend the range of the punch-card collection and obtain a wider basis for the evaluation. At this stage, the results of the statistical processing may continue to be published in the usual form as a book or as an article in a periodical.

Second Step

Several researchers or institutions interested in the same technical field (which might for instance be gynaecology or algenocology) should get together and work out a code for common use, so that their individual collections can be exchanged with one another or can be consolidated into a common archive. In this way an appreciably wider foundation is provided for statistical evaluation.

Third Step

Central punch-card archives with a suitable equipment of machines are established to serve one or several technical fields, which collect the research material as recorded on punch-cards by the participating workers and research groups. At the same time they store up in punch-card form those results of statistical evaluations and other data which have hitherto been published in book form. The cards, like other publications, carry the names of their authors. Either they are made accessible to the scientific public in the central archive or duplicates are made available. Examples of arrangements similar to this are already to be found in meteorology (the

German Weather Service, Deutsche Wetterdienst, has a punch-card archive) and in molecular spectroscopy (edge-notched cards carrying details of spectra can be bought from the Institut für Spektrochemie und angewandte Spektroskopie in Dortmund and from Butterworths Scientific Publications in London), as also in phonetics and linguistic research (at the Institute for Phonometry in Brunswick and at the Computing Centre for Mechanized Analytical Linguistic Research at Gallarate near Milan in Italy). Independently of these archives, technical documentation centres could be set up in which useful data and indications are extracted from existing literature and transferred to punch-cards under the guidance of subject specialists in order to build up documentary archives supplementing the other punch-card archives. This last is a true documentation activity, but it should not be called *Befunddokumentation* and I have called it *Auswertedokumentation* (evaluative documentation). Above all, it should not be confused with primary fixation or with statistical scientific work. Like all documentation, it is an ancillary discipline.

The execution of such a program is bound by various principles and rules which, on the basis of experience to date, can already partly be set down:

(*1*) Not every branch of knowledge is suitable for processing or recording by means of punch-cards.

(*2*) In no field of work can recording on punch-cards entirely replace the normal linguistic method of fixation by printing and so on. Generally speaking, machine punch-cards are the kind to be preferred for primary fixation and for the statistical purposes under discussion here.

(*3*) The machine punch-card method, and electronic computing machines depending on this, are the only method known up to now for the analysis of complex subjects and for carrying out extensive correlations in research.

What experiment offers us for the causal understanding of nature, comparisons between distributions of characteristics offer us for the correlative appreciation of phenomena. That is what has today become so important; but we need a mechanical process in order to obtain a sufficient quantity of comparable distributions for us to be able to arrive at conclusions that can form the basis for a thesis on the factors involved (Proppe and Wagner, 1957).

Considered as a heuristical instrument, the punch-card method compels uniform and disciplined expression. By so doing it secures a new kind of objective appreciation for the characteristics observed, and it makes comparisons possible in fields which hitherto have been accessible only to individual observers exposed to errors which are very difficult to check.

It is a fact that the study of histology became possible only after the discovery of the microscope. Likewise, so far as can be seen at present, an acceptable anthropology, especially on its psychological side, can be developed only on the basis of the punch-card method (Derbolowsky, 1952).

(*4*) With the aid of the machine punch-card method, an enormous saving of time will be secured at the evaluative stage. This saving in time will occur especially in monotonous tasks which, because they can be done by machine, are looked upon by human beings as second-rate and which inherently are very sensitive to careless mistakes. The machine, however, works not only very quickly but also with a virtual freedom from any risk of error, even apart from the fact that checks are possible. By reason of these qualities it becomes possible in a rational way to handle questions and correlations which are regarded as secondary, or which may not appear worthwhile, but which nevertheless—as so often happens in research—may turn out to be the very ones which yield interesting results.

I hope it has been made clear what the punch-card method is capable of doing. To demonstrate the economy of the punch-card for medical purposes, I need only mention the fact that I have passed every card belonging to our obstetrical physiological collection through the sorting machine about 3000 times in five years. When, further, it is recalled that by the use of hand methods it is possible to accomplish only one-hundredth of the sorting work which the machine performs without any error, then calculation shows that instead of these five years I would have had to go on sorting for about 500 years in order to reach my conclusions. This statement makes the saving in time more apparent than many words (Hosemann, 1951).

The basic studies in application of the punch-card method have yielded us an extraordinary amount of help. These have made it possible to process varying amounts of basic material in a fraction of the time which would have been necessary using the manual methods that have hitherto been normal. Besides this, second grade work was able to be transferred to machines and in this way greater care and attention devoted to the evaluation of the results. The favorable experience obtained in using the Hollerith system for establishing genetic values, and especially the discovery that the great mass of existing data which had proved impossible to evaluate by the ordinary methods for lack of money and time could now be systematically treated along with the rest, encouraged us to investigate other genetic questions in the same way. At this moment we are occupied with the evaluation of entries in the bovine yield book, results from pig fattening tests, inferences drawn from milking yield tests and matters connected with poultry records. All these have the same objects, namely, to perfect the methodology of genetic research, to increase the understanding of characteristics which are important in heredity and to provide useful practical advice for breeding selection (Havermann, 1956).

In ecological work in botany, undertaken by the author in reference to the flora of algae in the Fulda river, two persons in the course of ten working days were able to evaluate the material which would otherwise have taken one person at least a year (Scheele, 1952).

Work in fisheries biology showed similar results (Müller, 1952). Likewise, experience is available in physiological tasks undertaken at the Max Planck Institute for Medical Research: 'Whereas, last year, two persons had taken altogether about six months to evaluate about the same amount of material by manual methods, on this occasion the actual machine work took three days and the further study of the tables took one person about a month.' [This information was contained in a letter from Dr Hörnicke, 1953. Using the latest machines, even the last mentioned stage of work is made unnecessary—Author.] Finally, the almost unimaginable speeds of electronic computers may be mentioned again here, the steps in a calculation being timed in microseconds.

(5) All research operations can be divided between those which relate to the study of additional material for the purpose of confirming existing hypotheses and those which relate to the first examination of new data. Corresponding to this distinction, the results of research fixed on punch-cards can serve two purposes: the testing of already available hypotheses by the investigation of large numbers of data, or the assimilation of a given complex of data such as medical case records, biological specimens, etc., according to as many characteristics and along as many characteristic dimensions as possible, without posing beforehand any definite scientific questions such as will be assigned precedence when the stage of evaluation is reached.

(6) A card collection of the second kind allows better and more favorable exploitation of the advantages which are inherent in the punch-card method. The great number of charactertistics which can be taken into account makes it more versatile, so that it can be used over and over again whenever someone wishes to try new combinations. Consequently it is worth while setting up such a collection of cards even for a few hundred working units (preferably each corresponding to one punch-card, if there is enough room on it).

> The special job of analysing complex subject matter has shown that what determines whether mechanical processing pays is not so much the extent of the material, as such, but rather the number of characteristics to be collected in relation to the object under investigation. In order to obtain deeper understanding of even a few hundred cases it pays to transfer the collected data on to punch-cards. Whether this technique is worth adopting should not be judged merely from what the rules of combination show to be the limits of probability that relevant phenomena will be encountered, for that would be to underestimate the importance to clinical research of the possibilities which mechanical evaluation opens up (Proppe and Wagner, 1957).

This statement applies equally, and without qualification, to other fields of research also. It should again be stressed, however, that it lies in the nature of punch-cards to serve not only for statistical work on the material available; apart from that, the individual cards which relate to particular working units (persons, specimens, etc.) can very quickly be picked out from the mass.   This is important, in medicine for instance when it is desired to know or confirm which ones of the patients suffered from particular diseases or combinations of diseases.

(7) In a collaborative or collective research in which several workers are taking part it is not desirable to divide up the task before the punch-cards have actually been established.   If that were done, each individual would be obliged to examine the same raw material from his own point of view alone, which would entail all the psychological dangers (such as pre-conceived opinions, etc.) that attend such a procedure.   It is best for each participant to take a portion of the whole material, assimilating from this and transferring on to punch-cards *all* (or as many as possible) of the characteristics he finds in it including those which appear unimportant. This procedure, whereby each worker does his work independently and records the results straight on to punch-cards, is particularly suitable where the material is geographically dispersed and relates to fields of research in which the basic records (such as medical case sheets) from which data are to be punched do not have to be sent forward and back.

Hosemann, from his great experience in the planning of collective research groups, has drawn up the following rules for guidance:

(*a*)   The original material should be shared among the collaborators not from thematic but from practical points of view.

(*b*)   Each worker should receive part of the raw material from which to extract as many characteristics as possible, without cognizance of his own particular scientific theme.

(*c*)   In accordance with basic written instructions, these extracts should be so prepared as to dovetail into a common scientific plan.

(*d*)   Uniformity of work should be ensured by supervising the collaborators and by holding collective discussions of unsolved and difficult questions.

(*e*)   When this collective research has been accomplished the scientific themes should be distributed.

(*f*)   Finally the whole punch-card collection should be placed at the disposal of each of the collaborators for the purpose of evaluating them from the standpoint of a particular question.

(8) In certain cases it may be useful to provide what are called 'coupled card' collections.   By this is meant the common mechanical processing of several sets of cards which have only one or a few punching fields the same, whilst the others have different contents.   The fields which are punched the same, corresponding to points of view or characteristic dimensions common to the several sets of cards, then serve as connecting links between these.

Coupled card collections of this kind may be useful for instance in ecological investigations.   First of all a physiographical working set of cards is constructed in which all chemical and physical data for the locality of the research (for instance a river) are incorporated.   Then data for each of the various groups of organisms which have been found in that locality are recorded by different workers on to separate biological working card sets. These are coupled, as required, with the physiographical cards, since the same physiographical data are pertinent to all the organisms found at the same place. This saves repeating the physiographical data in all the various sets of biological cards, and the space which would thus be taken up is freed for other uses.

(*9*) Whenever possible, the use of intermediate record sheets before the data are actually punched in the cards should be avoided. Instead the values read off, for instance in the microscope, should be marked directly on the appropriate cards (or on cards coupled therewith) by the mark-sensing method. Judging from experience up to now this will not, however, be possible in all branches of work, or always possible for the whole contents of the punch cards.

(*10*) Scientific evaluative work using punch-card machines is not of a kind which should be equated with commercial routine work using these machines, such as is entrusted to the ordinary punch-card staff of the firms concerned. Therefore in every case it is advisable, even if not essential, that the scientific specialist concerned should acquire familiarity with the machine techniques in order to carry out the evaluations. At any rate he must be enabled to understand the business as a whole. Often it is only when the sorting is actually being done that new possibilities are revealed of a kind which ought at once to be followed up, or that laboriously framed instructions are found not to correspond with practice. The evaluation cannot be adequately carried out from the desk alone, however carefully it has been prepared. It is easier for the scientist to make himself familiar with a method, here the punch-card method, than for the methodologist to acquire the necessary knowledge of the science and problems in question.

(*11*) For primary recording or for statistical processing with punch-cards, the following points require attention from each aspect of the work:

(a) *Aspect I* (*technical language*)
Statistical evaluation of scientific research data depends (even more than documentation work) on absolutely clear-cut decision or definition of the concepts. (See also Chapter 5.) No mastery of mathematical and statistical method, however complete, can be of any use if the concepts to which it is to be applied are inaccurate or not clear. Consequently no endeavors should be directed (anyway for the present) to arriving at a code applicable generally to all kinds of research problems. It is much more important that the scope assigned to each code should remain comprehensible so that the uniform application of all names and terms and of the necessary indications can continuously be checked and coordinated. 'In fact the greatest difficulty encountered in applying mechanical methods of evaluation in clinical work is that which arises in so formulating the concepts that these are clear-cut and sharply differentiated at the same time' (Proppe and Wagner, 1957).

(b) *Aspect II* (*theory of order*)

No classification, but only a logical scientific system in accordance with system theory, comes into question where primary recording or statistical evaluation are concerned.   Here the decimal classification would be quite out of place.   The ruling principles of the system adopted, and the technical requirements of punch-cards such as the arrangement of columns and so forth, need to be brought into harmony with one another.   Each characteristic dimension is assigned one column or group of columns.   No two dimensions must be entered in the same column even if they are limited to two or three characteristics only.

(c) *Aspect III* (*notation*)

For primary fixation and scientific evaluation a notation system is usually superfluous.   Instead, the indications can be directly assigned to the punching positions on the punch-cards.

(d) *Coding of the Indications*

Coding of the indications should be done by using only such codes as are suitable for statistical and computing purposes.

9. SIGNIFICANCE AND TASKS OF DOCUMENTATION

(A) Definition

The Deutsche Gesellschaft für Dokumentation has laid down the following definition of the concept: 'Documentation means collecting documents systematically and making them accessible and useful.' The author, in order to avoid exposing himself to any misunderstanding in this book, would like to amplify the above definition by a closer consideration of what is meant by the word 'document'. Only such records as have been prepared by optical, acoustical or mechanical means with the object of fixing knowledge, and of so making it accessible to other people, are entitled to be regarded as 'documents'. In the above quoted definition the words 'collecting', 'accessible' and 'useful' apply to ancillary and supporting activities. Documentation, then, is to be regarded as a 'supporting' science. It has the task of making documents ready for acceptance by the specialist user, but not that of solving problems of research by making use of their contents. Thus all documentary work is of a referencing character only. Assessing the value of the available basic material, and making a choice from this, can be included in this function of documentation, but the intellectual processing of the material procured by the documentalist cannot be so included. It is, for instance, quite wrong in every way to stretch the term 'documentation' over the preparation of a textbook, or even that of a summary report, upon any given subject or problem. In the interests of a clear separation of functions this should be avoided. Neither can the mental and moral sciences be included in the concept of documentation even though the work they involve is based almost exclusively on the contents of documents.

A similar confusion stems from illegitimate extension of the concept 'document'. Otlet, for instance, spoke of the 'documentation of museum materials', but, as has already been pointed out in the preceding section here, plants and animals, people and other 'museum material', are not documents. If they are included in the scope of that term almost nothing is left out and the concept of documentation becomes coincident with that of science itself.

Much has been said and written about the delimitation between librarianship and documentation. Without entering into detail about that in the present book, the author is of opinion that the field of work called 'bibliography' can to a great extent be assimilated to what is covered by the concept of documentation, at any rate this is so if the concept of bibliography is defined, with Totok (1956), as follows:

In general, bibliography is now understood to include:

(*a*) lists of writings established from certain points of view, apart from the question of their availability in a library (therein distinguished from a catalog)

(*b*) study of literature referencing (structure, purpose, knowledge of the different forms, historical development)

(*c*) study of the practice of compiling such aids (the methodology of their construction).

(B) Possibilities of Subdivision

In accordance with the subject matter, documentation can be subdivided as follows (with possible intermediate stages and transitions).

I. Reference Documentation

(Here subdivided in accordance with the German standard *DIN 1426*):

> (*1*) Bare titles
> (*2*) Indications of contents
> (*3*) Commentary.

Under (*1*), titles by themselves should be used only to supply information as to the availability of publications. They provide only reference to the literature, in accordance with *DIN 1505*.

Under (*2*), the compiler should amplify the titles so as to state the nature and kind of the publication as clearly as possible without, however, expressing any opinion. This can be done by indicating the contents, the problem treated, and the assumptions or opinions of the author(s). Alternatively, it can be done by reproducing the subdivision heads. The form should be brief, limited to keywords, but the indications given should cover everything that is essential.

Under (*3*), commentary on the contents of periodicals and books, normally reflecting the opinions of the abstractor or reviewer, should be so designed as to offer the reader a sufficient insight into the construction, conclusions and value of the publication in question that he can readily decide whether to read the original or not. Reproduction of illustrations and tables from the publication can be used to replace long explanations and facilitate understanding. (Here translated from *DIN 1426*.)

It should be added here that another way of conducting the second kind of documentation, that which relates only to indications of content, is to scan the publications and look at the tables, illustrations and so forth which they contain from some definite and self-sufficient point of view, citing from this the original literature. Tüxen, for instance, has built up a phytosociological reference card index on the basis of currently scanning the related literature in this way.

II. Evaluative Documentation

III. Documentation of Results

The methods call for discussion independently of this conceptual subdivision. They correspond with the procedures to be used for primary fixation, and in that context are discussed in Chapter 10 along with secondary fixation.

Reference documentation can be regarded as documentation in the narrow sense of the word. As already explained, it is largely preoccupied with the bibliographical field in the sense adopted by Totok. In a separate work (1955 a) entitled *Über einige Grundfragen der Dokumentation mit Lochkarten* ['On certain fundamental questions in documentation using punchcards'] I have tried to examine exhaustively the conceptualization and subdivision of documentation. As the mode of subdivision there proposed (see also what has been said above) has worked out well, I shall here quote part of that work with only slight alterations:

> In the opinion of the author, who himself came up against the literature problem from his involvement in research, documentation may perhaps be regarded as an independent field of work which lies midway between librarianship and research, whose objects are primarily to be of service and provide a transition.

This statement may be amplified in a picture of the present situation which clearly shows the status of documentation. The librarian observes, with growing concern, that the riches of his library are not being as much used and exploited as they should and could be. It is from this side that he is led to appreciate the demands of documentation. On the other side the research worker—and in industry or economic life, the practitioner— becomes more and more aware, in his own work, that oversight of the literature is eluding him and that the laboriously cultivated fruits of his activities are not being delivered at all the places where they might fertilize the work of others but merely being buried under the avalanche of literature. In this way he also, from his own point of view, is brought up against the literature problem. But neither the researcher nor the librarian is in a position to master the additional requirements which arise through this situation; hence the need to distinguish a new professional pattern, that filled by the 'documentalist' or information scientist.

A field of work, and the concepts which belong to it, can be delimited more clearly in proportion as the activities are fully and unequivocally defined and subdivided. Therefore a subdivision of what is meant by documentation will now be attempted. This has already been published in summary form and was agreed at an international meeting of the Food and Agriculture Organization at which Unesco also was represented (Scheele, 1955 b), but it seems useful and desirable to present it once again and discuss it more fully.

According to this, documentation can be divided into three stages, relating respectively to finding the documents, to evaluating them and to working up the results found in them in accordance with the objects of the research. Holmstrom has aptly named these three the bibliographic stage, the analytic stage and the synthetic stage (Unesco, 1955).

The subdivisions of documentation are as follows:

General—the Theory of Documentation

(1) *The bibliographic stage—*

(a) *The working unit* is the single publication.   (In applying the punch-card method, this means using only one punch-card for each publication.)

(b) *Purpose*: reference and procurement.

(c) *Relation with activities contiguous to documentation.*   There are no close relations with research, but there are with librarianship.

> (*i*) *Relation as regards the working unit.*   Libraries and librarians concern themselves only with monographs (single books) and with periodicals as wholes, whereas documentation centres or information scientists concern themselves with individual papers or articles.   Here then, there is a clear difference, though only of degree.

> (*ii*) *Relation as regards statement of the task.*   Here the two fields of work, librarianship and documentation, cut across and complement one another in many ways.   This is inherent in the nature of the case, since the difference as regards the working unit is only gradual. It can, however, perhaps be said that jobs connected with the primary collection, arrangement and custody of documents are proper to libraries, whence it follows that a documentation centre so described in the pure sense does not have the documents (literature, etc.) them- selves available.   But usually a library and a documentation centre are coupled together or at any rate collaborate closely.

(2) *The analytic stage (Evaluation)—*

(a) *The working unit* is an 'object', together with the particular publications that relate to it.   (There may be many punch-cards for each publication, since every object occurring in a new context must have its own card.)

(b) *Purpose*: literature research.

(c) *Relation with activities contiguous to documentation.*   (Research and librarian- ship.)   No close relations exist with librarianship but there are close relations with research.

> (*i*) *Working unit.*   In research, unlike at the bibliographic stage, the working unit is not the publication but is the object of the research— for instance, in chemistry the various elements, in biology the various organisms.

> (*ii*) *Purpose.*   Documentation and research frequently cut across one another since the working unit is the same for both.   The difference between these two fields is that the research worker procures his knowledge directly from the object by way of observation and experiment whereas the documentalist collects data and values appertaining to the object by searching among those already known and recorded in the literature.   It is the common aim of the research scientist and of the documentalist (information scientist) to achieve as certain and many-sided an understanding of the object as possible; this understanding is then elaborated at the synthetic stage of documentation.

(3) *Synthetic stage (elaboration of the results)*—

(a) *The working unit* is the object, independently of the separate publications. (Only one punch-card or group of punch-cards is made for each object.)

(b) The *purpose* is to establish an archive or conclusions contributing to the 'collective memory of mankind'.

(c) *Relation with activities contiguous to documentation.*   (Research and librarianship.)   There are close relations with research only.

  (*i*) In research and documentation the *working unit* is the object of the research, but at this synthetic stage of documentation it is independent of the individual publications or investigations.

 (*ii*) *Purpose.* Documentation and research cut across one another since both use the same working unit at the synthetic stage.   The purpose of documentation consists, however, partly in close collaboration with research and partly in further elaboration of the results obtained at the analytic stage in order to collect and fix all assured knowledge that bears upon the object of the research.   In this way an archive (or card collection) of results is constituted which the documentalist (information scientist) continuously amplifies and keeps up to date. This archive then affords the research worker the possibility not only of furnishing himself with any desired information but also of carrying out every kind of comparative statistical investigation, based on the properties and characteristics that are already known and assured in relation to his object.

As is apparent from this way of subdividing the subject, the bibliographic stage—hence its name—has much in common with librarianship whereas the other two stages have a closer connection with research.   At the same time, this subdivision of documentation into three stages helps to clarify the boundaries between the field of documentation as a whole and neighboring fields.   It is rather in this sense that Holmstrom (1955) wrote as follows (before the two Unesco committees were merged in a single committee) :

Arising from this, the use of 'documentation' as a term embracing all three stages may be helpful in differentiating it from 'librarianship'; for it is clear that whilst the first or bibliographical stage should be regarded as an extension of ordinary library cataloging technique, the second and third stages have necessarily to be carried out by scientists able to exercise critical judgment in handling the specialized subject matter. Incidentally, this differentiation may also be taken to indicate the boundary between the respective objects of the two linked committees which Unesco maintains: the International Advisory Committee on Bibliography which is concerned with questions needing to be considered collectively and to be standardized in the same way for all disciplines, and the International Advisory Committee for Documentation and Terminology in Pure and Applied Science which deals with those questions which are peculiar to each group or branch of the sciences.

Here an example which extends over all three stages in documentation may serve to illustrate once again what has been said. The author has chosen this example from his own peculiar speciality, the study of diatoms. At the same time, it will illustrate how each of the three stages in documentation builds upon what precedes it.

The purpose and ultimate aim of documentation in the study of diatoms is the establishment of a punch-card archive covering all their varieties and indicating the known properties of each.

First stage. Awareness and procurement of all publications in which diatoms are treated. For this purpose all available bibliographical and technical aids are utilized. Bibliographies made up of titles, as comprehensive as possible, serve for general orientation in the available literature. An aid to that is the existence of a reference card collection in which all publications appearing in the most important limnological periodicals are taken up. Often bibliographical bulletins, containing lists of contents or abstracts, make it possible to eliminate publications not suitable for the desired evaluation. Insofar as the literature is not already on file in the related periodicals, or in the form of off-prints, the publications containing it are obtained or borrowed either in the original form or reproduced in microfilms or photocopies.

Second stage. Evaluation of the literature referenced and procured at the first stage.

An example of this is the processing of a publication by Hustedt (1954) under the title 'Die Diatomeenflora der Eifelmaare' [The diatom flora of the Eifel lake-craters]. Several of these craters were explored and about five specimens were taken from each of them, each specimen yielding at least fifty different varieties. For the purpose of evaluation one machine punch-card (using the mark-sensing process) was provided, in principle, to correspond with each variety found in each specimen, totalling up to several hundred cards for each publication. The following points of view or values relating to each variety were taken into account when punching these cards insofar as the publications gave information on them: frequency, medium, temperature, current, depth, light, chemical factors (pH, SBV, O_2, Cl, etc.), mode of life, substratum, major biotope, minor biotope, elevation, geography of the locality where found, month and year of sampling, remarks about other properties of the varieties such as might lead to amplification or alteration of the diagnoses already on record.

Apart from these indications expressible as numerical values or by reference to established concepts and thus amenable to statistical processing, the work carried out on certain of the varieties also yielded indications of a kind which had to be expressed in short sentences and could not be translated into 'punch-card language'. These indications were copied by typewriting on to edge-notched cards, notched to indicate the number of the variety and the points of view treated. Edge-notched cards were provided also for indications of a general nature not relating only to particular varieties.

As far as possible the whole of the literature about diatoms (but for the author's purpose only fresh-water diatoms) is being recorded on punch-cards in this fashion. The next step following this is the actual evaluation, in which the collection of machine-punched cards is worked upon statistically in strict accordance with rule, so as to arrive at conclusions for each particular variety. This may be exemplified as follows: Variety X has been found to occur frequently in 2800 samples taken to date. In 80 per cent of these samples it occurs with a pH value of less than 7. In 78 per cent of them it was found only in stagnant moor waters, mainly during the spring and exclusively in the paleoarctic zone.

Next, the set of edge-notched cards is sorted so as to find out what other indications are available whereby the statistical results can be amplified.

Third stage. Incorporation of all such available information about the individual kinds of diatoms as can be regarded as reliable.

For each variety only one machine punch-card, or designated group of such cards, is provided. In close collaboration with a world-renowned specialist in diatoms, Dr F. Hustedt, all important references to siliceous algae are being collected, the basis of this collection being partly direct consultation of the related publications (especially keys, handbooks, etc.) and partly results obtained from the evaluation card collection. The following properties, among others, are noted for each variety. As regards morphology: length, breadth, height, conditions of symmetry, structure, kind and arrangement of the chromatophors. As regards physiology: movement, development, propagation. As regards ecology: colonization and the position in the temperature, current, pH and halobian systems. As regards chorology and biogeography: the geographical distribution.

Thus the position of each variety in the 'multi-dimensional system of properties' is unequivocally fixed in the punch-card archive. Newly obtained knowledge is continuously punched in and changes can be made without difficulty by replacing the appropriate punch-cards, so that the archive always represents the latest situation reached in diatom research. The completed archive enables all the advantages and possibilities of the punch-card method as described above to be exploited. Examples and more detailed information have already been given by the author elsewhere (Scheele, 1951). At the same time this card collection of conclusions can be used as a 'key'. *Mutatis mutandis*, this example taken from the field of diatoms can be applied to any other fields of work (Scheele, 1955 a).

After this full explanation of how documentation can be subdivided, the following point may once again be stressed: tasks can be handled more simply in proportion as solutions to the literature problem are solved at the stage of primary fixation, and in proportion as documentation itself becomes better and more rationally organized. In application to the various stages of documentation, this works out as follows:

Bibliographic stage. The total number of publications to be referenced becomes smaller, and at the same time bibliographical practice can be organized more simply, in proportion as it becomes possible in some measure to enlist authors themselves in the work of documentation. The very fact of good titling, and the fact that many periodicals now require the provision of a separate clear synopsis of each article, are extremely valuable aids. A more remote objective might be to have each author accompany his manuscript with a mark-sensing card ready completed.

Analytic stage (*Evaluation*). The extraction of data and values from the literature becomes unnecessary in proportion as these data and values are fixed on punch-cards in the first place instead of being printed. In fact, evaluative documentation can be regarded as a duplication of work which at present is unavoidable but which would be made redundant if publication were to be reorganized in a rational way.

Synthetic stage (*Exploitation of results*). As the difference between 'evaluative' (analytic) documentation and 'results' (synthetic) documentation has often been misunderstood an attempt must be made to make this matter clearer. Evaluative documentation is concerned only with the collection of individual data and values, that is to say of indications which, in biology for instance, relate to single individuals. Documentation of results is concerned, on the contrary, exclusively with general indications which can be regarded as established criteria for semaphorontes or higher collective categories. Whilst evaluative documentation is an aid to statistical research (see Chapter 8) the documentation of results provides a contribution to general systematics (see Chapter 11).

Since, up to now, the indications which provide material for the documentation of results have generally been published in handbooks and similar works of reference (for instance in *Tabulae Biologicae*), the possibility arises that simplification and rationalization might be achieved by replacing them with a punch-card archive, at the stage of primary recording; for in this way the secondary operation of transferring the indications from handbooks on to punch-cards would be saved.

(C) General Problems and Rules

The following detailed experiences and rules have emerged for carrying out documentation by means of punch-cards.

(*1*) From every point of view—organizational, technical and coding— the three stages of documentation which have been described above must be kept clearly apart. Their problems are completely different and cannot be solved either in a single operation or by following the same rules. Evaluative documentation is closely connected with research, and therefore is organized jointly with the primary records, using codes which correspond with those used in statistical research. On the other hand, documentation of results contributes to scientific theory of systematics as well as to building up the corresponding punch-card archives, for which reason it is discussed in Chapter 11. Therefore the only aspect of these operations which remains closely linked with librarianship, and which remains to be discussed as part of documentation in the narrower sense of the word, is that occupied by the bibliographic stage.

(2) An attempt to survey the numerous endeavors that have been made to solve the problem of bibliographic documentation, and to draw up a balance sheet of these, leads to roughly the following conclusions:

(a) There is no simple and cheap ready-made solution to these problems. All ideas and attempts to carry out effective documentation as cheaply as possible by depending on volunteer collaborators and on out-dated methods, or to solve the whole problem by these means, flatly contradict the difficulty and magnitude of the task.

(b) Numerous documentation centres and services existing side by side without interconnection or coordination are, in the aggregate, much more expensive and much less efficient than a single centralized or suitably coordinated documentation system would be.   This statement is true most of all when expensive experiments in the use of new methods, all aiming at the same objective, are being pursued independently at different places. Moreover, in the financial assessment of these problems, it should not be forgotten that the scope of documentation work carried on within scientific institutions practically cannot be evaluated in terms of money at all, because such tasks are merged in the normal expenditure for staff and material. Finally, even today it can be assumed with some certainty that the progress and output of the Soviet Union, and of other countries belonging to the Eastern block, derives not least from the existence of documentation services organized centrally and on a very big scale.   This should give us food for thought; and surely it is unwise to confuse these technical considerations with politics, or be prejudiced against forms of organization in quite unpolitical fields, merely because they are practised (with success!) in the Eastern block.

(c) Nevertheless a solution is possible, even within the framework of de-centralized documentation, insofar as either or both of the following things can be considered independently: it appears desirable and necessary to create on the one hand a *centralized bibliographic documentation*, and on the other a *de-centralized specialist documentation*.

(3) As regards bibliographic documentation there is at present lacking, so far as can be seen, any general and internationally accepted conception of what the aim should be.   Too many points of view and endeavors, partly bound up with tradition and partly modern, conflict with one another.

The author considers that for the present the best solution might be the creation of national documentation centers which would work with machine punch-cards (or with electronic computers as the case may be) and would take cognizance, systematically and completely, of the whole of the literature in each country, including periodical articles and the 'underground' literature.   These national documentation centers would need to be closely linked with one another internationally, all of them using the same methods and codes so as to make the whole of the material exchangeable between them. In this way everyone would be able to obtain, through the appropriate national documentation center, the whole of the international literature bearing upon any given question. The fact that today it is necessary, even within the same country, to address several documentation centers in order to obtain all the material that relates to a given question, and that even then the information received from them is not exhaustive, represents an unacceptable state of affairs when seen from a broader point of view.

Were documentation to be organized on this pattern all general and other bibliographies (such as national and special subject bibliographies, and abstracting services insofar as individual publications are referenced in them) would become redundant, for it is known that the punch-card method makes it possible quickly to compile *ad hoc* a bibliography based on the whole of the available material relevant to any desired question. Further, as a by-product of such work, there is no difficulty with the aid of punch-cards in carrying out statistical analyses of the literature (here see Scheele, 1958 b). Such an analysis provides us with a survey of the development and status reached by the scientific discipline in question, which in turn enables conclusions to be drawn as to what should be done to promote it or as to any other measures desirable. In this way documentation at the bibliographic stage can be made serviceable also to the overall organization and policy of science. At the same time, the national documentation center could be linked with the establishment of a union catalog for the libraries of the country in question. Without here going into details about this, it is obvious in principle that it could be achieved without any technical difficulties.

Finally, having regard to the progress now being made in the development of translating machines, the national documentation centers should assume the task of installing such machinery in order that foreign literature may be translated into the language of the country by the most rational means. Not least among the proper functions of such a center would be that of pursuing methodical research into the processes of documentation, so that duplication of effort may be avoided in this field also. It is in the nature of such research that it is possible only on a practical basis, and that moreover it cannot be left for the smaller centers to pursue.

The conclusions may be summarized as follows:

(*a*) On the organizational side, it is in the consolidation of all bibliographical and cataloging work along with documentation in a national documentation center that the most rational solution of all these questions must be sought; so far they involve a general and complete survey of the literature.

(*b*) On the technical side, too, a centralized solution is called for, because the installation of machine punch-cards, 'electronic brains' and translating machines does not become economic and rational unless it is carried out centrally. Taking a broad view of the matter, it is becoming more and more evident that the problems of bibliographic documentation can be mastered only by resort to these techniques.

(c) From the coding side, a splitting of the documentation centers into several sections would appear expedient.   These sections, corresponding to the major fields of classification as indicated on page 119—cultural sciences, mathematics, physics and chemistry, astronomy, earth sciences and biology, applied sciences and technology—would correspond also with a suitable coding system taking up the space available on one IBM card—see the example which begins on page 218).   Where a piece of work overlaps several such fields, several punch-cards must be provided.

Before such a plan for the creation of national documentation centers is more definitely conceived a large-scale experiment should be carried out, using several hundreds of thousands of punch-cards relating to one of the fields mentioned above, in order to collect experience which is still lacking; for this cannot be done either at the desk or on the basis of only a few thousand cards.   If anyone considers that comprehensive and boldly conceived solutions to the problems of documentation are utopian he must be countered with the reminder that about one hundred years ago modern post and telecommunications, such as now enable any information to be transmitted in a very short time to any part of the world, would certainly have been regarded as still more so.   Just as, in that sphere, the general need called forth the appropriate organizational and technical solutions which took shape in the Universal Postal Union and international telegraph and telephone networks, so the requirements of documentation will sooner or later compel their corresponding solutions.   Not least among the contributions to these may be such as have already been made possible by telecommunications to connect the documentation centers with one another, and with their 'customers', by the use of teleprinters, television and the like.

(4) Specialized documentation within each subject field can be conducted side by side with the central bibliographic documentation without the former needing to be centralized.   This is already the position in the German Federal Republic, for instance.   The special documentation bureaux can undertake the following tasks:

(a) Systematic scanning of certain periodicals on behalf of the national documentation centre.   For this work, uncompromising conformity with the methods and coding rules adopted by the center is essential.   In return for it, the center would provide special bibliographical references free of charge.

(b) Special processing and making ready of literature referenced by the center for the benefit of the particular circle of readers which the special documentation bureau was created to serve.   Such bureaux are likely to exist mainly for industry and applied research, since theoretical science can be served adequately by information from the national center.   As regards this kind of work the special documentation bureaux will be left quite free to choose their own methods, classifications and codes.   Experience has shown it is no longer possible to achieve unification and coordination on the plane where the special documentation bureaux operate; nor does this matter, provided that bibliographic documentation is unified.

(*c*) A department for evaluative documentation may be attached to such a bureau. Regarding this see 'Primary recording', page 141.

Apart from the special documentation bureaux, most of the separate scientific institutions and individual scientists will of course maintain literature card collections of their own. In so doing, they may adopt the methods and systems of the main center or of the special documentation bureaux, or may proceed in accordance with their own ideas. They need not, however, carry out any documentation work in the proper sense of the word, as all references can be obtained from the center.

(5) As contributions to solving the literature problem, apart from the above mentioned, short-term (annual) and long-term (decennial) reviews of progress will be issued, providing summary outlines of the status reached within each complex of scientific problems (like for instance the existing *Fortschritte der Zoologie*). Also publications in book form should be further studied (on which see Rothschuh, 1955). These questions, however, fall outside the scope of the present book.

(6) Something more needs to be said on the division of work as between the documentation center and the special documentation bureaux.

Since the purpose of documentation must be seen in a rationalization of those increasingly difficult labors which prepare the way for intellectual activity, this purpose comes down to the avoidance of duplication. That is something which can be attained only when cognizance of all literature within a certain scope (preferably the literature of a certain country—whence the argument for *national* documentation centers) either is concentrated at one point, or is centrally and systematically controlled from such a point by dividing up the task according to the periodicals in which the literature appears, instead of according to subject divisions. At the center, the whole literature is arranged multidimensionally in accordance with a suitable system of classification (see the example in Chapter 13, § 3), and thereby is rendered accessible so far as is possible by references to an order which is not highly specialized but is to be looked upon as preparatory. At this stage nothing is attempted in the way of subjective evaluation, since that is something which must be left to the specialist. On the other hand, it is the proper task of reference documentation to collect material however widely scattered; and at the same time, through the nature of the classification and the use of punch-cards, to bring together all those data which are relevant to the same subject, thereby serving the unity of the sciences.

The growing specialization of the sciences has another side to it also. Since an ultimate limit exists to knowledge the several disciplines tend to converge more and more. A continual increase takes place in their cross connections and in the development of 'bridge sciences', which modern reference documentation must take into account.

If the object of reference documentation is so stated, the following quotation from Gülich (1953) in opposition to the application of punch-cards loses its force:

Ultimately, mechanical selection means the disappearance of the visual catalog and thereby of all those stimuli which the consultation of a properly arranged catalog affords the user over and above his original question. Whoever resorts to one of these catalogs, not merely in order to pose the question whether certain known books or periodicals are available but eager to become acquainted with the material as a whole, is continually heartened by the experience of discovering new and larger questions formulated for him by the very manner in which the knowledge is arranged and presented. That, however, is possible only when he actually has the catalog before him and can, if need be, finger his own way through its leaves, whereas the mechanical selector gives only the answers to the particular questions which he asks.

This argument is particularly interesting because, in fact, it weighs much more in favor of mechanical selection than against it. What Gülich describes is indeed the general experience of every scientist. In fact his problem lies precisely in the fact that, using the classical methods such as catalogs and the like, it has now become impossible for him to become acquainted with all the material available and relevant to any particular question, with all its important cross connections. Here is an example from limnology. Suppose all works relating to Eastern European rivers are being sought for. These must include all publications in biology, geography, geology, hydrology and hydro-chemistry and many other fields, some of them relating to practical disciplines—such as fishing and drainage engineering—but all of them pertinent to the river systems in question. At the same time, it may for instance be necessary for the biological works to be made findable also under keywords denoting the systematic groups which are treated in them, and under the specialized questions in subordinate disciplines to which they may relate such as phytosociology, ecology, animal geography, etc. The same thing may be true for others of the named branches of science, such as geography, geology, etc. Failing this the whole mass of material simply is not made available to the enquirer, but most of it is denied him. The flood of literature being nowadays so overwhelming how can one catalog to meet this problem as here formulated? In fact, punch-card methods are the only answer.

One of the other arguments brought against the proposal that a central reference documentation should be set up, and the duplication of work by many documentation bureaux thereby be brought to an end, is that a central or coordinated reference documentation is made impossible by the need of different persons working in different fields to study the same publications from different points of view, wherefore multiple study of the same material does not necessarily mean duplication of work. But in my opinion this argument rests on a misapprehension. It is impossible, in any case, to draw more out of a publication than there is in it! By using an appropriate system of classification, whatever content it has can to a great extent be extracted objectively even though, of course, it is never possible to eliminate completely the subjective momentum of the documentalist working on it. But this residual subjectivity can never be sufficient to justify duplicating the work.

To take an example, suppose a publication relates to the chewing mechanism and feeding habits of the cockchafer. Keywords stating this to be so may be perfectly valid: but, even so, it does not follow that either a physiologist concerned with sense organs or an animal geographer will find anything in it of interest to him. If the animal geographer believes that he might be able to draw conclusions relating to animal geography by studying how the cockchafer feeds, he must refer not only to this but also to all other related publications to be found under the keyword 'feeding'.

If a documentation center as here envisaged were to be superimposed on the existing specialized documentation bureaux the efficiency of these would be considerably improved. People working in them would then be freed to devote themselves entirely to such tasks as the more specialized subdivision of their own fields, 'working up' the literary material referenced for them or evaluating it (page 157). They would be able also to give an important place in their activities to the production of review reports (see para. (5) in this section), although that lies somewhat on the boundaries of documentation work properly so called (see page 152).

The specialized documentation bureaux, by contrast with the center, should always proceed *evaluatively* and discard inappropriate material. For this reason they must be staffed by subject specialists.

There will, however, be many cases, as indicated by way of example in Chapter 13, § 3, when it will not be necessary to interpose specialized documentation bureaux between the center and the 'user', because the referencing or the subdivision done at the center will be sufficient and the specialized treatment of the literature beyond this stage can be undertaken only by the specialist himself following up the original literature to which he has been referred.

(7) Choosing the type of documentation. At page 151 the various kinds of reference documentation which are possible were explained. Working with IBM punch-cards, extensive experiments have shown that keywords give the best results in documentation or bibliographical work. Mere titles are not sufficient, for often the title of a publication does not correspond with the contents, or does not always adequately indicate their nature. ('Educating' authors to provide good titles plays a very important part in documentation!) On the other hand reviews or more or less detailed abstracts require too much time in proportion to the results obtained. Solutions somewhere between reference documentation and evaluative documentation, endeavoring to mention in the abstract as many indications and values from the original work as possible, are entirely to be deprecated. For the same money, or only a little more, a good evaluative documentation can be formed or the user may altogether prefer to go straight back to the original works.

If an abstract is very long the reader prefers the original work, especially if this at the same time brings the diagrams and illustrations under his eyes. The cost of scientific abstracts is high and their readership very small, so it is difficult to make them pay their way. One tends, therefore, to have the impression that nowadays the technical world is

M

inclining more towards the short abstract or the simple indication of contents (von Klewitz, 1957).

Indications of contents in the form of keywords, which have been found satisfactory by themselves as a rational form of documentation using punch-cards, should at the same time be built up systematically, in accordance with a fixed plan. Unfortunately, such a plan, which could be followed more or less by enquirers too, is missing from nearly all of the known abstracting services. In these, systematization is limited mainly to the bibliographical indications (such as title references in accordance with the German standard *DIN 1505*) and even this detail is not always consistently carried out.

Existing experience suggests that it might be expedient to divide the bibliographical indications of each publication into three parts, preferably all on one punch-card:

(*a*) Bibliographical indications in accordance with the German standard *DIN 1505* suitably adapted for application to punch-cards (see the example from page 218). In special cases this part might be amplified by indicating locations of the books and by a few symbols for enabling the punch-card collection to serve also as a catalog (see also page 158).

(*b*) Indications of the outward form of the publication—its 'informational characteristics'. This expression is meant to include everything which has been described by other authors (Rösch, 1951; Koller, 1955) as a 'literary critical code' and 'typification of a work'; that is to say, indications of its physical form, size and value, the language used, the numbers of illustrations, tables and literature citations—everything apart from the substantial aspect of the contents. In the author's opinion, anything in the nature of subjective evaluation should here be excluded. For mechanical selection of the literature, such indications as these have a significance which ought not to be underestimated, for they are often of great selective value. At the same time, they are easy to code. Hence it would be useful if such indications, too, could be standardized. But, so far as the author knows, nobody but the above mentioned authors and himself has paid any detailed attention to this problem. Here again it would be necessary, first of all, to investigate working times and to make comparisons of cost, so as to arrive at a basis for estimating the profitability.

(*c*) Indications of the substantial content by means of keywords. The basis for this must be a plan enabling the operator to proceed step by step in such a way that no important point of view is overlooked. Such a basis is offered by a suitable system of classification directly convertible to punch-card coding (see examples Chapter 13, §§ 2 and 3). This solution has been reached by several authors in different fields independently of one another (Riegels in aerodynamics, Steidle in chemistry, Scheele in biology). To extend the plan, or in cases where it cannot be applied, either coding lists or card indexes may be provided in which the assignment of holes or punching positions to the keywords is recorded.

(*8*) The most important part of reference documentation is indication of the substantial content. Here, care must always be taken that the keywords chosen are limited to indicating the contents of the publications and not extended to indicating the objects treated in them, which would be to trespass upon the stage of work proper to evaluative or 'results' cards.

What is meant by this may be brought out by the following example. Suppose it is required to reference and code a work on the orientative power of fish, a work in which details of the eyes, labyrinth and fins are morphologically and physiologically treated on the basis of appropriate investigations which relate to three different groups of fish and have supplied a wealth of numerical and tabular material. It will then be the function of the reference card collection to ensure that this publication can be found from the keywords 'morphology', 'physiology', 'orientative power', 'fins', 'eyes' and 'labyrinth' as well as under the systematic categories to which the types of fish treated belong. It is no part of its function, however, to record and render reproducible the special results achieved by the investigations in question. That, rather, is the object of the separate evaluative card collection. Still less must it be regarded as a purpose of the first named to register what is already known, or what has been newly developed in the work under reference, regarding the types of fish treated therein (as, for instance, the fact that they are aquatic animals living in salt water and preferring a certain depth, occurring in shoals, orienting themselves according to a certain type, etc.). To record all that is the purpose of the 'result cards' collection.

Repeating, in different words, what has already been stated here this amounts to saying that a reference card collection should not be designed to make it possible to answer 'multidimensional' questions about the objects treated in the publications under reference. On these cards the objects should be recorded along one dimension only; that is to say in a fixed sequence, the most appropriate sequence to adopt in biology being that of the natural system. This will make it possible, for instance, to meet requests for all publications dealing with fish, molluscs, green algae or siliceous algae—but not for works in which aquatic organisms that thrive in a particular salt content. If these fundamental considerations are not taken into account, an irreclaimable mix-up may very quickly result. Indeed, a publication which discusses the adaptation to aquatic life of a group of organisms occurring in water is essentially of quite different interest from one which deals with the orientative powers or the digestive physiology of organisms whose other properties, not here treated, happen to be conjoined with the fact that they live in water.

Nor should one be misled, as regards observing rules such as these, by the existence of a particularly well-developed object code in chemistry (Steidle, 1957). Chemistry is in the fortunate position of having, in its formulas, a notation which at the same time reproduces the properties (molecular structures) of its objects. Once a code is found, like that of Steidle, which adequately transfers this notation to punch-cards a real advance has been gained, which unfortunately cannot yet apply to biology and other less 'exact' disciplines and which, therefore, cannot in principle affect the above mentioned rules.

10. SIGNIFICANCE AND PROBLEMS OF SECONDARY RECORDING BY THE USE OF PUNCH-CARDS

(A) Definition

By secondary recording is meant the procedure for recording which belongs to the phase of documentation. This never embraces the direct recording of results but either is limited to 'referencing' where certain results are to be found or else such results, recorded elsewhere, are systematically extracted from the primary documents and are prepared for further study (evaluation and processing of results).

(B) Possibilities of Subdivision

The methods applicable to secondary recording are the same as those in primary fixation, under which heading they have already been discussed. What concerns us here is only secondary recording assisted by the punch-card method.

(C) General Problems and Rules

(*1*) The various kinds of reference documentation on the one hand, specialist documentation and personal card collections on the other, do not involve the same methods of using punch-cards. As already explained in the preceding section, only machine punch-cards or electronic computers developed from these are suitable for reference documentation, whereas for specialist documentation and for the individual user needle and visual punch-cards can also play an important role, provided that the material be documented does not exceed a certain range of quantity.

(*2*) Since the results which are available from trials in different subject fields agree in indicating that the established methods of using punch-cards, such as the IBM system with standard equipment, are very well suited for documentation when properly applied, it seems pointless and inexpedient to design and construct special machinery for that purpose. This conclusion is supported by the following arguments:

Machine punch-cards, and the machines in which they are used, are in such worldwide use as practically to constitute an international standard. This already gives them so great an advantage in documentation work (as for instance to allow exchanges of cards) that any new method must be handicapped by comparison with them. Present tendencies in the application of punch-cards in the most varied directions make it quite certain that this advantage and progress will not be overtaken.

Electronic computers are developed on the basis of their input and output units being punch-cards, so that *in this sense* they are themselves to be reckoned as punch-card systems.   It can, indeed, be taken as fairly certain that this kind of electronic computer will eventually be relied upon for reference documentation.   For this very reason it would seem desirable to retain the punch-card as the elementary unit in literature referencing, especially since, when intelligently applied, it may generally be made to correspond with *one* publication so as to embody a single unit of literature and to provide, both in input and in output, the best and most convenient link between man and machine.   This advantage is further realized in the fact that punch-cards can also be filed in an ordinary card index, whereby their user is enabled to consult them without needing apparatus of any kind. This is another way of saying that the 'customer' can, if he finds it convenient, make direct use of punch-cards produced by electronic computers and supplied to him through a documentation center.   If it should prove possible—and endeavors in this direction are already being made—to work out a code which can be generally applied both in the various types of electronic computers and in ordinary punch-card machines, there are grounds for the hope that these techniques may lead the way to the optimal solution for reference documentation, through the same punch-cards being used (*a*) manually, (*b*) in standard machines, and (*c*) in electronic computers.   In this context it may be pertinent to recall that, given good programming, electronic computers can be made to deal with about a hundred enquiries at the same time.

(*3*) The referencing and the procurement of literature are tasks which must be considered separately.   Machine and visual punch-cards are suitable only for referencing the literature; that is to say, for indicating (see page 151) where the publications that bear on a particular theme are to be found.   On the other hand, needle punch-cards can also be used in such a way that referencing and procurement are to some extent coupled with one another.   On this type of card it is possible, without great difficulty, to attach an abstract in addition to the title and all necessary information about the publication.   This may be done in many different ways, ranging from handwritten notes to ordinary letterpress or, if convenient, abstracts collected from other sources may be pasted on to the cards.   For the latter purpose it has often been suggested that abstract bulletins should be supplied with printing on one side of the paper only, so as to allow of individual abstracts being cut out from them.   Going to the limit in this direction, the whole of a publication may, in the form of a microfilm strip, be attached to a needle punch-card.

In all these cases the final answer to an enquiry which a card collection and the appropriate selecting procedures are capable of yielding directly may include, besides the title, the corresponding abstracts or the work itself on microfilm.   How far a microfilm can and should take the place of the printed original text remains, however, a controversial question.

Various attempts have been made likewise to provide machine punch-cards with film windows or to find other ways, such as by photosensitizing these cards, to make them capable of combining the two purposes of referenc-

ing and of conveying the actual literature.   As already indicated in Part I
of this book, however, the author is led by his own experience to discountenance any such procedure, since machine punch-cards are in principle
not suited to it.

As regards the many methods—even apart from punch-cards, for instance
the Minicards, or the Rapid Selector—which aim to combine referencing
with procurement data, the remark by Rothschuh quoted on page 161
should not be forgotten.   This was to the effect that, when the literature
problem is broadly contemplated as a whole, its most important aspect is
seen to be not the referencing but the assimilation or 'utilization' of contents
of the publications.   Rothschuh found from his enquiries that no scientist,
or at least none working in physiology, is any longer able to read or still
less to study all the publications which appear in his specialty.   The
situation in other disciplines cannot be very different.

From this point of view, even taking no account of the real difficulties
which reproduction involves, is it not perhaps altogether beside the point
to develop methods of supplying the user with whole publications in some
such form as microfilm, alongside or instead of the reference?   Is it not
better to limit documentation to the referencing operation which is always
necessary for the purpose of reconnaissance, and to procure the literature
itself only in those cases where the user asks for it?   The money that can
be saved in this way might more profitably be devoted to evaluative documentation.   In my opinion that applies equally to any methods which aim
at coding the whole of the running text found in publications.

(4) In building up a collection of needle punch-cards it has often been
found useful to have two card sets side by side, one composed of these cards
and the other an ordinary static card index.   Both sets can be prepared
without additional labor by typewriting the latter as a carbon copy, it
having been found that normal punch-card material allows doing this
legibly.   Such a procedure is always a practical one when the card collection
is consulted frequently in a certain order of arrangement, such as the
alphabetical order of authors' names.   The ordinary card index can then
be arranged in that order and the punch-card collection utilized only for
the purpose of selecting in accordance with other characteristics.   Considerable time may thus be saved, which easily outweighs the cost of
stationery and space as it is, of course, possible by consulting the ordinary
card index to search for any publication whose author's name is already
definitely known much more quickly and simply than in the punch-card
set which is not filed in any order.

(5) As the various punch-card methods and codes have been discussed
in Part I of this book, and the several stages preliminary to fixation have
been treated in the chapters of Part II preceding this, it may be useful to
insert here a complete survey (see table, page 169), of the various combinations and interconnections that are possible in recording.   Rather than
merely enumerating as many disconnected isolated examples as possible
without the possibility of treating them fully, a scheme will be described

TABLE

Section I **Technical language**	Section II **Theory of order**	Section III **Notation**	**Coding of indications**
Names	**Formal arrangement**	**Without notation**	**Simple codes**
Personal names Fritz Meyer	Alphabetical	Direct assignment to holes or combination of holes	*Direct code* One hole
Specific names e.g. Iron	**Systematic arrangement**		*Abridged code* Combination of holes
Group names Metals	According to properties (characteristics and characteristic dimensions)	**Numerical notation**	**Combined codes**
Terms		*Unrelated to properties or order* Running numbers	*Hierarchical code* Code for multi-digit numbers
Characteristics Round		*Related to properties* Definite measurements	*Associative code* Punching pattern method
Characteristic dimensions Shape		*Related to order* Universal Decimal Classification	
		Letter Notation (*Subdivided as above*)	
		Notation using other symbols (*subdivided as above*)	
		Mixed notations (*subdivided as above*)	

whose categories are illustrated by examples. The author hopes that, by his adopting this method of explanation, the reader may be enabled to make his own choice and combination of the available procedures.

Referring to the diagrammatic scheme as here set out and taking the example of personal names (in Section I) with formal arrangement (in Section II) various possibilities of combination will now be examined for the sake of explaining it.

Case 1.   A research institute has five collaborating workers.   For their common use a literature card set is maintained on needle punch-cards, providing one card for each publication.   As there still is enough room on the cards, it has been agreed that each worker will mark on these needle punch-cards the publications that interest him.   For this purpose no notation is needed.   The names (Fritz Meyer, etc.) are directly printed close to a pair of holes on the needle punch-cards (which, let us assume, are double-row edge-notched cards).   The coding is done with direct codes, because it is possible that all five workers might be interested in the same publication.   Deep notching means 'specially important literature for the worker marked against this' and shallow notching 'normally important literature for this worker'.

Case 2.   In a large institute, where some 70 to 80 workers are collaborating, a 'personnel' card set is kept, using needle punch-cards.   For this case a numerical notation with serial numbers of the personnel is adopted. Supposing that double-row edge-notched cards have again been chosen, a hierarchical code may be formed by combining two additive abridged codes (because only one personal number needs to be notched on each edge-notched card).

Case 3.   It is required to record the authors' names of publications.   For this purpose a letter notation has most often been found best and in the majority of cases it has seemed natural to base it on abbreviations of the full names, such as their first three letters.   There are, however, alternative possibilities, such as to notch the first, third and last letters of the names. For coding on edge-notched or slotted punch-cards, hierarchical abridged codes may be used, such as a triangular code (see the example on page 85). If machine punch-cards are used the whole of the surnames may be punched in addition to the initials of given names.   The coding can then be done by way of the letters provided in the internal abridged code of the method in question.   Coding, therefore, raises no questions apart from the assignment of columns.

Finally, it seems necessary here to refer separately to a much discussed method, that known as Uniterms. Here, according to the available literature, names and terms (not concepts)—see Section I in our scheme—are used as headings for cards arranged in formal alphabetical order (Section II) without notation (Section III) and without coding, each corresponding to the heading of one visual punch-card. Transfer to machine punch-cards or needle punch-cards is, however, also possible with the aid of a combined associative code. The following quotation (Kreithen, Gull and Miller, 1954) will serve to explain the matter:

Language is built up from words.   Concepts, ideas, expositions, are expressed through language in the form of single words and combinations of these.   The number of combinations for any given content of information can be very large, but the number of basic forms or basic concepts, from which compound concepts are built up, is in general comparatively small.   An example of this is provided by the relatively small number of chemical elements, which is infinitesimal by comparison with the number of chemical compounds.

In the Uniterm system the information which is contained in a document is re-disposed in the linguistically simplest word units that characterize the information—the name Uniterm being derived from this principle and the essential basis being as follows:

(*a*) One Uniterm card is provided for each fundamental concept or keyword.

(*b*) Each document received for evaluation is given, at the time of its accession, a serial number which may also serve as a filing number, and its title or content is analyzed.

(*c*) This number alone is entered in all those Uniterm cards which correspond to the fundamental concepts found by analysis to be represented in the document.

The word units (basic concepts) generally consist of single words which straight away cover the essence of one concept, corresponding partly or wholly to the information content of the document.   Thus the word 'wind' can be associated with several different concepts or images to form for instance 'wind channel', 'wind velocity', 'cold wind' and so on.   In the conceptual combination 'wind channel', for instance, two separate concepts are joined together, one of which belongs to the conceptual group 'channel'.   When two such concepts are brought together, the operation known as logical combination is achieved.   In itself this denotes only the combination of 'wind' and 'channel', so the same combination might also be expressed as 'channel' and 'wind'. Thus a simple method of arranging the individual concept in a meaningful order is provided.

By means of the Uniterms—which need not be limited to two—any given concept may be built up in this way.   One great disadvantage of the method is, however, the fact that it is not based on the actual concepts— that is on the *meanings* of the words—but only on the *words* as such, so the method is always bound up with the use of one particular language.

Another circumstance which must be reckoned as a notable disadvantage is that *no systematic order* is used, whereas many writers on these questions agree in holding that an effective systematic classification is one of the indispensable pre-requisites for documentation, for which a merely formal order like that of the keywords used in the Uniterm system is no sufficient substitute.

These disadvantages can be avoided by using the punching pattern method (see the example on page 242).

11. SIGNIFICANCE AND PROBLEMS OF THE PUNCH-CARD METHOD IN SCIENTIFIC SYSTEM THEORY

(A) Definition

For the definition of 'system theory' see page 155. According to this, the purpose of a scientific system theory consists of tracing and exhibiting the order which is inherent in data.

If I have succeeded in making intelligible my line of thought in the section so far, and if these lines of thought are pursued to their conclusion, it will be recognized that in system theory the aims of research and documentation in a sense converge; hence a separate treatment of system theory is justified at the end of the most important part of this book.

One may agree with Hennig that system theory (or, as he still calls it generally, 'systematics') may embrace all questions of order and rationalization of the phenomenal world and therein all nomothetical activity in the natural sciences. In the system theory of any given field, all knowledge appertaining to that field finds its shortest possible, most pregnant and most unambiguous outcome. Loosjes (in 1957b) has explained very well how a science develops from its unsystematic enumerative stage through a 'mono-hierarchical' to a 'poly-hierarchical' stage—here using 'hierarchy' to mean the same as 'independent point of view'. Adopting the terminology of this book we would say that three stages of science can be distinguished: one in which objects and characteristics are more or less arbitrarily collected, enumerated and described, a systematic unidimensional and a systematic multidimensional stage. (Here see Chapter 6.)

The present status of science (particularly in biology) can properly be represented only as a multidimensional system, and it is just this field for multidimensional systematics—still only slightly developed—that we have here called 'system theory'. As was explained in detail, system theory begins by dividing the disciplines in question (for instance, biology) into a system of objects and a system of properties. It is the interweaving of these two systems that supplies the texture of science. Assuming every property of every object and all their interconnections and inter-relations to have been established—or in other words assuming that every object viewed from every possible 'independent point of view' (or 'characteristic dimension') could be fitted into its place in a coherent multidimensional system— the science in question could be regarded as complete. In practice that, of course, is a state of affairs which can never be attained; but it must nevertheless be regarded as the aim of science.

If, on the other hand, the object of documentation is 'collecting documents systematically and making them accessible and useful', neither can there be any doubt that its aim—likewise never fully attainable—is to render the treasure of knowledge latent in the literature available for 'utilization' in a coherent scientific system, as fully and at the same time as concentratedly as possible. This third and last stage of documentation was described above as 'documentation of results'. The referencing and the evaluative documentation serve and assist this aim within documentation and within research, insofar as it is capable of realization.

The author is of opinion that this aim must be kept in view, for everyone seems to be agreed—see the writings and results of Rothschuh and others—that complete referencing of all the available literature is not enough in itself to solve the existing problems (see also page 161).

If the foregoing arguments are correct it remains an open question why, although science reaches the 'polyhierarchical' or 'multidimensional' stage in many directions, virtually no multidimensional 'system theory' exists. Manifestly the reason seems to be that it has not been possible to realize any such system with the methods of fixation hitherto current. It is practically impossible to arrange the contents of a book otherwise than in linear order; that is to say, along a single dimension. In principle the same thing applies to any known optical or acoustical method of fixation. For this very reason, the planning and subdivision of a paper or book is the most difficult part of the whole job, since one has to subdivide the material in such a way as to keep down the repetitions to a minimum. Nevertheless, as is illustrated for instance by the present book, the same lines of thought often are necessary and pertinent at different places and have to be repeated unless the author is content with a cross reference. In tabular presentation not more than two dimensions can be used; beyond these the transmittal becomes complicated and soon reaches its limit.

In fact, a solution to the problem of multidimensional systematics is offered us for the first time by the punch-card method and by electronic computers developed on that basis.

(B) Possibilities of Subdivision

The *scope* of 'system theory' does not require further subdivision. Subdivisions of the particular systems covered by 'system theory' must, by definition, be in accordance with whatever order is inherent in the data they embrace.

(C) General Problems and Rules

(*1*) In the section on 'Theory of order' it has already been brought out that the task confronting system theory begins with recognition of the characteristics, and characteristic dimensions, of the objects treated. The circumstance that most research works cannot be regarded as 'systematic' in the sense here intended is simply due to the facts and characteristics discovered not having expressly been arranged on any particular system (here see also Hennig). Yet *order* already is implied in any scientific statement about an object which can be expressed in words. In principle, therefore, it is possible and necessary, once the 'frameworks' for such systems have been

erected empirically or deductively, that all objects (in biology, the semaphorontes) should be fitted into their proper places in some appropriate
system according to their various characteristics.

Thus for biology a 'system theory' must aim to develop systems able to
accommodate as many characteristics and characteristic dimensions as
possible, and to transfer these on to machine punch-cards.   Progress must
be accomplished step by step, so that it may continuously be attended by the
acquisition of new experiences.

(2) In order to collect the characteristics of objects, the following sources
may be drawn upon:

(a) The objects themselves, in the case of characteristics which, because
they are obvious or well known, are nowhere fixed in writing, or for
characteristics which have not previously been known or investigated.

(b) Original works in the shape of primary documents such as books,
periodical articles, etc., in which newly discovered characteristics are
published.

(c) Biological keys.   These, as is known, serve for the diagnosis of
unknown kinds of organisms, referring almost solely to those characteristics
which are important diagnostically and are easily recognizable.

(d) Handbooks (secondary documents).   Two types of handbook may
be distinguished.   In one of these the aim is a complete summary treatment,
within a particular field of science, of all objects and their most important
characteristics.   Those objects are dealt with one after the other in a
systematic order.   Examples are provided by the famous German chemical
handbooks of Gmelin and Beilstein, in which all known chemical elements
and compounds are systematically treated.   Undoubtedly it is this type of
handbook which occupies the front rank, since it unifies the concentrated
knowledge of mankind within the given field.

The other type is more modest.   It offers only a general prospect of the
field of science in question and its construction is not so strictly systematic,
in the present sense, as is that of the first type.   The most important of the
characteristic dimensions (or aspects of enquiry) are separately treated as
ancillary disciplines, citing certain objects as examples.   It is in this fashion
that the *Handbuch der Biologie* is constructed.

(3) Punch-card archives, adopted as the basis for a comprehensive exposition and study of all objects falling within a given range of science, take the
form of a multidimensional systematics and offer the following advantages,
apart from those of the punch-card method in general which have already
been mentioned several times here (see page 142):

(a) Regarded as sections of the 'collective memory of mankind', they can
take the place of existing handbooks of the first named type which, by reason
of the continually growing volume of knowledge in their respective fields,
no longer can be brought out quickly enough.   In this form, 'the archive
must have indicative possibilities corresponding to the efficiency of the
standard handbooks hitherto relied upon; but over and beyond that it

must, archivistically and potentially, incorporate knowledge accruing in the field to which it relates up to the latest moment' (Pietsch, 1951a).

(b) The archive can meet this need to be continually up to date as the cards can at any time be exchanged and amplified.

(c) Not merely would the archive make it possible, for instance, to select all semaphorontes showing particular properties or particular combinations of characteristics—such as all land plants with red flowers appearing only in spring—but, offering these possibilities of combined selection, it would constitute a new special methodology of identification.

The advantage of basing identification on punch-cards lies, above all, in the fact that it would no longer be necessary to rely upon proceeding step by step as we do when using the existing keys, which, being mainly dichotomous, entail the risk of starting to follow a completely wrong road each time a choice of alternatives or divergences has to be made. On the contrary, it becomes possible to indicate whatever characteristics are most conspicuous in the object to be diagnosed without having to follow any definite order and in accordance with whatever key and method is used, and to make the selection in accordance with several characteristics at the same time. Examples of diagnostic card collections on these lines are described in Chapter 14 of the book.

(d) The punch-card archive makes it possible to carry out many-sided correlational research based on the whole of the knowledge embodied in the archive (here see also Scheele, 1951). The fundamental significance of correlational research, especially in biology, has been recognized and explained by well known workers in botany, zoology and anthropology such as Troll, Remane, and Kretschmer. As the last mentioned has remarked, 'correlations have natural laws hidden behind them, and it is because true correlations are due to the true causations behind them that we investigate them by research'.

(e) By following the rules of the theory of order, the relationships between the various characteristic dimensions are automatically ascertained in the very act of fixing all the dimensions and characteristics. By this statement the following is meant. In biology we are aware, for instance, of the concept of sexual dimorphism, meaning that in the same kind of organism the two sexes may more or less differ from one another structurally. If, then, the semaphorontes are established in the course of recognizing and fixing the characteristics, separate semaphorontes will of course be recorded for each sex, and the corresponding morphological characteristics will be separately fixed. This makes it unnecessary for the concept of sexual dimorphism, as such, to be anywhere recorded as an additional characteristic because, so to speak, it amounts to a 'concept of relationship' which the machine itself will arrive at by the logical operations it performs, namely by comparing the morphological characteristics of the two sexes. Always presupposing undefective terminology, order and coding, the machine can expose the concept of sexual dimorphism, which cuts right across the range of organisms in all their variations and interconnections, much better and more quickly than a human brain. Apart from this, the machine makes it possible to establish hitherto unknown interconnections and inter-relations (correlative research).

It follows from these considerations that in the construction of system theory 'elementary concepts' must be distinguished from 'relative concepts', and that only the former must be fed into the machine. Assuming a good system of order and coding the 'relative concepts' will then emerge automatically from the logical operations of the machine.

(*4*) A punch-card archive of the kind here envisaged makes particularly heavy demands in the way of preparatory work as follows:

(*a*) Section I (Terminology and nomenclature). Unless concepts are unequivocally clarified the whole work remains hanging in the air. It is better to work out a conceptual apparatus unchallengeable in itself, even a new one, than to admit compromises of any kind.

(*b*) Section II (Theory of order). The requirements of logical theory of subdivisions must be strictly obeyed (see Chapter 6).

(*c*) Section III (Notation). For purposes of notation, numbers and capital letters which can be handled by the machines should be chosen.

(*d*) Coding of indications. Mainly machine punch-cards are in question, but needle and visual punch-cards also are useful in biological key work in parts of the field. For the purposes of coding, use should be made only of the internal code of the method adopted. Particular attention must be paid to matching systematic order with notation and with the internal code (see the example at page 61).

PART III

PRACTICAL EXAMPLES OF THE APPLICATIONS OF PUNCH-CARD METHODS IN RESEARCH AND DOCUMENTATION

In this last part of the book it follows from the nature of the case that wherever the author is not giving examples of his own he must depend mainly on letting others speak for themselves. All unnecessary ballast will, however, be omitted and only what is essential will be reproduced here, with a view to offering the reader a general oversight of some practical solutions in the application of punch-cards.

N

12. EXAMPLES FROM RESEARCH

(1) **MORPHOLOGY**

(From Knese, Voges and Ritschl, 1954.) This example is an especially instructive one because the authors have developed a way of using (IBM) machine punch-cards for a purpose of research which could not be attained either by the normal *descriptive* method or by statistics as ordinarily considered—namely, for the purpose of investigating the microstructure of human bone. They write:

'To characterize the osteon (Haversian system) as being a vascular canal (Haversian canal) surrounded by layers of collagen fibers, most of which are joined in lamellae, is to be quite general and unspecific. In fact each osteon exhibits individual perculiarities as regards the number of lamellae, their varying positions (their asymmetries, etc.) in relation to the vascular canal and the different ways in which they are built up. The problem is to determine whether these features (or combinations of features) in a single osteon, or in the relation of an osteon to the region in which it occurs, have any significance as regards second order structure.

'Altogether 42 forms of osteon were distinguished. Any one of these may occur in any of ten groups according to the way it is built up. As an absolute total, the combination $\binom{42}{10}$ gives $3\cdot 6 \times 10^9$ possibilities, but the picture becomes still more extensive if account is taken also of asymmetries and of the possibility that concentrations of osteons may tend to occur which do not depend only on the combinatorial probabilities. If there is no region in which the possibilities of combination are limited in absolute number, the second order structure may nevertheless be too finely differentiated for it to be detected either by direct observation or by photography. Thus the investigator is placed in the same position as when confronted with a large population of people and called upon to draw some conclusions as to their differentiations by age, sex, height, weight, etc., or even according to combinations of these features. The phenomenon "many", with all its attendant possibilities for subjective error, renders any direct judgment impossible.

'In these circumstances, an attempt was made to trace out the pattern of second order structure for osteons by statistically examining their features and combinations of features, using the same mechanical methods as are applied in population statistics. Out of 34 cross sections, 20 were chosen for this treatment, including three each of the femur, tibia, humerus and fibula with four each of the radius and ulna, corresponding in total to 161 regions having a surface of 1 151 mm^2 and comprising 11 000 osteons. The question to be answered on the basis of this survey is whether the distribution of osteons is statistical or topographic. At the first stage of the work, the distribution within the material as a whole was compared with that ascertained within the individual bones. As the comparison revealed no percentage of agreement between the respective features or combinations of features, the topographic dependence of the structure may be taken as confirmed. The question has now to be extended to the regions. Further, it is desired to arrive at positive conclusions as to what osteons or features of osteons, and what kinds of combinations, characterize the individual regions.

'Investigating the population statistics of osteons offers an opportunity to extend anatomical method. Morphological technique undergoes continual development. Its aim is to render structures visible, but only two morphological methods exist: that of description and that of measurement. Descriptions of shape, color, consistency, etc., can be compared in such a way as to reveal the intrinsic nature of the material. Any kind of measurement or computation leads to collectivities of numbers; these tell us nothing more about the original material but serve to disclose whatever regularities may occur in statistical variations of quantities that seem to be conditioned by the material—though only as regards their orders of magnitude. In this respect it does not matter whether lengths of objects, sizes of nuclei or volumes are in question. Such statistics do not make it directly possible to draw conclusions referring back to the nature of the material itself, for they are not governed by the properties of the material: they are governed by the occurrence of regularities among the properties that relate to certain chosen features of the material. Conclusions of that kind are, therefore, deprecated even from the mathematical standpoint for the reason that their truth cannot be checked. It follows that such statistics can be used for investigating quantitative regularities only within such ranges as are determined by the material.

'This way of utilizing numerical data is what distinguishes the studies in population statistics of osteons here discussed. The wish to collect every variety of structure, and to fit them all into patterns not directly obvious, made it necessary to look for a way of resolving the manifold into individual structural properties capable of being described and recorded. Such analytical description, undertaken with the object of discerning the theme of the pattern, is here associated with a mode of computation which in itself has almost nothing to do with the principle underlying the procedure of investigation adopted. The computation is not part of the recording procedure as such, which consists of description; it is something carried out by the machine at a second stage, for the purpose of selecting those features whose frequency of occurrence incites to elucidation by way of further structural description. With the methods of computation hitherto usual in morphological work, as for instance the determination of percentage relations, the line which later has to be followed in evaluating the data is predetermined and the material cannot suddenly be switched to another form of questioning. Here, however, the form of questioning can be altered during the actual course of the evaluation in whatever ways the combinability of the numbers may allow—but with the difference that the outcome instead of being a nameless number is a firmly delineated morphological picture. As such results can equally well be obtained from cases where the material has in fact been recorded unambiguously and with any necessary degree of completeness, an attempt can be made to forge a link between accurate description and the differentiative and correlative possibilities of mathematical theory.

'In osteon statistics there are no nameless numbers. It is a question of round, oval and other osteons of quite definite sizes, build-up, asymmetries and topographical positions. These characteristics are internally connected with one another as means of describing the disposition of collagen fibers around a vascular channel: and it is this composite picture of how the collagen fibers are bundled together with determines the shape of the osteon, perhaps further characterized by its asymmetries. Thereupon the number of lamellae or size of the osteon determines, in one degree further of fineness, how the collagen fibers are arranged, and finally their build-up shows the relation of the bundle of fibers to the vascular canal.

What are recorded here are not numbers which theoretically might be the basis of any pattern whatever, but numbers which express the properties of an actual structure. It is this fact which makes it possible to adopt an altogether different working method. It is true that the work is done by using statistical tools: but no use is made of statistics of variations in accordance with the laws of probability and the task is essentially one of description—that is to say, of morphology. The reliability of the conclusions is conditioned by that of the descriptions, each stating that in an individual case, within a particular region, the course of the collagen fibers showed certain quite definite characteristics. Here the number of structures noted in a given region matters hardly at all. The quantity factor is significant only insofar as there is a risk, where only a few cases are available, that important things may have been overlooked in the descriptions.

Thus population statistics of the kind here described offer a working method for effecting comparisons between one region and another, between one cross section and another, between one bone and another, more reliable than can be achieved by any other method. Further, the evaluation by mechanical means makes it possible to compare isolated characteristics or combinations of characteristics, as illustrated in the examples of build-up and asymmetry given in the first publication (Knese, Voges and Ritschl, 1954a). In anatomy the problem so treated is by no means rare. By this means the percentage indications of different types of cells at different places can be amplified. An example might be glandular cells or the construction of the cerebral cortex, which it has hitherto been possible to describe only by reference to the stratification of characteristics.'

(2) PHYSIOLOGY

(From Hörnicke, 1956.) Dr H. Hörnicke of the physiological section in the Max Planck Institute for medical research has been so kind as to make available his experiences in using punch-cards for climatological-physiological investigations on miners, a piece of work which offers us a further beautiful example of applying the punch-card method in research.

Here the measured data were evaluated by punching them in cards and processing those cards in IBM machines, two sets of cards being provided under the respective designations 00 Climatic data and 01 Physiological data.

(a) *Climatic Data Cards*

These cards contain the following indications in this order:

	Total columns	Numbers of columns
Kind of mine	2	8–9
Mine number	2	10–11
Shift	1	12
Working time	1	13
Day of week	1	30
Date	5	31–35
Time of day	4	36–39
Measuring point	3	40–42
Travelling time	1	43
Air pressure	3	56–58
Dry temperature	3	59–61
Wet temperature	3	62–64
Relative humidity	2	65–66
Air velocity	2	67–68
American effective temperature . .	3	69–71
Belgian effective temperature . .	3	72–74
Wet bulb temperature . . .	3	75–77

For the purpose of evaluating the climatic measurements the cards in this form were sorted according to these various points of view and the indications tabulated. Supplementary cards were then prepared in reference to cases where the measurements had been taken only at 1100 hours and 1300 hours, by punching a duplicate of the 1100 hours card and on those containing assumed values for 1300 hours.

b) *Physiological Data Cards*

These cards contain the following indications:

	Total columns	Numbers of columns
Miner's serial number	4	14–17
Employment	2	18–19
Age	2	20–21
Years employed in mine . . .	2	22–23
Months employed in mine . . .	1	24
Height	3	25–27
Weight	2	28–29
Day of week, date, time of day, measuring point, travelling time as in climatic cards	14	30–43
Pulse	3	44–46
Rectal temperature	3	47–49
Systolic blood pressure . . .	3	50–52
Diastolic blood pressure . . .	3	53–55
Range of blood pressure . . .	3	78–80

'The following code numbers were adopted:

Kind of mine   01 coal, 02 potash
Mine number: 01 Buggingen
Shift: 1 early, 2 midday, 3 late, 4 night (Guide hole 11: 4 shifts)
Actual working time on the job
Day of week: 1 Monday, 2 Tuesday, etc.
  Measuring points: identified by numbers.
  Travelling time: 1 for 0–13 minutes, 2 for 16–30 minutes, etc., as estimated.
  Employment: in accordance with code numbers, the following being added:

> 01 physiological measuring group
> 02 climatic measuring group
> 05 not fully acclimatised group.

After the physiological values had been punched in them, the 00 and 01 cards were associated by means of the machines according to date, time of day and measuring point so as to bring together the climatic cards and the cards of those individuals who were tested at the same time and place. Then, by the use of the calculating punch, the climatic values taken from the climatic cards were transferred to the corresponding cards containing climatic values. In the same run through the machine the systolic and diastolic blood pressures were utilized for calculating the amplitudes of blood pressure and the latter were automatically punched in columns 78 to 80.

Thereupon, as the 01 cards now contained all the necessary indications for evaluating the physiological measurements, the 00 cards could be sorted out and put away. The results were printed out by the tabulating machine, and the main part of the evaluative process could then be undertaken from the final totals so delivered, by plotting the individual values read from the tables on graph paper.

In order to calculate the correlations, the individual values and squares and products taken from the appropriate groups of cards were added up and calculated mechanically.

(3) GYNAECOLOGY

(From Hosemann, 1951.)   In the medical field Hosemann's work using the IBM system calls for mention.   He has written:

'In statistical processing, the punch-card takes the place of the counting sheets hitherto in use. By contrast with these the punch-card makes possible purely mechanical sorting and counting, which not only is incomparably quicker but above all is more reliable.

'In working on the punch-card material I followed the principle that only a medical man can direct the selection in a way appropriate to his own field. Each question which arises requires its own special procedure, aimed partly at sorting out those cases which disturb the regularity, partly at bringing together those characteristics which belong together, partly at further subdivision when regularities and inter-relationships are perceived, partly at the standardization of particular characteristics. The key to success was found to lie in immediate mathematical statistical evaluation of each piece of output from the sorting, thereby enabling new cues to be

9   Oblique presentations:
90 without indication of position

Dorso-anterior oblique presentations:

91 first dorso-anterior oblique presentation
92 second dorso-anterior oblique presentation

Dorso-inferior oblique presentations:

93 first dorso-inferior oblique presentation
94 second dorso-inferior oblique presentation

dorso-posterior oblique presentations:

95 first dorso-posterior oblique presentation
96 second dorso-posterior oblique presentation

Dorso-superior oblique presentations:

97 first dorso-superior oblique presentation
98 second dorso-superior oblique presentation
99 other oblique presentations

Using this code, the first column of numerals gives information about the child's presentation and position. This information is adequate for most purposes of evaluation as the cephalic presentations can easily be juxtaposed with pelvic and transverse positions, likewise extended presentations with flexed positions in cephalic presentations. The situation of the part coming first cannot, however, be indicated; nor is it possible to subdivide breech and transverse presentations more exactly into complete and incomplete, etc. The second column of the code numerals supplies information missing in the first. Herein a system is clearly apparent which makes it possible to work from this column alone: it will be noticed that in the case of cephalic presentations 0 always indicates the absence of further detail, 1 and 2 that the child's back is disposed symphytically, 3 and 4 that it conforms to the legs being crossed—1 and 3 being the first presentation, 2 and 4 the second. The odd numbers for the first and even numbers for the second presentation are retained also for breech and transverse presentations, with the addition of further numerals to show finer subdivisions.

It is clear from this example that often a decade code can be used without needing to take up the whole of a column. Since only 62 cases had to be accommodated it would have been possible to save using the numerals 5 to 9 in the second column for cephalic presentations, these being necessary only for breech and transverse presentations. Such saving would not, however, increase the capacity of the columns, as 62 cases require two columns anyway.

Finally, Hosemann (1951) makes the following remarks:

It would be wrong to conclude from this that the punch-card method is unnecessary or even that it is to be avoided because it distorts for the sake of convenience, or to argue that we have hitherto managed without punch-cards and it is not desirable to make life too easy for the rising generation of scientists. Whoever feels the attraction of science will devote to it whatever time is left over from the burdens of his professional life. If no technical aids are at his disposal he will direct his research to questions in which success is possible without them. If, however, he does have access to a punch-card installation, he will perform neither more nor less than he otherwise would, but he will be inclined towards investigations which, without the possibilities offered by these methods, would exceed the available amount of working time.

I am therefore of the opinion that the punch-card is suited for enabling us to open up hitherto untrodden regions of our science, and thereby ultimately to help the sick who are entrusted to us.

Meanwhile, these works have set an example and invited followers. Hosemann's many years of experience of service to this end have led to the development of proposals for collaboration between several clinics concerned in the field of statistics. On this matter Hosemann has written as follows:

At the request of the German Gynaecological Society, Professor Hosemann has worked out a plan for evaluating case records as fully as possible with the aid of the punch-card method. In earlier attempts to do this, punch-cards have been used as in other fields of application, such as economics and technology, so as to result as it were in only a single instantaneous photograph of a condition at a given moment. The new plan, however, envisages annual amplifications of the cards.

By way of regular additions extending over a period of more than ten years it has proved possible to make a continuous record of each individual case comparable with making a kinematographic film. This was achieved by the device of making a duplicate of the punch-card, prepared for the purposes of the polyclinic, and arranging for the investigating physician to mark this duplicate with the annual check record of each patient by use of the mark-sensing process. At regular intervals of time, these additions are automatically converted into holes, and are transferred to the basic card collection with the aid of the card mixer. Apart from the practical advantages of this method which amount to a big step in rationalization, it has the advantage that now all time entries consistently begin from the month when they were handled, so that it is no longer even necessary to treat them as if they corresponded to calendar years. This means that the material available on punch-cards can be evaluated as for any desired point in time, and makes it possible to count cures and death rates on an annual basis corresponding with the years of treatment. Hence, first of all, the calendar error is avoided, which amounts on the average to plus or minus half a year. Secondly it is made possible, after two or three years, to answer therapeutic questions on the basis of death rates.

In order more quickly to obtain the large number of cases necessary for statistics of this kind, collaboration between a number of clinics is desirable. This is facilitated by their adoption of the same suggested technical procedures. The cooperation relates above all to the fundamental principles of punch-card evaluation. Each clinic is given an evaluative statistical code which has been elaborated in common, but which leaves sufficient latitude for the separate wishes of each clinic. The evaluation is not, however, centrally carried out. Each clinic arranges to put its own results together and then ultimately to make them available for combination. Thus, what is sought is not centralization but coordination. This 'kinematographic' way of using punch-cards is something new. It is logically well founded and has already given good results in some clinics. It remains to be seen whether the desired collaboration of many clinics in this technical facility will be achieved. Should this be so, as we hope, we may be enabled to look forward to a larger scale application on the international plane.

(4) **METEOROLOGY**

(From Guss and Reichel, 1950 and Guss, 1953.) 'By and large, the underlying principle of the punch-card method can now be taken as known. When, nevertheless it continues to attract attention, this is because the method is notably well suited for the treatment of many climatological questions which hitherto it has been practically impossible to investigate because of the excessive range of the work that would be necessary. Such questions can now, however, be fully processed, whereby it has become possible to attack meteorological and climatological problems on a wide basis in directions which in recent times have been attracting more and more interest. Thus, the punch-card method promises to form an important link between synoptic meteorology and climatology, and considerably to promote meteorological research. This will help to meet the continually increasing demands of technology, industry and transport for climatological data, not so much for average values as for frequency distributions. For this reason it appears desirable to present in summary fashion the complex of meteorological questions which rationally can be worked upon by means of punch-cards.

From the mass of problems amenable to punch-card treatment, there can of course be selected here only a few examples which will serve to show the wide range of applicability and the successful utilization of this method for all meteorological statistical questions. It will be best to begin with a short recapitulation of the developments which the use of meteorological punch-cards has undergone.

Here two different kinds of application may be distinguished. First, punch-cards serve as a basis for systematically arranging and juxtaposing the wealth of results obtained by measurement and observation, and for calculating their totals and averages. Secondly, punch-cards serve for the scientific, statistical processing of this material from the most varied points of view, following the exact methods of mathematical statistics. It is no mere chance that the introduction of this method occurred first in maritime meteorology, for it was in this field that systematic processing of the great number of observations which are collected in the meteorological logs of ships had become very difficult to carry out by manual means. All these observations covering the oceans of the world, recorded in the ships' logs of all seafaring nations, are completely scattered in time and place. Their continuous speedy evaluation to meet the needs of navigation had become an urgent necessity, for which the punch-card method seemed predestined.'

'The first application of the punch-card method to scientific work in meteorology had been carried out two years earlier by D. Brunt (1925) in his examination of weather periods by harmonic analysis. A few years after that Pollak developed a completely mechanical procedure for the analysis of periodograms by using the indices of terrestrial magnetic activity in accordance with Schuster's method for transforming the data by a system of 'trial' waves, arriving at group totals for the phase diagram and grand totals for the amplitude periodogram, as well as for increasing the density of the periodogram, in accordance with Darwin's method. Likewise K. Stumpff used punch-cards for analyzing relative numbers of sunspots by Schuster's method, and S. Chapman in the same way calculated the lunar pressure wave for a large number of stations.'

'In most of the more advanced countries, as distinct from this application for calculating quite definite problems its general introduction of the punch-card method into meteorology followed, upon its application to applied climatology; first of all, as already mentioned, to maritime climatology in England during 1921, a few years later in Holland, and in 1930 in Germany. Air transport being more dependent on the weather than any other human activity, its development led naturally to a corresponding need for climato-logical work enabling the flight meteorological service to provide synoptic observations of the degree of cloudiness, the heights of clouds, the range of visibility and ground winds, as well as the aerological elements, upper wind, turbulence and icing. Just as exact knowledge of these weather conditions is necessary for the safety of each individual flight, so also meteorological statistical studies of flying weather are necessary for airlines to plan the siting of airfields, and as aids for advisory purposes. Since these questions always bear upon the probabilities for the occurrence and duration of weather phenomena, the only conceivable method of working was through frequency studies in climatology. Consequently, the calculation of frequency distributions for the most important elements in flight meteorology on the basis of synoptic observations, and the evaluation of these for the purposes of flight weather service, occupied an ever increasing proportion of space in the *Erfahrungsberichte des Deutschen Flugwetterdienstes* (these being a series of experimental reports issued by the German aeronautical weather service) from 1928 onwards. As already stressed, this work was hampered on the one hand by its volume where climatological frequency investiga-tions are involved, and on the other hand by a lack of sufficiently long series of recorded observations. But the longer these grew, the more urgent appeared the necessity for using the punch-card method. Consequently, the rapid increase in flying was attended by a development of flight climato-logy as a separate branch of applied climatology, based almost entirely on the use of punch-cards. In Germany the first experimental punchings date back to K. Keil in the year 1930, and the systematic processing of synoptic observations was undertaken in 1936 by the Reich Weather Office. As climatic observations for purposes of investigations in flight climatology can readily be extracted for the purpose of complete examination, the transfer of current climatic material, as well as of that stored in the archives, was at first postponed.

It was natural that the first investigations to be undertaken in flight climatology should have related to compiling the usual distribution tables as regards the most important of the elements, enabling the greater part of meteorological statistical questions posed by air transport to be answered straight away. By reason of the small number of available observations, derivation of more complicated relationships does not lead to usable results, the mean error being greater than the relationships themselves. For this purpose, however, annual distributions have only a limited value. Therefore, along with special individual computations, a computation of the monthly distribution tables for the elements visibility, height of cloud, amount of clouding (N_h and N), direction and speed of wind, was undertaken on the basis of the available seven-year period from 94 German stations. Some 4·3 million observations taken from 700000 punch-cards, which also carried a further 10 million values of the remaining meteorological elements, were worked up into 1692 tables containing not less than 190000 calculated relative frequencies, all this being achieved in about one year's work by a relatively small expenditure of staff time. In the flight climatologies these statistics were carried further, especially as regards combinations of certain elements for European stations, namely height of clouds and amount of clouding. These in their turn, as well as visibilities and temperatures, are combined with direction of wind, as is now being done also at the airfields in accordance with the recommendations of the World Meteorological Organization, and with a still wider scope by H. Guss.

Among other work carried out in the Reich Weather Office by means of punch-cards, the following may be mentioned:

Calculation of the mean daily air pressures and maps showing changes in air pressure for Europe and the North Atlantic.

Calculation of the average changes in wind at 1000 m height over Germany.

Calculation of wind gradients and their application as an indicator for weather situation statistics, and for frequency distributions of the meteorological elements.

Cloud statistics for Germany and the diurnal investigations of vapor pressure and ground wind on the basis of hourly measurements at Potsdam by F. Möller. In this way, the inter-diurnal variability of these elements and of wind components, as well as the application of the difference method for compensating the fine weather bias of upper wind data, have to a large extent been carried out by mechanical means.

The enormous growth of meteorological work during the 1939–45 war, and the demand for quick answers to enquiries, further considerably increased the importance of the punch-card method in applied climatology. In all such projects it was not only the general weather conditions that were significant but often quite special meteorological requirements. Nearly always, and to the exclusion of almost everything else, these reduced themselves to estimates of the probability for the occurrence and duration of particular values. For instance, it might be required to know the frequency distribution of single or combined elements such as winds of particular strengths in particular directions combined with clouding, with temperatures at certain intervals above or below certain limits or with fog, sand-storms, particular ground conditions and so forth—all this more especially in little known regions and extreme climates.'

'Applications of the punch-card method to climatic data are of no less importance for the advancement of agricultural meteorology also.   It is generally recognized that average and extreme values for calendar months, although they may suffice to give a general picture of the conditions in a large region, are inadequate for appraising local conditions and for estimating the limits of profitability for cultivations with the accuracy needed to ensure optimal utilization of the land.   The proper basis for answering the mani-fold climatological questions which in this connection are important to agriculture is that provided by frequency distributions of periodical and diurnal mean values and of certain combinations of meteorological ele-ments.   Here it is the frequencies that are needed instead of the usual monthly divisions corresponding to natural phases in the development of vegetation, and F. Schnelle has shown how to integrate average values of temperature and precipitation for this purpose.   Limits to the phases of plant growth not only depend on phenological data but are considerably affected by different types of soil and regional conditions—a particular circumstance which makes it necessary for compilations of the meteorological elements to be made at such widely differing intervals of time that manual methods cannot cope with the task.   On the other hand, using punch-cards the appropriate distribution tables can be prepared by purely mechanical means.   From these tables, the probabilities of magnitude and duration for the relevant meteorological values, and the deviations of these from the average weather conditions and related mean values, which are important in their effects on the growth of the crops, can be read off or calculated. W. Haude has worked out a combined scale for estimating the sensitivity of harvests to combinations of mean temperatures and mean monthly precipita-tion values during the period of vegetation; a scale which should be capable of further refinement by establishing the frequencies of these elements and the exact periods of growth.   If so, the present wide margins between the estimated and the actual harvests may be reduced or eliminated.   In evaluating the useful effect of the total precipitation, not only must the frequency with which the separate rainstorms occur and the conditions of temperature and radiation prevailing at the time of their occurrence be taken into account, but also the water content of the ground and the level of the water table.   In this connection, the rating of agricultural land for purposes of taxation, as for instance in making valuations, probably can be better based on climatological frequencies than on mean values.   This consideration will gain more and more weight in proportion as account is taken of individual harvest years in climates where large variations in the meteorological elements occur, especially as regards precipitation and tem-perature.   Even when the data are insufficient for it to be possible for all these influences to be taken into account exactly, it is evident at once what great advantages the punch-card method offers for handling the copious numerical material in all the manifold ways that are necessary for that purpose.

The same thing applies to the processing of phenological observations, since it is in the nature of such data that their regional distribution is not constant. Isophenes, or lines or equal phases, are attended by some uncertainty so that, although distributions over large areas can very well be expressed in this way, statistical investigations of frequency are as essential for the intensive study of the phenological material as they are for that of the meteorological elements. W. Boer, by treating a series of growth phases in Thuringia according to this method, has shown that even when only a small number of observations is available useful results can be obtained from a classification of the frequencies of phenological values, whether integrated into groups or as regards their regional distributions. It is to be expected that the study of distribution tables combining phenological and meteorological observations will lead to a still more quantitative understanding of the dependence of plant growth upon climate, and in this way to improvements in harvest forecasting. Many questions necessary for elucidating the effects of weather on the growth of plants can, of course, be answered only by establishing correlations, for the yield of many crops is influenced not only by the weather that occurs during the period of vegetation but also partly by the weather a long period ahead. This is especially evident with cereals, including summer wheat, and with fruit, as W. Zielke was the first to show. Thus, for the cherry crop in the country around Basel, the combination of rainy days from August to October and in December, January, April and May during the years 1934–44 was shown to have a correlation coefficient as high as 0.95 ± 0.02. It has already been mentioned that this method too, which involves much calculation and which is applicable especially to agricultural meteorology as well as for the study of cosmic influences, can be carried out with punch-cards.

In bio-climatology, H. Cordes has introduced the concept of 'cure days' for studying meteorological conditions as a means of describing the kind of weather that prevails in a particular health resort. The number and frequency distribution of these days, as well as the average frequencies of those meteorological elements which are important to the human organism, provide a much better basis for evaluating the climo-therapeutic factors of such a resort than do the total climatic mean values which hitherto have been widely used for the purpose. Once the punch-cards have been established, the values of means, frequencies and extremes needed to form a collective whole can be arrived at without difficulty by following the proper principle of selection mechanically. The same is true in any other comparable case.

By way of intensive statistical processing, many problems of climatological frequencies which contribute to our understanding of applied climatology can be made to yield results of value for the climatology of weather systems, which is one of the directions in which research is now being pursued. The following is an example: for the purpose of establishing the purely formal statistical probability of favorable cloud conditions, the United States Weather Bureau investigated the frequencies with which different degrees of clouding amount observed at many stations in a given region corresponded with complete cloud cover at a particular 'indicating station'. Thus it

o

was found that within a short distance of Nagano, as the indicating station for Japan, there are places where the complete cloud cover coincides in as many as 75 per cent of all cases, that is to say with a high degree of probability, obviously by reason largely of their insular and leeward situation. For any chosen indicating station, the distribution of clouding frequencies among the remaining stations is of course different. By this method it is possible accurately to establish the probable suitability of any given airfield to serve as a relief for another and to take account of this in the planning of airlines. Thus Reykjavik and Akureyri constitute excellent relief airfields for one another, for whilst each of these places separately has 12 to 15 per cent of days with bad weather on the ground, the two simultaneously have only 2 per cent. Also in the United States, distribution tables for the elements producing different weather conditions have been prepared, including "gradient wind" and ground wind, cyclonic and anticyclonic curvature of isobars, and according to air masses. This last method of computation, known in the United States as synoptic climatology, which is applied to planning and as an aid to prediction, likewise is handled by means of punch-cards. It leads directly to an analysis of climate considered as a complex of weather conditions, similar to what was proposed by T. Bergeron from a strictly dynamic point of view based on the components of circulation, air masses and fronts. As early as 1922, K. Knoch and E. Rubinstein drew attention to the need for adopting the natural weather periods as units of time for examining the interactions of elements with one another and their dependence on geographical data, as well as for studying genetically the changes of weather in time and the anomalies which can occur. 'Arbitrary division into months breaks up the natural periods of weather,' he remarked so that 'many interrelations are overlooked or may even be mistaken for their contraries.' More recently H. Flohn has put forward the idea of dividing the year into natural weather periods in accordance with singularities, and also that of adopting large weather areas when describing climate genetically. E. Reichel, in particular, has drawn attention to the significance of air components, masses and fronts as the essential synoptic base for dynamic climatological research and has given details of practical working methods for applying these conceptions, as well as stressing the utility of the punch-card method in handling such problems. It is a question primarily of frequency statistics of the air masses themselves, and of considering geographical distribution over large spaces. This involves the statistical description of individual air masses in accordance with the changes that occur in their properties as they move from place to place and therefore the exact quantitative understanding of the changes of those properties consequent upon orographical influences, which qualitatively are already known. In similar fashion weather processes dependent upon the passage of a front can be statistically examined in relation to those effects which are attributable to the shape of the ground.'

'Finally, it would be wrong not to mention also the economies that can be realized in the running of weather services through simplifications made possible by the punch-card method. Thus tabulating machines may be used for reproducing directly the contents of the punch-cards, either completely or selectively, in any desired sequences and for combining the tabulated data in various ways. If the number of cards is not too great to permit several successive runs through the machine, making up to five carbon copies in each run, a sufficient number of the copies of the tables can be made in this way to save any need for further reproduction. Once the punch-cards have been prepared the usual monthly climatic tables can, with the exception of remarks, be compiled and computed mechanically and duplication of copying work can be avoided. If, however, a larger number of copies is required the tabulation can be printed on to albuminous paper and reproduced by lithography, without any intermediate operation being necessary. This is already the practice followed by the meteorological office of North-West Germany for its annual publications. As a further development in the application of the punch-card method in this direction, there may be mentioned the preparation by mechanical means of the aerological section in the German meteorological yearbook, whereby it will be possible to save the writing and computing work otherwise unavoidable and at the same time to collect experience bearing upon the applicability of mechanical methods in a small and self-contained department of work; for here again the road leading to the ultimate goal runs across a very large number of technical difficulties, which call for further tests before the process can be regarded as fully operational. The same mechanical process of using punch-cards can be applied to working out the monthly averages and the other contents of the monthly and pentade summaries of the various tables. The conversion of these punch-card records to numerical notation provides data for the compilations which are made in every meteorological central institute, which serve as a basis for calculating and establishing average values over periods of many years.

The further possibility exists of carrying out re-coding. For instance, the synoptic reports which earlier were punched in accordance with the Swedish code have been converted in accordance with the Copenhagen code, and results obtained from German ascents with radio-sondes which had been recorded in the American code have been transferred to punch-cards prepared in accordance with the German system—an operation which involved not only re-arrangement of the values but mechanical conversion of measurements from the Anglo-American to the metric system.'

These lengthy quotations all go to show that in meteorology the machine punch-card method has taken such firm root that this field of science is no longer conceivable without it. I would particularly like to add to them the following further observation:

Many years ago, A. Schmauss aptly observed that he never could pass through a meteorological library without a feeling of awe and the impression that it contained buried riches; that material lay dormant which could lead to great advances in our science. Today the punch-card method seems destined to play an ever more important role in the exploitation of these riches and to become an indispensable aid to meteorological research.

Next I shall quote—in translation as before—the summary of a work by Guss (1953):

The introduction of the punch-card method in meteorology has given the elaboration of meteorological statistical problems a decisive turn. Complexes of questions whose investigation was formerly quite impossible because of the amount of work entailed can now be quickly and comprehensively handled. As all four of the basic arithmetical rules can be operated mechanically and the interim results stored on the punch-cards it is possible, once the meteorological measurements and observations have been so punched, for any problem in statistical meteorology to be carried out entirely by automatic means. The prerequisite for manifold application of this method to rationalizing statistical counting and computation is, therefore, a comprehensive meteorological punch-card archive. Obviously such an archive can be constituted only in a large central institute, and many years must elapse before it becomes extensive enough to meet all requirements. For this reason, the Deutscher Wetterdienst (German Weather Service) has for some years past been punching in cards a large part of its current and retrospective meteorological observations, along with all the weather elements measured and observed. The German meteorological punch-card archives in Bad Kissingen and Hamburg already include meteorological material of many kinds. Besides the 50-year and 80-year series of all climatological elements they include many 5-year and 15-year series of synoptic and climatological observations from German stations along with evaluations and aerological measurements of European and world climatological data, especially maritime meteorological material. They further include special runs of punch-cards recording major European weather situations, air masses and geomagnetic characteristic data, mostly extending over periods of 60 years, as well as yet other material. The total adds up to over 30 million cards, which record from 10 to 20 times that number of individual values.

In order that proper advantage may be taken of the possibilities for exploiting this material it appears necessary that every meteorologist occupied with climatological questions, in the widest sense of that expression, should broadly understand the main principles underlying this important mechanical aid to statistical work. As, however, many of the pertinent explanations are still not very clear, the more important methods of processing these meteorological punch-cards will be shown by a few examples.

Finally, in order to show the later development of this method, I give the following extract from the *Jahresbericht des Deutschen Wetterdienstes* (Annual Report of the German Weather Service) No. 3 (1955):

Punch-card work. Current work in punching the climatological synoptic and aerological observations received from land stations within the Federal Republic of Germany had to be limited, again in 1955, to a selection of these stations. The only data to be completely punched, up to and including the year 1954, were the synoptic observations from stations in South Germany and from all airports in the Federal territory, as well as results from the radio-sonde measurements of pressures and height layers. Altogether, 696 000 meteorological punch-cards were prepared during the year under report. At the same time 1 040 000 cards showing air pressure values and intersection coordinates for ground points in the Northern Hemisphere, over a period of 40 years, were received from the United States in exchange for a similar number of German punch-cards.

The demand for punch-card evaluations to meet the needs of applied climatology and medium-term forecasting shows a continual increase. It is intended, in the near future, to make use of electronic computers in carrying out statistical evaluations of the data on large numbers of cards, as well as for interim computations to relieve the load on the punch-card machines in readiness for further increases in the material and in the demands made upon them.

The greater part of the evaluative work carried out upon punch-cards was for research in medium and long-term forecasting. To an increasing extent the questions handled refer to areas outside Europe.

(5) **ECOLOGY**

(From Scheele, 1952 and 1956 b.) Every specialist in a particular group of animals or plants of a greater or less extent meets with the need to evaluate, from as many points of view as possible, the material he has collected himself or which others concerned with the same field have passed to him to work up systematically. The greater the number of factors he takes into account in such work, and the more numerous and accurate the records of specimens placed at his disposal by other collectors, the more valuable will be the aggregate results of such investigations and the more quickly shall we attain a fundamental and many-sided understanding of the group of organisms in question.

A specialist has further to meet the requirement that his task must be carried out with as small an expenditure of time and material as possible, since otherwise the work may rapidly swamp him. According to experience to date, a combination of needle punch-cards with the IBM system has been found best. The working procedure is as follows:

(1) The material, which in the present example consists of siliceous algae specimens, is collected in the field, all the specimens being numbered and the location factors recorded.

(2) Indoors, the record is transferred to needle punch-cards. The material is systematically worked upon and the results of the identifications are immediately entered on the same needle punch-cards.

(3) The more frequently occurring varieties are transferred from the needle punch-cards to IBM machine (mark-sensing) punch-cards with a view to separate statistical evaluation entirely by mechanical means.

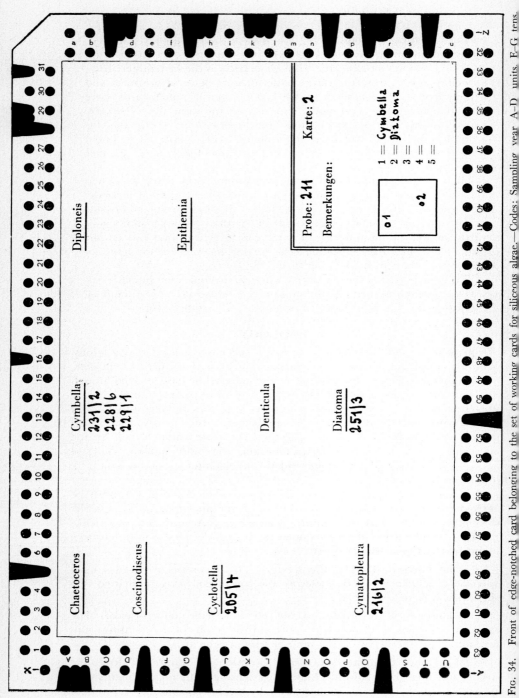

FIG. 34. Front of edge-notched card belonging to the set of working cards for siliceous algae.—Codes: Sampling year A–D units, E–G tens.

200

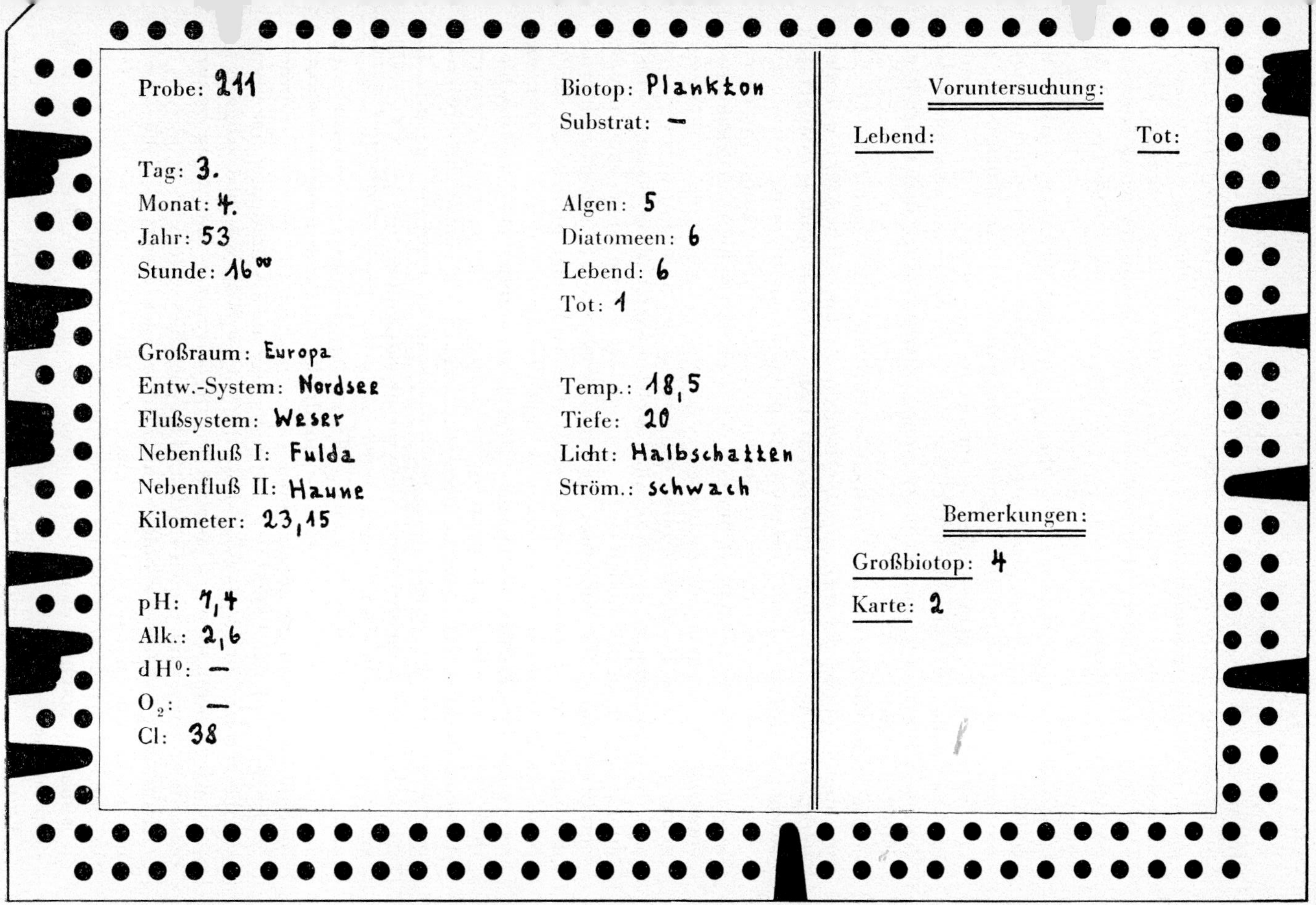

Probe: 211

Tag: 3.
Monat: 4.
Jahr: 53
Stunde: 16^w

Großraum: Europa
Entw.-System: Nordsee
Flußsystem: Weser
Nebenfluß I: Fulda
Nebenfluß II: Haune
Kilometer: 23,45

pH: 7,4
Alk.: 2,6
dH°: —
O$_2$: —
Cl: 38

Biotop: Plankton
Substrat: —

Algen: 5
Diatomeen: 6
Lebend: 6
Tot: 1

Temp.: 18,5
Tiefe: 20
Licht: Halbschatten
Ström.: schwach

Voruntersuchung:

Lebend: Tot:

Bemerkungen:

Großbiotop: 4

Karte: 2

Fig. 35. Back of the edge-notched card for siliceous algae.

Figs. 34 and 35 show the layout respectively on the front and the back of the needle punch-cards used in the present example. The left hand side of the writing field on the back serves for entering all recorded data which apply to all the specimens alike. The right hand side is used for entering the results obtained by preliminary examination of the specimens along with any special remarks. The front of the card contains the genus names of the diatoms. During his biological analysis, under the microscope, of the siliceous algae specimens or preparations the investigator has before him a large cardboard list showing how the various kinds of diatoms are to be coded, each type being designated by a number. Very quickly these numbers become memorized in place of the names and can immediately be entered, under the genus names on the needle punch-cards. The printing of these names beforehand on the card has been found valuable for better control. Besides the number, a frequency category which may range from 1 to 8 is added.

The right bottom corner is framed for entering any special remarks and the number of the specimen appears there once again. The grid is intended to represent the cover glass of the preparation. It is not feasible to interrupt biological analysis of the specimens or preparations in order to consider critical forms or those which are not known to the investigator; moreover, it is necessary to be able to retrieve any such forms for more exhaustive checking and systematic examination. For this purpose, using a diamond point, a circle is scratched around the form in question on the cover glass and the approximate position of such circles is sketched on the grid which appears on the needle punch-card. If there are several circles they may be numbered and at the same time the genus designations of the critical forms may be written directly against them. The two long sides of the needle punch-cards, containing the pairs of holes numbered 1 to 63, serve for recording the varieties of diatoms. The large number of forms in which these occur make it necessary to use six different cards for each specimen. These cards differ from one another only as regards the genus names printed on them, since the general data for the specimens apply of course to all six cards for the same specimen. On the six cards altogether $6 \times 63 = 378$ varieties of diatoms can be designated using the direct code. In case of need, further cards may be added. Three-digit numbers of varieties were adopted for the coding, the first (or hundreds) digit indicating at the same time the number of the needle punch-cards on which the variety is recorded whilst the other two digits (tens and units) are always limited to one of the numbers from 1 to 63, so as to show the pair of holes which is assigned to the variety in question. This code has the advantage that it can be used equally on the needle punch-cards and for the IBM system.

Thus one pair of needle holes is provided for each variety. If the variety in question does not occur in the specimen, the related pair of holes is left un-notched. If it rarely occurs in the specimen (frequency category 1 or 2) it is shallow-notched, or if it often occurs (frequency categories 3 to 8) it is deep-notched.

One of the vertical sides of the card serves for coding the specimen number and year. Notching of the x-hole indicates that in that specimen an unidentifiable critical form was found, which belongs to one of the genera entered on the card. Thus all critical forms which require further work to be done upon them can later be retrieved from the card collection as a whole by selecting in accordance with the x-hole.

The specimen number has three digits and is coded by means of the '7 4 2 1' code. An addition 'thousands pair' of holes makes it possible to code up to No. 3000. Full thousands are coded using all three places in these specimen numbers as 10 (7 + 4). For the numbers 1001 to 2000, the thousands-pair of holes is shallow-notched in addition and for numbers 2001 to 3000 this pair is deep-notched.

The year the specimens were taken is expressed by two digits, but the following device makes it possible for any of the years 1951 to 2010 to be indicated: using an abridged '4 2 1' code, the decades are punched according to the scheme 5 = 1, 6 = 2, 7 = 3, 8 = 4, 9 = 5 and 10 (denoting 2000) = 6. The years within the decades are indicated by the full '7 4 2 1' code.

So as to be able to enter as many specimens (numbers) as possible, the specimens taken in each year are separately numbered beginning again from 1. Hence the exact indication of a particular specimen includes both the specimen number and the year.

The y-hole is left spare.

The other vertical side of the card serves for notching the number of the card in accordance with the abridged code '4 2 1' (Card Nos. 1 to 6). Notching of the z-hole shows that still further cards (7 to 12) have been incorporated. Apart from this, the same vertical side is used for recording the most important indications of the specimen as a whole: month and major biological class using a direct code (notching table), pH and Cl according to the '7 4 2 1' code, and frequency of occurrence of algae in the other algae groups, as well as frequency of dead diatoms, in direct order (shallow = rare, deep = frequent).

After the analytical work has been performed on each specimen, the six cards are notched in accordance with the coding scheme explained above. All notchings on the vertical sides, apart from those of the card number, apply to the whole of the specimen and are made on all six cards. Experience shows that three cards laid over one another can be notched simultaneously, so that four working operations are saved. The general indications for each specimen, entered on the back of the cards, need only appear on its card No. 1, since the more important of these indications have been notched and, moreover, the appropriate No. 1 card can at any time be retrieved quickly if needed, with the aid of the specimen number and card number.

The working method here explained results, then, in the production of a multidimensional needle punch-card collection which does not call for any use of gummed slips, lists or separate card indexes for varieties, locations, etc., but which itself holds the most important punched data and factors for all varieties, ready for evaluation.

To show the many possibilities which are open, only a few examples will be given. Any one of the 378 kinds of diatoms recorded on the long sides of the six cards in each set can be separately selected. That is to say, a single sorting operation (shallow needling) brings out the references to all those specimens in which any given variety was found to occur. By a second sorting operation (deep needling) the specimens in which that variety occurred frequently can be separated from those in which it occurred rarely. All specimens taken in the same month or belonging to the same major biological class, the same pH or Cl group, etc., can be extracted (by needling the vertical sides of the card) in order to find out which varieties within these groups are the most frequent. Furthermore, these various points of view can of course be combined with one another.

As soon as a sufficient wealth of material has been collected, or a particular major project is complete, the needle punch-cards are sorted according to the individual varieties. The most frequently occurring varieties, or those it is proposed to evaluate statistically, are transferred to IBM mark-sensing cards (Fig. 6). These IBM cards are coded to correspond with what is printed on the reverse of the needle punch-cards. But, by contrast with those, the indications are now all punched, for which purpose a separate IBM card is provided for every variety occurring in every specimen.

For indications which are to be repeated on all or several of these punch-cards, use is made of template cards whose contents can be transferred mechanically to the final cards. Template card 1 carries the following indications which are applicable to the whole contents of a card set (relating to a particular region, such as, for instance, the Werra river).

Column 1	Kind of card
Columns 32 to 33	Major region
Column 34	Drainage system
Columns 35 to 36	River system

Template card 2 carries all the indications applicable to all cards relating to the same specimen. These depend on the pertinent data and it is not necessary to discuss them here.

The template cards are not prepared by the mark-sensing process, but are punched in an ordinary punching machine by reference to needle punch-card No. 1 of each specimen.

The mark-sensing cards are used to receive only the following indications:

1. Object No. (variety)
2. Frequency
3. Specimen No.
4. Year (two digits)

Thus one mark-sensing card is necessary for each variety and specimen. The cards so marked are then automatically punched by machine. After that, in accordance with the specimen numbers and years, they are placed in the card mixer to be intercalated with the template cards, and finally in the card copying machine for the punching to be automatically completed.

Statistical evaluation of the cards can now be begun, its objective in this example being first to obtain a general view of how the most important varieties of diatoms are distributed in the river. By means of the sorting machine, the cards are first arranged according to frequency, variety number and location. Separately for each location, they are then placed in the tabulating machine for the frequencies in which the different varieties occur to be added up, and for this total as well as the total number of specimens in which each variety occurs in that location to be automatically transferred on to total cards. (For the statistical ascertainment of the diatom population several specimens must be available from each location.) With the aid of the total cards, the computing punch is used to work out the quotients which represent the average frequency of occurrence of each variety at the location in question, and to punch this result in the total cards. Thereupon the tabulating machine is used to print out a list of these average values, which can be used as a basis for the corresponding graphical presentation.

The working procedure varies a little according to the available machines, and the card collection can correspondingly be evaluated in accordance with any other factors and combinations of factors.

Finally, it may be remarked that this example has purposely been gone into with as much detail as possible, as the methodical principles it exhibits can be adapted to any other field of work. Above all, it also illustrates how needle punch-cards and the IBM system can be used for the same purpose, either separately or in combination, in accordance with their respective characteristics and possibilities.

On such a foundation of ecological investigations and uses of cards, the scientific substance of extremely varied fields can be unified in a punch-card archive.

Water resources, with the many problems to which they give rise—both quantitatively (as regards shortage of water) and qualitatively (as regards pollution)—are becoming more and more focused at the center of interest for public economy as a whole. There is, however, a lack of any numerical or research material correspondingly concentrated, or capable of concentration, which could serve as a basis for the study of all these problems as and where required. Such a basis could be supplied by classifying drainage systems, catchment areas, river systems and streams of various ranks down to individual kilometre lengths of these, so as to cover the whole of a country in the form of punch-card records.

This card system could then be used for incorporating all conceivable characteristics and factors, beginning with those which can be read off maps (showing the geology, climate, heights, vegetation, hydrological densities and utilization, etc.) and which include the data needed by hydrological bureaux, water and navigation services such as water levels, flows, quantities of water taken out and of waste water added, etc. This would provide a definite and consistent basis, quantitatively and qualitatively, for the appropriate research centers to carry out special investigations. Such a collection of cards, with its manifold possibilities of use, could attain great significance for the whole economy as well as for science. (Compare with the examples under 4 Meteorology.)

(6) **LINGUISTIC RESEARCH**

(From Busa, 1957.)   In order to show the suitability of the punch-card method not only for application in very varied fields of natural science but also for the successful pursuit of projects in other intellectual fields, I shall now refer to the researches of Father Busa, S. J., which are well known in specialised circles.

'After a preparatory period of ten years, the first computing center in the world for mechanized linguistic analysis was opened on 15 December 1956 at Gallarate near Milan in Italy.   As our first piece of research there, we are registering the contents of the works by Thomas Aquinas, with the intention of improving the method which has been developed and of informing science and linguistic research about similar questions and problems, so as to help in promoting such work.

A linguistic analysis consists of the examination of categories in which the elements of a recorded train of human thought can be grouped, classified and described, so as to be able to fit these elements into the appropriate categories.   Analytical work of this kind can be divided into: (*a*) indications of the contents and concordances of words, and (*b*) literary statistics.   It is conducted by the following stages:

(*1*) Sounds and letters . . .
(*2*) Letter groups and syllables . . .
(*3*) Word formations.   Prefixes, suffixes, endings, roots . . .
(*4*) Tone, accent . . .
(*5*) Words, considered solely according to their graphical and phonetic construction, or in accordance with their similar construction plus their meanings . . .
(*6*) Sentences, paragraphs, passages and their parts . . .

Mechanization is necessary in linguistic analysis because the work of collecting, grouping, comparing, inter-relating and counting linguistic elements often is very time-absorbing when carried out only with pen, paper and ink or with the aid of a typewriter and duplicating apparatus, so that under those conditions it is never performed on a very large scale, very accurately or in a very suitable manner.   Nor can the results so obtained be easily checked by others.   Mechanization of literary analysis includes two phases:

(*i*) The text must be made capable of elaboration by machine:

All the characters must be presented in a form which can be handled by machine.

The elements (words) must be so characterized (mainly by arranging them in alphabetical sequences, both from left to right and from right to left) that any further analytical operation can be carried out easily, quickly, economically, reversibly, accurately and on a large scale.   These latter operations are more or less similar to the preparation of word indexes and concordances.

(*ii*) Further analyses and statistical computations.

I myself [Busa] became interested in the mechanization of linguistic analysis because, as a teacher and researcher in philosophy, I found that an author's work could best be translated by starting from a preparatory linguistic examination of his vocabulary and syntax. As the Faculty to which I belong has been working for over 130 years on the philosophy of St Thomas Aquinas, I suggested to my chief and other specialists, in 1946, that a card collection recording all the words used by St Thomas Aquinas

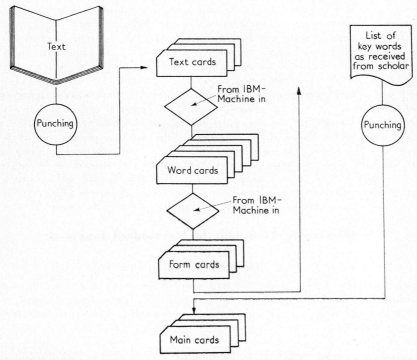

FIG. 36. Mechanization of linguistic analysis with the aid of IBM punch-cards (Busa, 1957).
Text cards: one for each line of text.
Word cards: one for each word in the text with its characteristics.
Form cards: one for each written variant of the same base word (thus 'house' and 'houses' will have two cards; 'am', 'are', 'was', 'were' will have four).
Main cards: one for each keyword under which all the different variants of what is essentially the same word are brought together and the frequency of their total occurrence is recorded; thus 'am', 'are', 'was', 'were', etc. all are brought together under 'be'.

in all his works should be set up, wherewith to follow the example set by the *Thesaurus Linguae Latinae* (TLL) in Munich, Bavaria. After surveying all the technical possibilities then known to me, I began experiments using the IBM punch-card system in 1949.

In the course of time I became cognizant of how wide a range of sciences is being drawn upon in order to improve the methods of linguistic analysis, and I discovered relationships between my own problems and the questions which are nowadays posed by documentation.   I used first those electrical IBM machines in which partial application is made of electronic techniques, whereby small electrical impulses are strengthened, as for instance in the sorting machine.

By the adoption of the punch-card method and the establishment of indexes, the working time can be reduced to between one-twentieth and one-fortieth of that hitherto needed using manual methods or with duplicating apparatus, according to the accuracy of the results desired.

The plan here reproduced (Fig. 36) shows how the contents are divided up.   The four sets of cards carry the author's text and the word index. With their aid, linguistic analysis can be carried out easily, quickly and accurately on a large scale and, above all, economically, since the same card can be used over again as often as is desired for checking, examination and evaluation.   Thereby many important research projects can be accomplished with the sorting, card mixing or calculating machines.   I would particularly like to draw attention to the working possibilities of the Type 101 electronic statistical machine, and to the new special form of this machine.   In the same context, the possibilities should be borne in mind of proceeding, by mechanical means, from punch-card indications to a graphical presentation in the form of a curve, and conversely from a drawn or photographed graphical presentation to punch-card indications.

The Electronic Technique in Mechanized Linguistic Analysis

My information as to the present situation is as follows:

(*1*) The Rev. John Ellison, a clergyman of the Episcopal Church, was working at Harvard University on a Mark IV computing machine to produce a report on the relations between the fourth chapter of the Greek Gospel according to St Luke and the deviations from this text in 311 manuscripts.

Using the Univac machine of Remington Rand, jointly with Professors L. B. Kiddle and J. W. Carr from the University of Michigan, he is now completing a concordance to the Authorized Version of the English Bible. He is also working at a concordance to the works of Cervantes.

Ellison has also devised a program whereby the contents of a work can be indexed by the use of computers.   He says that this program can be carried out on the computing machines supplied by several of the various companies.

(*2*) IBM have supplied me with their experience, and placed their machines at my disposal, for the philological, statistical examination of the Dead Sea Scrolls in the Hebrew language.   The final processing of these texts published to date will not involve more than 50000 words.   It is being carried out with the IBM 705 machine.   We estimate that the punching and checking will take from three to four weeks and that establishing the program for the IBM 705 will take one person three weeks.   But when this is done the machine will be able to print the whole of the word index in two hours.   The completion of this program will be of considerable help for further work not only on the Scrolls but also on other texts, including different languages.

For the *Summa Theologiae* which already has been completely punched and checked, the IBM 705 took 13 hours 20 minutes to transcribe the text from punch-cards on to a magnetic tape. This involved about 16 million signs including the spaces between words, and 222 000 index references. Sixty hours were needed to arrange in alphabetical order the 1 600 000 words contained in the *Summa*. A total of 266 hours and 40 minutes was needed to punch the 1 600 000 cards which correspond to the alphabetically arranged words, and 30 hours to print the 1 600 000 lines.'

'Following this, I may be allowed to state six guiding principles:

(*1*) The EDPM installation (which is a large electronic computing installation of IBM—Author) needs to be used for the improvement and development of linguistic analysis.

(*2*) This system does not replace the use of punch-cards, but amplifies it.

(*3*) The use of punch-cards and of electrical punch-card machines must be further extended. Often they are more practical than the EDPM installation. Thus the punch-card continues to gain in significance as a simple and reliable vehicle of information of the first rank.

(*4*) Unless, however, the punch-card system is used conjointly with the EDPM installation, scientific linguistic analysis will never be carried out on a sufficiently large scale, and financially will remain beyond the reach of many scholars.

(*5*) We now know that the use of the EDPM installation for linguistic analysis must be centralized. The punching, checking, mixing and sorting machines can, however, be distributed among the scholars and schools interested.

(*6*) The EDPM installation must be made available for linguistic analysis in a simple and inexpensive form.'

'Special machines for literary research and for linguistic analysis are being constructed by private persons and particular institutions. Consequently there is some danger that in this field a variety of methods, codes and systems will be adopted, as unfortunately has happened in librarianship and microfilm work. We ought not to forget that we all belong to one large family of peoples on this earth, living and working in the same house, which is the House of God. Perhaps I am wrong, but I would like to say here and now that in our quest for the best scientific tool we should not be afraid to institute a "trust".

At any rate, I would like to put the question whether large international companies may not in fact be the only form of organization by which researchers in linguistics and documentation can be helped to develop a uniform system with a uniform code, and finally uniform principles, for the whole world. In my opinion, anyway, nobody can have greater interest in the adoption of uniform principles than research workers in linguistics and documentation, whose function in human society is that of "communication".'

13.   EXAMPLES FROM DOCUMENTATION

(1) **AERODYNAMICS**

(From Riegels, 1955.) 'What, now, are the possibilities offered by mechanical selection as a working tool?   First of all, the edge-notched card calls for further examination.   When made in the format *DIN A 5* ($5\frac{7}{8}$ in. $\times$ $8\frac{1}{4}$ in.) it allows the title to be followed by short notes, abstracts, critical remarks and the like.   Its further novelty, as compared with the usual form of bibliographical reference, lies in the possibility of characterizing the contents by punching individual holes or combinations of holes, which later make mechanical selection possible.   Suppose, for instance, that there is a work dealing with the flow over a delta wing with fuselage and at supersonic speeds, from the point of view of the longitudinal and transverse forces and the moments about three axes, treated theoretically and experimentally in summary fashion.   By punching the holes which correspond to particular features—summary report, theoretical, experimental, delta wing, fuselage, supersonic speed, lift, lateral forces, moments about the longitudinal and transverse and vertical axes—the detailed contents of this work can be fixed and later be sought for in a selecting device, even though its title may simply be "Aerodynamic forces and moments on a supersonic-speed wing."   Obviously for this purpose the concepts used in the technical speciality must be clearly defined.

In order to make it possible quickly to obtain an idea of the topics treated in a work by briefly looking through it a questionnaire has been designed which takes up four pages of *DIN A 5* format ($5\frac{7}{8}$ in. $\times$ $8\frac{1}{4}$ in.)—that is, both sides of a *DIN A 4* sheet ($8\frac{1}{4}$ in. $\times$ $11\frac{3}{8}$ in.) folded in two—in which the concepts necessary for referencing are arranged in groups.   These concepts are, for instance, the nature of the work (whether it is a publication, the report of an institute, a microfilm, etc.); general indications (for instance: historical, bibliographical, descriptive, design, theoretical, experimental data); shape of the object treated (such as tube, channel, slot, tapered wing of rectangular, trapezoidal, swept back, triangular or dihedral form, with slotted or split flaps; ball, cone, solid of revolution, frame); nature of flow (for instance frictionless, laminar, turbulent, incompressible, velocity low, medium, high or supersonic).   Those concepts to which substantial reference is made in the work are then simply underlined when scanning it and serve as a basis for punching (see Fig. 37).

With the IBM (Hollerith) punch-card, the "reference" card collection is complemented by a "contents" card collection maintained in parallel with it, the two being linked by identification numbers and each of them carrying indications of content in the form of combinations of holes.   To answer any given question these cards are mechanically scanned and compared in the

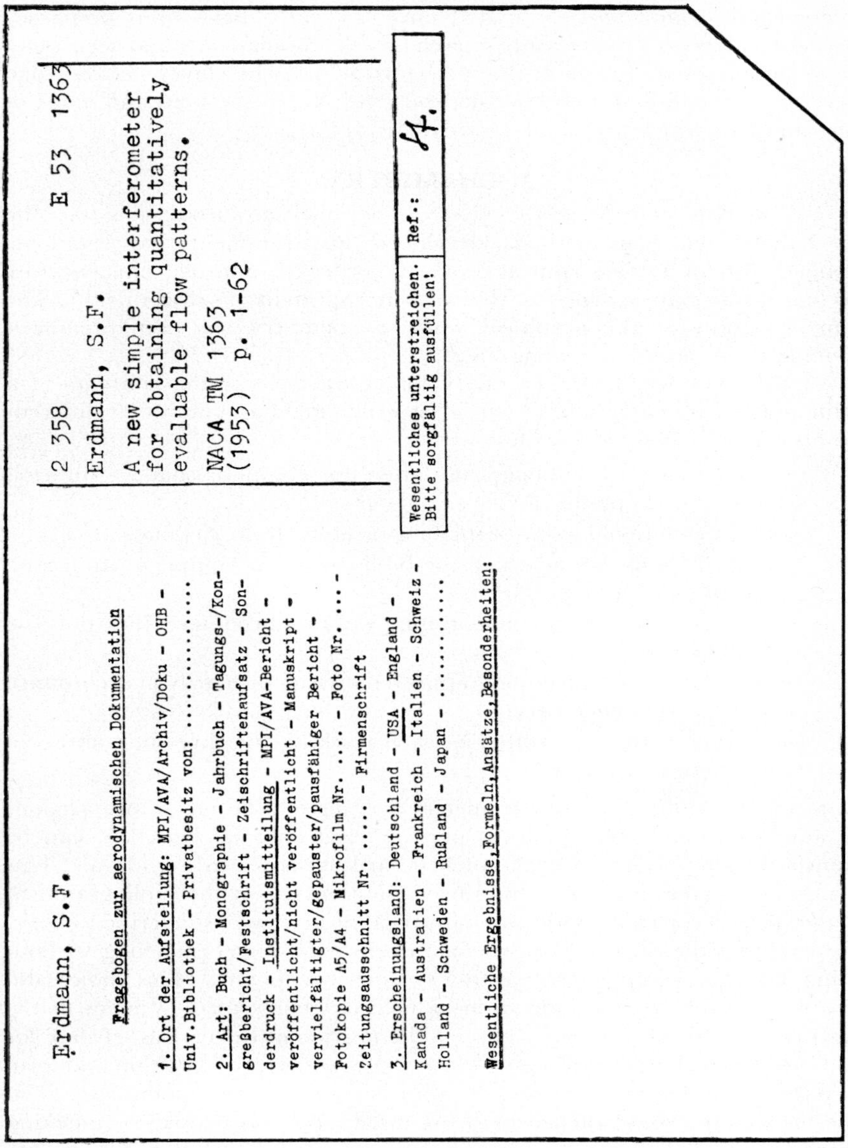

Erdmann, S.F.

2 358   E 53 1363
Erdmann, S.F.
A new simple interferometer
for obtaining quantitatively
evaluable flow patterns.
NACA TM 1363
(1953) p. 1-62

Ref.:

Wesentliches unterstreichen.
Bitte sorgfältig ausfüllen!

Fragebogen zur aerodynamischen Dokumentation

1. Ort der Aufstellung: MPI/AVA/Archiv/Doku – OHB –
Univ.Bibliothek – Privatbesitz von: ....

2. Art: Buch – Monographie – Jahrbuch – Tagungs-/Kon-
greßbericht/Festschrift – Zeitschriftenaufsatz – Son-
derdruck – Institutsmitteilung – MPI/AVA-Bericht –
veröffentlicht/nicht veröffentlicht – Manuskript –
vervielfältigter/gepauster/pausfähiger Bericht –
Fotokopie A5/A4 – Mikrofilm Nr. ..... – Foto Nr. .... –
Zeitungsausschnitt Nr. ...... – Firmenschrift

3. Erscheinungsland: Deutschland – USA – England –
Kanada – Australien – Frankreich – Italien – Schweiz –
Holland – Schweden – Rußland – Japan – ....

Wesentliche Ergebnisse, Formeln, Ansätze, Besonderheiten:

FIG. 37. Part of front of punching instruction sheet (questionnaire) (Riegels, 1955).

IBM card mixer, after which the indications on the pertinent reference cards are converted by the IBM tabulating machine into the form of bibliographical lists or transferred to ordinary filing cards (which may, if desired, but need not, be of the internationally standardized library format) at a printing speed of 1000 references an hour. One important advantage of this fully mechanized method is that all need for proof reading of the

P

references is completely eliminated once the cards have been prepared. Any later collections of literature references will automatically and accurately be incorporated by reason of the mechanization. The choice between one selecting procedure and another depends entirely on the kind and scope of the questions which are liable to arise.'

(2) CHEMISTRY

(From Pietsch and Mulert, 1955.) 'The question arose how far the mechanical selection methods developed for documentation could be applied also in bibliographical work, in order to improve efficiency by adding to the expressiveness of the titles in a specialized subject field. The Gmelin Institute bibliographical work in chemistry has been organized systematically on the following lines.

All the data which are necessary for characterizing the contents of a bibliography are entered on a check list which takes account of 99 different points of view, subdivided as follows:

(a) Characterizing the bibliography after the manner usual in libraries, according to 25 points of view.

(b) Noting the national scope of the bibliography, from 26 points of view.

(c) Noting the language in which the bibliography is compiled, from nine points of view.

(d) Noting the date that the bibliography was produced, for which purpose five subdivisions of time are provided.

(e) Subject division of the bibliographical material, primarily in accordance with 33 parts of chemistry.

(f) Indication of the first author of each work by the three first letters of his surname (see Fig. 38 b).

Data for the multiplicity of parameters that have to be taken into account in any particular bibliographical unit, entered on this check list, can be transferred directly to an edge-notched card as shown in Fig. 38 a. This being done makes it possible to answer questions about the bibliographical material in accordance with any named point of view, as described above. In designing the card to be used for this purpose, direct punching without using any code except for the author's name was chosen. This choice also made it possible for the indications which are represented by holes in the card to be read off directly. The middle portion of the card is left free for copying in the characterization of the work by author, title, edition and form of publication directly from the top right portion of the questionnaire. On the back of the edge-notched card the middle portion is used for indexing three letters of the author's name by the use of the X–1–2–4–7 code (see Fig. 38 b).'

(3) BIOLOGY AND EARTH SCIENCES (PHYSIOGRAPHY)

(From Scheele, 1951–58, here published together for the first time.) Here a complete account will be given of the reference system for biology and physiography which the author and his collaborators developed at the documentation centre for limnology in Hannover-Münden during the years 1953–56. In this system, an attempt is made to take into account, as fully as possible, all the experiences which have been described in the earlier sections of the book—although, for various financial and organizational

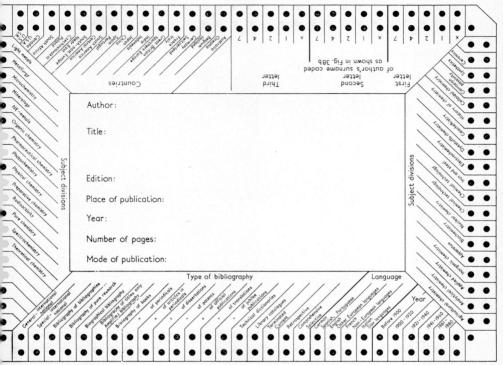

FIG. 38a. Front of edge-notched card for compiling chemical bibliographies (Pietsch and Mulert, 1955). [On the original card the indicators are in German.]

reasons, it has not yet been possible to try it out on as wide a basis as is desirable, seeing that tens or hundreds of thousands of cards cannot be prepared in a relatively short space of time.

At the time when development of the modern system of punch-card documentation described below was begun, only very scanty experience existed in this field. It was something quite new; and looking back it is possible to say that maybe the courage to face such a prospect would have failed if it had then been possible to foresee the kind of difficulties which were in fact to be encountered. I am saying this quite deliberately, so as to stress once again that whoever aspires to complete success in applying the punch-card method to documentation must face up to demands which he will be unable to meet single-handed. As, therefore, it may interest the reader to follow the early course of the evolution which has resulted in the system now about to be described, its actual description and explanation will be preceded by a short historical account.

In giving this, the errors which became manifest in the course of feeling our way will not be discussed at too great length, it being thought better to

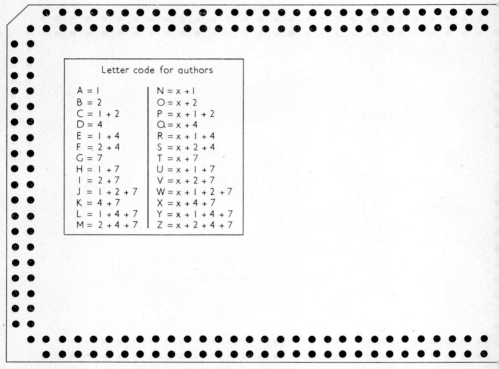

Letter code for authors

A = 1	N = x + 1
B = 2	O = x + 2
C = 1 + 2	P = x + 1 + 2
D = 4	Q = x + 4
E = 1 + 4	R = x + 1 + 4
F = 2 + 4	S = x + 2 + 4
G = 7	T = x + 7
H = 1 + 7	U = x + 1 + 7
I = 2 + 7	V = x + 2 + 7
J = 1 + 2 + 7	W = x + 1 + 2 + 7
K = 4 + 7	X = x + 4 + 7
L = 1 + 4 + 7	Y = x + 1 + 4 + 7
M = 2 + 4 + 7	Z = x + 2 + 4 + 7

FIG. 38b.   Back of edge-notched card, with code for authors' names (Pietsch and Mulert, 1955).

use the space for describing the system as finally established and accepted as satisfactory for its purpose.

After 1949, when the author first met the punch-card method, he conceived the idea of punch-card documentation in limnology around 1952–53. In 1953 the preparatory work for this was intensively begun, the first task being to build up a collection of concepts on needle punch-cards which, with the help of students, grew finally to more than 1 000 cards.   In this set of cards only terms as distinct from names were collected, since biological nomenclature is more easily worked upon than its terminology.   In collecting these concepts particular attention was paid to the inclusion of synonyms.

When the collection of concepts had reached a certain size, allowing it to be assumed that the resulting picture would not be wrong or biased, the work of arranging it in an orderly pattern was embarked upon. This second step involved fitting the concepts into their places in a usable system in practice. It became clear even at this stage that limnology cannot be torn from its context of biology, geography and other neighbouring disciplines without rendering punch-card documentation irrational. This led to the decision that a complete system, broadly embracing biology and the physiographical sciences of the earth, must be set up if the work was not to remain merely fragmentary—a decision which, of course, entailed some delay to further development. In the sense adopted by Thienemann and Friederichs, the systematization of sciences to which it gave rise can be described as general ecology.

When attention was concentrated on applying the punch-card method in the most rational possible way, the first attempts at establishing such a system and at arranging the numerous concepts in a meaningful order continually came up against obstacles which seemed insurmountable. It soon became clear that these difficulties led back to the difficult question of how the concepts ought in fact to be subordinated and coordinated, a problem which has been exhaustively described in Chapter 6. At the time, in 1953, when this first came to light no immediate solution could be found, because the first step required for overcoming these difficulties had not yet been appreciated: namely, the splitting of the system into two major parts—respectively a system of objects and a system of properties. For the purpose of constructing the system of properties, experiments were carried out on the basis of the Universal Decimal Classification, but these proved abortive. In order to make progress, we thereupon turned to the question of notation, and still having the Universal Decimal Classification in view we chose a numerical notation. Here it became clearer than ever, as regards applying the punch-card method, that any kind of notation constitutes an unnecessary detour. The idea then arose of directly associating concepts with multiple punchings within each column of the machine punch-cards, but this way seemed at once to be blocked by the absence of any experience in that direction as well as by the fact that IBM strongly advised against multiple punching. After various practical experiments, however, the last mentioned principle was found to work well enough in documentation, and in that context it was found possible to carry the classification through. At the same time the idea of associative codes arose, and on this basis the 'punching pattern' method was developed, which in the author's opinion offers the best solution proposed up to now to the problem of classification so far as fixation on punch-cards is concerned.

In parallel with these lines of thought and development it had, of course, to be considered what kind of documentation was in fact to be undertaken. Was preference to be given to bare titles, to indications of content in the form of keywords or to a complete abstracting service? This again was a question which could be answered only in relation to the punch-card technique adopted, and at that time I decided in favor of complete abstracts as being the proper form of documentation to adopt.

The outcome of the considerations described up to this point was the creation, in the year 1954, of a very complicated system of documentation which at that time appeared to us ideal. Broadly it took the following form. A needle punch-card of *DIN A 5* format ($5\frac{7}{8}$ in. $\times$ $8\frac{1}{4}$ in.), printed with a special layout, was provided for each publication. On this card the documentalist entered first of all the bibliographical indications, reserving the back for the addition of a complete abstract. Then, on the front of the card, the necessary coding was marked both for the needle punch-card itself and also for the intended IBM machine punch-card, so that the former could at the same time serve as punching instructions for the latter. Next a set of five machine punch-cards was prepared for each publication, as follows. Two of these IBM cards, described as 'contents cards', were punched in accordance with the 'punching pattern' system so as to indicate the contents of the publication in question, one of them representing its place in the system of objects and the other its place in the system of properties. Two further IBM cards, described as 'alphabetical cards', were used to receive continuous alphabetical punching of the author's name, the title and some further bibliographical indications of the publication in question. The fifth and last card of the set was a Powers machine punch-card serving as a matrix to link up the whole of this system with the needle punch-card technique.

There can be no doubt that this system had many advantages, but it was so clumsy and irrational to operate that it tended partly to defeat the inherent advantages of using punch-card methods. One of the possibilities it allowed was that of supplying the customer of the documentation service with lists of titles printed in the tabulating machine or with complete needle punch-cards, or alternatively with duplicated IBM cards. Attractive as such possibilities had seemed, it was found again and again that the results bore no acceptable relationship to the expense.

The first simplification which now followed was the abandonment of the edge-notched *DIN A 5* cards. Experience showed that these cards were used solely as punching instructions for the machine punch-cards, afterwards remaining filed in the same sequence as the publication numbers and never themselves being used for purposes of selection, so it was an obvious decision to replace them simply by a file of ordinary index cards.

The next step in the direction of further simplification consisted of combining the two contents cards into a single card.

When the coding system had been further simplified and developed it became possible, in 1955, to embark on a major experiment in documentation. The *Archiv für Hydrobiologie* journal was chosen as the object of this experiment and an additional collaborator was enlisted so that other periodicals, too, could be included in the scheme. The working staff of the documentation center now comprised a leader whose role was to watch over the experiment as a whole and at the same time over other jobs, the two abstractors, a corrector and a girl secretary working half time.

With this increased working staff the experimental work gathered speed, and meanwhile the following further simplifications had been adopted. Whereas, hitherto, a full abstract of each publication had been insisted upon the other extreme solution was now tried of producing a bibliography containing only titles, supplemented by objects treated in the contents but not expressed in the titles. As that type of documentation also did not work well, it was replaced finally by indications of contents in the form of keywords and this solution proved more and more successful. Meanwhile, on the technical side, the Powers card had been discontinued, so that only an ordinary punching layout marked on a card of *DIN A 5* format ($5\frac{7}{8}$ in. $\times$ $8\frac{1}{4}$ in.), one contents card produced by the mark-sensing method and two alphabetical cards were now necessary. In the course of the work a form of compound code, defined with ever increasing strictness, had crystallised out into the shape of a large coding table that could be consulted at a glance without need for the troublesome turning of pages forward and back. It seemed that the greatest possible simplification had been attained.

By the time, however, that several thousands of publications had been coded and that an IBM card collection for the whole of the *Archiv für Hydrobiologie* was ready for use in evaluative work, so much new experience and so many new points had been perceived that in 1956 a further review of the whole system and procedure had to be undertaken.

Meanwhile the author had moved over to the Deutsche Forschungsgemeinschaft (the German Research Association) in the capacity of specialist for documentation, with the task of carrying out a survey of the present situation in that field. This assignment provided him with the opportunity of critically examining over again all the experience so far obtained in applications of the punch-card method. When the results of this check were complete, and the author had come back to the Max-Planck-Gesellschaft, the system and procedure were given the definitive form in which they are now presented.

This final review had suggested yet another series of important simplifications which in the nature of the case would have been quite impossible at the initiation of the development. First of all, the further evolution of the classification of sciences and of the classification system used in punching the cards resulted in space being saved on the cards, which opened the way for additional simplifications. These may be summarized by saying that the whole process now consists principally of having, for each publication, one photographic contact-printing negative of the punching pattern and one IBM card in which the whole of the important bibliographical indications are combined with indications of the contents of the publication in question.

Although it has not been possible, in this short account of how the present system was evolved, to mention all the snags and difficulties, the changes of direction and retracing of steps which in fact occurred, the reader will perhaps have received a good enough picture of them. Before he starts to criticize, let him remind himself that everyone is cleverer in retrospect than in foresight. Many of the stages in development which have been described may look like detours that could have been avoided; but theory and practice are two different things. As long as the experience of others is not on record one has no option but to try out for oneself, in a practical way, every possibility that seems to promise success. Nobody will seriously contest that such experimenting is as justifiable and necessary in methodology as in research. And finally, the main importance of the whole of this book is to make all experience so obtained, whether positive or negative, accessible to others interested.

The Organization of Literature Referencing

The first item to be reproduced here will be the list of contents of a loose-leaf binder supplied to each of the collaborators for the purpose of ensuring

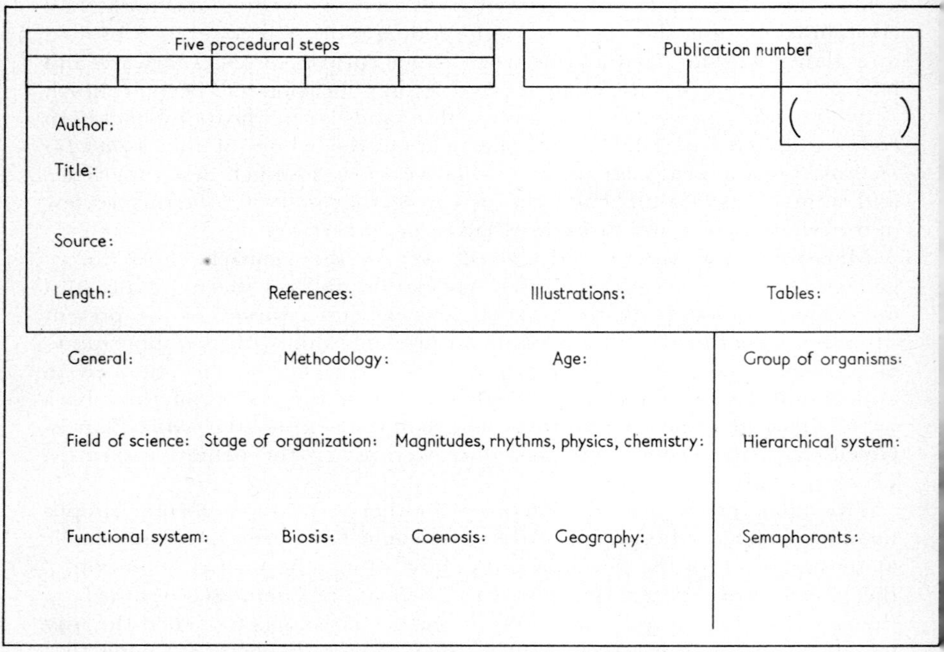

Five procedural steps					Publication number	
						( )

Author:

Title:

Source:

Length: References: Illustrations: Tables:

General:	Methodology:	Age:	Group of organisms:
Field of science:	Stage of organization:	Magnitudes, rhythms, physics, chemistry:	Hierarchical system:
Functional system:	Biosis:	Coenosis:	Geography:	Semaphoronts:

FIG. 39.   Punching instructions for biological-physiographical reference card.

that all the processes may be truly uniform and can be correctly carried out in all their details. Working instructions of this kind, carefully thought out to the verge of pedantry and practically tested, are amongst the pre-requisites for punch-card work.

Contents

A. General
      I. General instructions for the input
     II. General instructions for the output
B. Notations and codes
      I. Properties system and code for biology and physiography (general ecology)
     II. Notation and code for objects
   III. Notation for sources
   IV. Notation for informational characteristics

C. Plugboard connections
  I. Card reproducer (mark-sensing automatic punch)
  II. Card collator
  III. Punch-to-print interpreter
  IV. Tabulator.

Details of the instructions and codes now follow:

A. *General, I. General instructions for the input*

The following basic forms are provided: one card of transparent material for photographic contact-copying (see Sample 1, Fig. 39) of *DIN A 6* format (4 in. × 5¾ in.). One paper slip of the same size to be prepared as a carbon copy from this card (see Sample 2).

One IBM mark-sensing card (see Sample 3, Fig. 40).

(1) *Completion of the* DIN A 6 *cards and slips by the secretary*—These cards and slips are supplied in sheets of *DIN A 4* format (11⅔ in. × 8¼ in.) each containing a series of four, so as to make them easier to type. For each publication one card, and one slip as a carbon copy, is completed by using the typewriter. For publications which appear by instalments each instalment is treated as a separate unit. In the topmost field, the following are entered:

(*a*) Bibliographical indications in accordance with the German standard *DIN 1505*

(*b*) Extent of the work

(*c*) Number of literature references

(*d*) Number of illustrations

(*e*) Number of tables.

In the upper right corner the number of the publication is entered, this being made up of the source number (five digits), the year (two digits) and the page number (four digits).

For periodicals the year is designated by the date that the volume in question was published.

In a separate space provided underneath the page number, a roman number identifying successive publications of the same source and year is inserted in brackets as a check.

The lower field is left vacant.

Finally the *DIN A 4* sheet of paper is cut up into separate slips whilst the corresponding sheet of cards is left intact and put aside till later. The slips are marked 'Aufg.' (input) in the top left corner and are then passed to the coder as covering slips attached to the literature to which they refer.

(2) *Scanning and coding of the publications by the documentalist (coder)*—First the covering slip is compared with the original literature and checked for correct referencing. Following the 'guide' which appears in the lower field of the covering slip each publication is scanned according to the codes for 'aspects

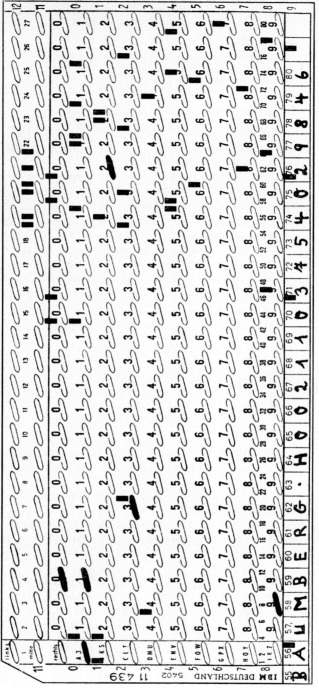

FIG. 40. Mark-sensing card for the recording procedure of the biological-physiographical card collection.

of search' and 'objects'. Within each category that appears on the covering slip the corresponding keywords for the publication in question are entered and the code numbers are added. With the hierarchical objects code, whatever higher collective category is shared by all of the objects treated is the one to be coded. The covering slip is then marked 'Verschl.' (coded) and the covering slip, accompanied by the literature, is sent back to the secretary.

(3) *Preparation of the* DIN A 6 *cards and completion of the IBM mark-sensing cards by the secretary*—(*a*) By reference to the covering slip, the related *DIN A 6* cards are completed on the typewriter. In so doing only the keywords and not the code numbers are typed. After this the sheets of cards are cut up into separate cards.

(*b*) Thereupon a mark-sensing card is prepared by reference to the covering slip of each publication, the mark-sensing card being divided as follows:

Hole 12 in column 1: indication that this belongs to the reference card set	
Columns 1–38	'Aspects of search' or 'properties' system (associative code)
Columns 39–43 and one additional hole in each column 1–38	Semaphorontes and large groups in the objects system (associative code punching pattern)
Columns 44–45	Left vacant for further subdivisions (hierarchical code)
Columns 46–54	Hierarchical subdivisions of the objects system (hierarchical code)
Columns 55–78	Bibliographical indications (hierarchical code)
Columns 79–80	Informational characteristics (direct code).

The next stage in preparing the card consists of filling in the spaces along the lower edge on the front, each space corresponding to one column. Here the bibliographical data as well as the extent of the publication and the number of literature citations in it are to be entered according to the following rules:

(aa) The author's surname, by nine letters in columns 55–63. If the name is longer than this the additional letters are omitted. The German *Umlaute* ä, ö, ü are represented by ae, oe, ue. Aristocratic prefixes (*von*, *de*, etc.) are, in principle, abbreviated following the names after one letter space, or if the name itself is too long to leave room for them they are omitted. If there are several author's names only the first is entered.

(bb) The first of the author's given names is indicated by an initial letter (column 64) if there is only one author. If there are several authors, hole 11 is punched in column 64.

(cc) The source number in accordance with the notation for sources (columns 65–69).

(dd) The volume number (columns 70–72).

(ee) The year as shown by two numerals such as 58 instead of 1958 (columns 73–74). The year 1900 is denoted by 00, the year 1901 by 01 and so on; for years previous to 1900, hole 12 is to be marked as punched in column 73.

(ff) The initial page number (columns 75–78).

(gg) The number which indicates the size of the publication in accordance with the notation for informational characteristics (column 79).

(hh) The notation number which indicates the number of literature references (column 80).

In addition, the mark-sensing cards are marked with the code numbers for properties and for objects shown on the covering slip, using electrographic ink. Finally the covering slip is checked 'Geschr.' (meaning that it has been typed) and 'Angestr.' (marked on the mark-sensing card), whereupon the original literature, the covering slip, the *DIN A 6* cards and the mark-sensing cards are passed to the corrector for checking.

(4) *Checking of the completed punching, by the corrector*—The corrector checks:

(a) the correctness of the coding
(b) the correctness of the typing on the *DIN A 6* cards
(c) the correctness of the completion and marking of the mark-sensing cards.

Thereupon the covering slip is marked under 'Gepr.' (checked). The covering slips are filed according to authors and the *DIN A 6* cards in the order of publication numbers (put together from the source number, year and page number). The mark-sensing cards are then sent to the punch-card department for punching.

(5) *Punching and checking of the mark-sensing cards in the punch-card department*—

(a) The mark-sensing cards are automatically punched in the appropriate machines.
(b) The indications shown in the spaces along the bottom edge of the front of each card are then punched using the alphabetical punch.
(c) The completely punched cards are examined by spot checks as regards correct punching in accordance with the mark-sensing, and are fully checked in the proving machine for correctness of the remaining holes.
(d) Using the punch-to-print interpreter with connections III/1, the cards are imprinted in type and are put aside.

II. *General instructions for the output*

The following kinds of output are possible either in answer to individual enquiries or by subscription:

Supply of the IBM cards (see sample 4, Fig. 41).
Supply of bibliographical lists (see sample 5, Fig. 42).
Supply of cards contact-printed from the *DIN A 6* cards (see sample 1, Fig. 39).

(1) *Supply of IBM cards*—

(a) In accordance with the enquiry—for instance, a request for all literature relating to the digestive physiology of the bat—the stock of punch-cards is put through the sorting machine, care being taken to sort first according to whatever concept gives the greatest degree of selectivity.
(b) The cards which have fallen out are put through the card reproducer to be copied on to cards like sample 4.
(c) The copied cards are put through the punch-to-print interpreter, with the connections III/1, to be imprinted in type.
(d) The cards are sent to the customer.
(e) Instructions for use by the customer. As seen in sample 4, Fig. 41, the IBM card carries along its upper edge:

   (aa) the author's surname, here limited for technical reasons to nine letters even though the name may actually contain more. (The name in this form is to be regarded merely as an indication useful for retrieving the wanted literature.)
   (bb) Where there is only one author, the initial letter of his first given name. If there are several authors only the surname of the one first mentioned in the publication appears, followed by an asterisk in the space marked 'Vorn.' ('given name') to indicate that there are several authors.
   (cc) The source number.
   (dd) The volume number.
   (ee) Year of publication (abbreviated to last two digits).

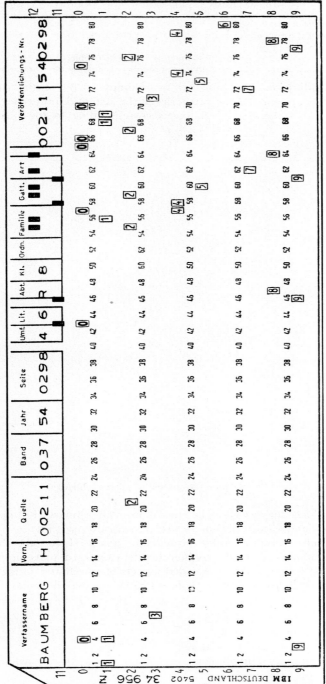

Fig. 41. Indicative card (IBM) for a user of the biological-physiographical card collection.

(ff) Initial page number.
(gg) Notation corresponding to the informational characteristics 'extent' and 'literature citations'.
(hh) The notation corresponding to the hierarchical code of objects.
(ii) Separately on the right, the publication number identifying the work in question.

All these indications are punched in columns 46–80 of the card. In columns 1–45 are entered the categories of the system of properties and the major groups of the system of objects corresponding to the work under

Author's surname	Initial	Source	Vol.	Year	First page number	No. of pages	No. of refs.	Biological data				
AMMANN	H	1 1	8	1 3	2 8 9	5	3	C	6	N	0 5	
ARNDT	W	1 2 7	3 1	3 7	4 7 8	6	5	N	1	B	0 2	
AUERBACH	M	B 3	1 0 1	·5 3	1 2	3	2					
BAIER	C	1 9	1 5	4 9	1 7 3	7	9	B	1			
BUSSE VON	L	1 1	4 3	4 6	7	5	4	C	3	D	1 1	0 9
DUNZINGER	G	3 8 4	6 1	5 4	1 2 3 5	9	7	O	9	L	2 6	K 5
EFFENBERG	W	1 1	4 0	4 3	7 5 6	5	3	R	4	F	1 8	2 3
EICHLER	H	1 2 7	1 0 6	5 8	2 1 3	2	0	C	6	M	0 3	1 2
FREIDENFE	T	3	1 2	2 3	9 8	8	4	C	4	A		
GEITLER	L	1 9	3 1	3 7	6 7 8	8	9	C				
GRASSE	G	5 3	4 8	2 9	3 1 8	4	4					
HARTMANN	O	1 1	4	0 9	2 0 2	6	8	H	4	C	1 0	1 6
HOFFMANN	E	6 1	1 8	2 7	6 1 6	3	2	K	4			
JUERGENSE	C	4 8	2 8	3 5	3 6 1	7	9	C				
KAHL	A	3 8 4	1 9	2 8	5 0	7	0	K	7			
KAMMERER	P	6 1	2	0 7	5 0 0	6	3					
KIEFER	F	1 1	3 6	4 0	9 4	6	5	O	3	E	0 9	2 1
LANGE	K	1 2 7	2 1	3 0	1 4 7	3	3	M	1	B	1 2	0 3

Fig. 42. Literature list printed by an IBM tabulator.

reference, which can very easily be read off from an ordinary IBM numbered card placed underneath the literature punch-card (see Fig. 41) so that the line numbers become visible through the holes. These, together with the column numbers printed in red on the literature card, make up the code numbers that correspond to the coded aspects of search and to the objects code under which the related keyword (or category) may be found.

Thus the example in Fig. 41 can be interpreted as follows from left to right:

1/1 = main subject: biology
3/9 = quaternary and present age
4/0 = pertaining to idiobiology, the main theme being structure and
4/1   morphology

7/3 = an organ
21/2 = teeth
43/0 = Monotremata and Marsupialia
43/11 = Placentalia.

It is made evident by these indications that the work refers to the morphology of teeth as organs common to the recent groups of mammals, and that in this instance the work does not refer to anything else even as a secondary theme.

In this way the IBM card can practically be read off as a keyword abstract, but in addition it can be mechanically selected and sorted in an ordinary IBM sorting machine.

(2) *Supply of bibliographical lists*—

(a) Selection as above.
(b) The cards which have fallen out are sorted according to authors' names.
(c) Cards are set to the tabulating machine with connections IV/1.
(d) The lists so produced are sent to the customer.

(3) *Supply of contact-printed cards*—Customers for whom the indications on the IBM card are not sufficient, and who wish to receive also the title, etc., can be supplied with a photographic copy contact-printed from the original *DIN A 6* card either on card material or on paper.

(a) Selection as above.
(b) A clerk refers to the cards which have fallen out and finds on these the publication numbers of the corresponding *DIN A 6* cards. These being contact-printing negatives they are used for making positive copies and are then put back.
(c) The contact-prints are sent to the customer.

B. *Notations and Codes, I. Properties System and Code for Biology and Physiography (general ecology)*

Remark: The numeral before the oblique stroke indicates the column number and the numeral after the stroke the line number.

Main categories

General main categories

1/0 General ecology in general	2/0 General methodology
1 Main subject biology	1 Open field methods (observation, collecting, fishing, hunting)
2 Main subject physiography	
3 Secondary subject biology	2 Captivity and breeding
4 Secondary subject physiography	3 Operational methods (performed upon the living object)
5 The subject extends beyond the scope of general ecology	4 Methods of preparation (handling of dead object)
1/6 Bibliography (containing more than 200 literature references)	5 Microscopy
7 Theory of science, general theories, general propositions	6 Methods of measuring and examination
8 Works of reference, literature relating to identification, nomenclature, terminology	7 Methods of illustration (drawing, photography, film)
9 Organization of science, historical, memorial notices and miscellaneous	8 Devices, apparatus and machines
	9 Other methods

Historical main categories

3/0 Eras in general	5 Triassic
12 Precambrian and Cambrian	6 Jurassic
1 Silurian	7 Cretaceous
2 Devonian	8 Tertiary
3 Carboniferous	9 Quaternary, including present era
4 Permian	

Main categories relating to space and contents

Idiobiology

Main subject

4/ 0 'Gegebenheitslehre'*
11 Ontogenetics
12 Phylogenetics
1 Structure
2 Antecedents
3 General laws

Subsidiary subject
4 'Gegebenheitslehre'*
5 Ontogenetics
6 Phylogenetics
7 Structure
8 Antecedents
9 General laws

Cenobiology

Main subject

5/ 0 'Gegebenheitslehre'*
11 Ontogenetics
12 Phylogenetics
1 Structure
2 Antecedents
3 General laws

Subsidiary subject
4 'Gegebenheitslehre'*
5 Ontogenetics
6 Phylogenetics
7 Structure
8 Antecedents
9 General laws

10/8 Comparative in general
(applicable from cells to holocoon)
10/11 Further subdivision for special cases

Organizational stages of idiobiology

6/11 Natural separations and substances (excretions, secretions, milk, etc.) .

6/0 Cells
1 Cell membrane
2 Plasma
3 Nuclear
4 Plastides
5 Vacuoles, inclusions
6 Cytocentrum
7 Chondriosomes
8 Golgi-apparatus
9 Chromosomes

7/0 Tissues
1 Structural tissues
2 Wood

7/3 Organs
4 Organs without ascertainable function
5 Rudimentary organs
6 Hearing organs
7 Cleansing organs
8 Leaf
9 Root

	8/0 Whole organism	
	1 Head	
	2 Breast and neck	
	3 Stomach, abdomen	
	4 Back	
	5 Extremities	
	6 Tail	
21/0	8/7 Nutritive powers (including webs, etc.)	
21/0	8/8 Excretion	
27/0	8/9 Orientative powers	

8/0	9/0	Powers of construction
8/0	9/1	Psychology, theory of behavior
8/0	9/2	Total metabolism and energy exchange
8/0	9/3	Cleanliness, purification
8/0	9/4	Regeneration
8/0	9/5	Asphyxia, states of rest
8/0	9/6	Immunity, resistance
8/0	9/7	Autotomy
8/0	9/8	Protection
8/0	9/9	Other powers

* A word invented by the author to designate those aspects of biology which (by contrast with the subject matter of ontogenetics and phylogenetics) are not affected by the passage of time.

Organizational stages of cenobiology
Main subject

10/0 Organism + environmental factor
   1 Bioses (organism + organism)
   2 Cenoses (biocenosis + biotope)
   3 Holocoon of the earth (totality of cenoses)

Subsidiary subject

10/4 Organism + environmental factor
   5 Bioses (organism + organism)
   6 Cenoses (biocenosis + biotope)
   7 Holocoon of the earth (totality of cenoses)

10/8 General comparisons
    (applicable from cells to holocoon)
10/9 Non-terrestrial factors

Basic scientific categories
General basic scientific categories

11/0 Magnitudes in general, space
   1 Number, quantity
   2 Length, width
   3 Height, depth
   4 Content, weight, mass
   5 Shape, limits
   6 Symmetry conditions
   7 Subdivision, structure
   8 Interval, distance
   9 Other magnitudes

12/0 Rhythms in general, time
   1 Rhythms of less than one hour
   2 Rhythms within one hour
   3 Rhythms within one day
   4 Monthly rhythms
   5 Annual rhythms
   6 Rhythms of several years or more
   7 Equilibrium, regulation
   8 Decay, death
   9 Duration

Physical basic scientific categories

13/0 Medium and condition general, and others
   1 Water
   2 Air
   3 Damp
   4 Dry
   5 Solid
   6 Colloidal, mucous
   7 Liquid
   8 Gaseous
   9 Isotope, radioactivity (as a whole phenomenon)

14/0 Mechanical factors in general
   1 Movement, flow
   2 Velocity
   3 Permeability
   4 Vibration, harmonic motion, sound
    (including ultrasonics)
   5 Temperature
   6 Pressure, elasticity
   7 Compactness, viscosity, strength
   8 Surface phenomena
   9 Other mechanical factors

15/0 Energy factors in general
   1 Gravity
   2 Light (including infra-red and ultra-violet)
   3 Color
   4 Polarization
   5 Radiation other than light
   6 Electricity
   7 Electrical conductivity
   8 Magnetism
   9 Other energy factors

Q

Chemical basic scientific categories

Inorganic chemistry

16/0 Inorganic chemical factors: general and others	16/0	17/0 Aluminium
1 Smell, taste	16/0	17/1 Boron
2 Alkalinity, hardness	16/0	17/2 Iron
3 pH and hydrogen	16/0	17/3 Potassium
4 Carbon and CO_2	16/0	17/4 Copper
5 Calcium	16/0	17/5 Magnesium
6 Chlorine	16/0	17/6 Manganese
7 Phosphorus	16/0	17/7 Sodium
8 Oxygen	16/0	17/8 Silicon
9 Sulfur	16/0	17/9 Strontium
11 Nitrogen	16/0	17/12 Zinc

16/12 Complex inorganic compounds

Abridged code for inorganic chemical factors

18/a Arsenic	j Rare gases	s Hafnium
b Barium	k Rare earths	t Indium
c Lead	l Act. protactin.	u Iridium
d Bromium	m Antimony	v Masurium
e Chromium	n Beryllium	w Molybdenum
f Cobalt	o Cadmium	x Niobium
g Fluorine	p Cesium	y Osmium
h Gold	q Gallium	z Palladium
i Iodine	r Germanium	
19/a Lithium	j Polonium	s Thorium
b Nickel	k Rhenium	t Titanium
c Platinum	l Rhodium	u Uranium
d Mercury	m Rubidium	v Vanadium
e Radium	n Ruthenium	w Yttrium
f Selenium	o Scandium	x Zinc
g Silver	p Tantalum	y Zirconium
h Bismuth	q Tellurium	z Transuranium and hitherto
i Tungsten	r Thallium	undiscovered elements

Note: Always punch 16/0 in addition

Within each vertical column of elements as many indications as desired may be combined, provided that *no* indications from either of the other two columns are punched.

Organic chemistry

20/0 Organic chemical factors in general
1 N-free substances: hydrocarbon
2 N-free substances: carbohydrates, etc.
3 N-free substances: fats, waxes, etc.
4 N-containing substances: albumen, etc.
5 Vitamins
6 Hormones
7 Ferments, enzymes
8 Poisons, antibiotics, inhibitives, harmful substances
9 Other organic compounds

Detailed categories in idiobiology

21/0 Digestive system: general and others
1 Oral cavity
2 Teeth
3 Digestive tracts, oesophagus
4 Stomach
5 Small intestine
6 Large intestine and rectum
7 Liver and gall bladder
8 Other glands secreting into the digestive tract
9 Reserve storage

22/0 Urogenital system; general and other
1 Kidney
2 Bladder and urinary tracts
3 External male sexual organs
4 External female sexual organs
5 Internal male sexual organs
6 Internal female sexual organs
7 Hermaphrodite sexual organs
8 Glands secreting into the evacuative tracts
9 Non-sexual reproductive organs

23/0 Defensive and protective system: general and other
1 Envelopment, shell
2 Epidermis, Epithelium
3 General protective organs (hair, nails, etc.)
4 Captive and offensive organs
5 Poison organs
6 Smell organs
7 Electrical and phosphorescent organs
8 Glands secreting externally
9 Pigmenting and coloring organs

24/0 Circulation system: general and other
1 Blood vessels
2 Blood, serum
3 Lymphatic vessels
4 Other kinds of animal systems
5 Vascular channels of plants
6 Heart
7 Spleen
8 Glands secreting internally into the blood
9 Red marrow, bone marrow

25/0 Supporting system in general
1 Skull
2 Shoulder, fore extremities
3 Pelvis, hind extremities
4 Spine and ribs
5 Bones, cartilage
6 Other ligaments
7 External supporting skeleton
8 Plant stalks, stems
9 Other

26/0 Movement system in general
1 Muscles
2 Tendons, ligaments
3 Joints
4 Fixing organs
5 Stabilizing organs
6 Running organs
7 Swimming organs
8 Flying organs
9 Other

27/0 Sensory system; general and other
1 Sense of smell
2 Sense of taste
3 Sense of light
4 Sense of temperature
5 Sense of flow
6 Sense of touch and pain
7 Sense of weight and equilibrium
8 Sense of hearing (including ultra-sonic)
9 Sense of position, muscle, space, vibration, depth
12 Sense of time

28/0 Breathing system: general and other
1 Nose and throat
2 Wind pipes
3 Larynx
4 Bronchiae
5 Lungs

28/6 Nervous system: general and other
7 Brain, ganglia nodes
8 Spinal marrow
9 Nerves

Detailed categories in cenobiology

Bioses

29/0 Metabolism relations: general and other
1 Symbiosis (on organisms) and commensalism

2 Metabolic symbiosis
3 Parasitism (also parasitic diseases)
4 Feeding relations

29/5 Reproductive relations: general and other
  6 Sexual relations (within the species)
  7 Fertilizing relations (between different species)
  8 Descendant relations (with own descendants)
  9 Care for descendants (with the aid of other species)

30/0 Social relations: general
  1 Swarming, herding
  2 States, peoples
  3 Colonies
  4 Ranking
  5 Competition, conflicts
  6 Protective relations
  7 Domestication, service
  8 Other social relations

30/9 Expansive relations

Cenoses

31/0 Sea: general and other
  1 High seas and coastal zone
  2 Deep sea
  3 Shallows

31/4 Inland waters: general and other
  5 Groundwater, springs
  6 Wells
  7 Flowing waters
  8 Standing waters
  9 Small waters and phytothelmae
  12 Snow, ice

32/0 Land: general and other
  1 Forest
  2 Open country other than desert
  3 Deserts
  4 Heath
  5 Cultivated land
  6 Island
  7 Mountain, ⎤ with 32/0 on land
    hill   ⎮
  8 Valley,   ⎬ with 31/0 or
    depression ⎮   31/4 under water
  9 Cave   ⎦

33/0 Air space: general and other
  1 Air strata close to the ground
  2 Sea level zone
  3 Medium zone (medium mountains)
  4 Upper zone (high mountains)
  5 Troposphere
  6 Lower stratosphere and ozone layer
  7 Upper stratosphere
  8 Ionosphere
  9 Outer atmospheric strata

34/0 Substratum: general and other
  1 Suspensions
  2 Sediment
  3 Ground
  4 Rock
  5 Surface layer, boundary layer
  6 Free space, pelagial
  7 Underground, benthos
  8 Dead organisms
  9 Artificial living environments

Terrestrial holocoon (geography)

35/0 The earth as a whole
  1 Arctic and antarctic zone
  2 Temperate zone
  3 Subtropics
  4 Tropics
  5 Pacific Ocean
  6 Atlantic Ocean
  7 Indian Ocean
  8 Arctic waters
  9 Antarctic waters

36/0 Europe
  1 Asia
  2 Africa
  3 Australia
  4 North America
  5 Central America
  6 South America
  7 Greenland and Arctic
  8 Antarctic
  9 Islands in Pacific Ocean

Hierarchical further subdivisions

37/0 Europe general
  1 Scandinavia, Denmark, Finland
  2 Lithuania, Latvia, Esthonia
  3 Soviet Union (in Europe), Poland
  4 Balkans

  5 Italy, Switzerland, Austria
  6 Spain, Portugal
  7 France, Benelux
  8 Great Britain, Ireland, Iceland
  9 Germany

38/0 Germany: general
   1 Schleswig-Holstein, Mecklenburg, Pommerania
   2 East Prussia, Danzig, Memel
   3 Brandenburg
   4 Silesia
   5 Bavaria, Württemberg
   6 Baden, Palatinate
   7 Rhine Province
   8 Westphalia, Oldenburg, Hannover
   9 Saxony, Anhalt, Thuringia, Hesse, Hesse-Nassau

Use of the spare columns—Columns 39 to 43 are intended for the major groups in this object system which can all be coded together—see below.

Columns 44 to 45 also are spare. These provide the possibility for further subdividing any of the concepts in the system of properties. In the case of the even-numbered columns this subdivision is always by way of hole No. 12 in column 44 and in the case of the odd-numbered columns by way of hole No. 11 in column 45. For each publication only *one* further subdivided concept in an even-numbered column and *one* in an odd-numbered column may be used in addition to as many basic concepts as desired.

In a column used for the further subdivision of a concept, any other concepts besides this which have lower line numbers may also be marked (the 0 being counted as 10) but concepts with higher line numbers must not be marked.

In practice a further subdivision takes the form which may be exemplified as follows. If standing waters are to be subdivided into natural lakes, lakes retained by dams, ponds and ditches, then besides being punched 31/8 they may be marked and punched 31/11 to show that a further subdivision of the contents of this column follows in the spare column 45, and the latter can be punched according to a supplementary code for 'standing waters', subdividing the concept in question as 45/1 natural lakes, 45/2 lakes retained by dams, 45/3 ponds, 45/4 ditches.

II. Notation and Code for Objects

   2/11 New descriptions
   7/12 Trial organisms

Semaphorontes

39/0 Nuclear cells (ovum, sperm)
   1 Fertilized ovum, non-sexual spores, embryo, seeds of plants
   2 First state
   3 Second state
   4 Third state (chrysalis)
   5 Fourth state (imago, adult)
   6 Polymorphisms, varieties within the species
   7 Non-inheritable adaptations, modifications
   8 Diseases, anomalies
   9 Male
  12 Female

Major groups in the object system

Hierarchic notation	(All usable in combination)	Code for punching pattern	Hierarchic notation	(All usable in combination)	Code for punching pattern
S	Organisms		M 5	Ctenophora	30/11
A	Plants		—	Platyhelminthes	32/11
B 1	Schizomycetes	12/11	N 4	Nemertini	37/12
B 1	Bacteria	12/11	N 5	Rotatoria	33/12
C 1	Cyanophyceae	13/12	N 6	Gastrotricha	34/11
C 1	Schizophyceae	13/12	N 6	Kinorhyncha	34/11
C 2	Phytoflagellata	40/11	N 8	Nematodes	35/12
K 1	Zooflagellata		N 7	Nematomorpha	36/11
C 2–	Dinoflagellata	40/0	N 6	Acanthocephali	36/11
C 2–	Silicoflagellata	40/1	N 4	Entoprocta	37/12
C 9	Heterocontae	15/12	N 9	Annelida	38/11
C 3	Chlorophyceae	40/2	O 1, 2	Malacopoda	43/1
C 3–	Protococcales	40/2	O 3	Crustacea	
C 3–	Ulotrichales	40/3	O 3–	Trilobita	43/2
C 3–	Siphonocladiales	40/3	O 3–	Phyllopoda	43/3
C 3–	Siphonales	40/3	O 3–	Ostracoda	43/4
C 4	Conjugatae	41/11	O 3	Branchiura	43/5
C 4–	Desmidiales	41/12	O 3–	Copepoda	43/5
C 4	Zygnemales	41/11	O 3–	Cirripedia	43/6
C 5	Charophyta	24/11	O 3–	Malacostraca	43/7
C 6	Bacillariophyta	37/11	O 6	Arachnomorpha	43/8
C 7	Phaeophyceae	9/12	O 5	Linguatulida	43/9
C 8	Rhodophyceae	17/11	O 5	Pantopoda	43/9
D 5	Lichenes	8/11	O 8	Myriapoda	38/12
D 3	Eumycetes	20/11	O 8	Chilopoda	38/12
D 1	Myxomycetes	14/11	O 8	Apterygogenea	38/12
F	Pteridophyta	21/12	O 9	Insecta	
E	Bryophyta		O 9	Orthoptera	42/12
E 1	Hepaticae	41/0	O 9–	Thysanoptera	42/11
E 2	Musci	41/1	O 9–	Corrodentia	42/12
G	Gymnospermae	22/11	O 9–	Embidaria	42/11
G 1	Cycadofilicales	22/11	O 9–	Plecoptera	42/0
G 2	Cycadales	22/11	O 9–	Odonata	42/1
G 3	Bennettitales	22/11	O 9–	Ephemeroidea	42/2
G 4	Ginkgoales	22/11	O 9–	Neuroptera	42/3
G 5	Cordaitales	22/11	O 9–	Panorpatae	42/11
G 6	Coniferae	22/11	O 9–	Trichoptera	42/4
G 7	Gnetales	22/11	O 9–	Lepidoptera	42/5
H 4	Monocotyledoneae	40/4	O 9–	Diptera	42/6
H 2	Archichlamydeae	40/5	O 9–	Aphaniptera	42/11
H 1	Dialypetalae	40/6	O 9–	Coleoptera	42/7
H 3	Sympetalae	40/6	O 9–	Strepsiptera	42/11
T	Viruses	11/12	O 9–	Hymenoptera	42/8
J	Animals		O 9–	Rhynchota	42/9
K	Protozoa		P 2	Amphineura	41/7
K	Rhizopoda	40/7	P 3	Gastropoda	41/8
K 6	Sporozoa	40/8	P 1	Solenoconchae	41/7
K 7	Cytoidea	40/9	P 5	Lamellibranchiata	41/9
K 7	Ciliata	40/9	P 6	Cephalopoda	41/7
L 3	Planuloidea	36/12	P 7	Tentaculata	23/12
L	Spongiaria	36/12	Q 3	Enteropneusta	23/12
M	Cnidaria	29/12	Q	Echinoderma	25/12

Hier-archic notation	(All usable in combination)	Code for punching pattern	Hier-archic notation	(All usable in combination)	Code for punching pattern
Q	Chaetognatha	23/12	R 6	Rhynchocephalia	41/4
R 1	Tunicata	26/11	R 6–	Testudinata	41/4
R 2	Acrania	26/11	R 6–	Crocodilia	41/5
R 3	Cyclostomata	44/11	R 6–	Squamata	41/6
R 4	Pisces	44/11	R 7	Aves	45/12
R 5	Amphibia		R 8	Mammalia	
R 5–	Stegocephali	41/2	R 8	Monotremata	43/0
R 5–	Gymnophiona	41/3	R 8	Marsupialia	43/0
R 5	Urodela	41/2	R 8–	Placentalia	43/11
R 5	Anura	41/3	R 8–	Hominidae	43/12
R 6	Reptilia				

<u>Hierarchical subdivision of the object system</u>

(The subdivision extends only to species)

General subdivision

Column 46	Division	(Letter notation)
Column 47	Class	(Numeral notation)
Column 48	Order	(Letter notation)
Column 49/50	Family	(Numeral notation)
Column 51/52	Genus	(Numeral and letter notation)
Column 53/54	Species	(Numeral and letter notation)

<u>Special notations and codes</u>

(Here extending only to classes)

Division (Column 46)

<u>12 = Plants</u>   <u>11 = Animals</u>   <u>0 = Organisms in general</u>

A = Plants in general	J = Animals in general	S = Organisms in general
B = Bacteria	K = Protozoa	T = Viruses
C = Algae	L = Spongiae und Planuloidea	
D = Fungi and Lichens	M = Coelenterata	
E = Bryophyta	N = Vermes	
F = Pteridophyta	O = Arthropoda	
G = Gymnospermae	P = Molluscs and Tentaculata	
H = Angiospermae		

Q = { Echinodermata, Enteropneusta, Chaetognatha

R = Chordata

<u>Classes (Column 47)</u>

B 1 = Bacteria	D 1 = Myxomycetes
C 1 = Cyanophyceae	2 = Phycomycetes
2 = Phytoflagellata	3 = Eumycetes
3 = Chlorophyceae	4 = Fungi imperfecti
4 = Conjugatae	5 = Lichens
5 = Charophyta	
6 = Bacillariophyta	E 1 = Hepaticae
7 = Phaeophyceae	2 = Musci
8 = Rhodophyceae	
9 = Heterocontae	F 1 = Psilophytinae
	2 = Lycodiinae

F 3 = Psilotinae
   4 = Equisetinae
   5 = Filicinae

G 1 = Pteridospermae
   2 = Cycadinae
   3 = Bennetittinae
   4 = Ginkgoinae
   5 = Cordaitinae
   6 = Coniferae
   7 = Gnetinae

H 1 = Dialypetalae
   2 = Monochlamydeae
   3 = Sympetalae
   4 = Monocotyledoneae

K 1 = Zooflagellata
   2 = Amoeba
   3 = Foraminifera
   4 = Heliozoa
   5 = Radiolaria
   6 = Sporozoa
   7 = Ciliata
   8 = Suctoria

L 1 = Calcispongia
   2 = Siliceratospongia
   3 = Planuloidea

M 1 = Hydrozoa
   2 = Scyphozoa
   3 = Anthozoa
   4 = Conularida
   5 = Ctenophora

N 1 = Turbellaria
   2 = Trematoda
   3 = Cestoidea
   4 = Nemertini, Entoprocta
   5 = Rotatoria

N 6 = Gastrotricha,
     Kinorrhycha,
     Acanthocephala
   7 = Nematomorpha
   8 = Nematodes
   9 = Annelida

O 1 = Onychophora
   2 = Tardigrada
   3 = Crustacea
   4 = Gigantostraca,
     Xiphosura
   5 = Pantopoda,
     Linguatulida
   6 = Arachnoidea
   7 = Symphyla, Pauropoda
   8 = Diplopoda, Chilopoda,
     Apterygogenea
   9 = Insects

P 1 = Solenogastres
   2 = Placophora
   3 = Gastropoda
   4 = Scaphopoda
   5 = Lamellibranchiata
   6 = Cephalopoda
   7 = Tentaculata

Q 1 = Pelmatozoa
   2 = Eleuterozoa
   3 = Enteropneusta

R 1 = Tunicata
   2 = Acrania
   3 = Cyclostomata
   4 = Pisces
   5 = Amphibia
   6 = Reptilia
   7 = Aves
   8 = Mammalia

III. Notation for Sources

Sources include any of the following:

(1) Periodicals
(2) Books (monographs) and non-periodical collective works
(3) Unprinted academic dissertations and theses at all levels
(4) Other

Each of these kinds of sources is denoted by a five-place number or letter group.

(1) For periodicals this number consists entirely of numerals, each periodical being given a running number which is always to be filled up with zeros. Precise indication of the individual work is given by the page number.

(2) For books and collective works, sources are indicated by the letter A followed by numerals in the remaining four places. Each publisher is assigned a number and the zeros are always to be written in. The books issued by each publisher within each year are denoted by 'volume numbers' in columns 70 to 72. In a normal bibliographical reference the page number is necessary only for collective works.

(3) Dissertations and the like are denoted by the letter B followed by numerals to fill up the remaining places in the source indication. Each university is assigned a running number and the zeros are always to be written in. Within each university, each year, the individual works are denoted by 'volume numbers' in columns 70 to 72 in the order they occur. In a normal bibliographical reference no page number is necessary.

(4) In accordance with requirements.

Source Cards

(1) Cards for periodicals
Subdivisions (according to the German standard *DIN 1503*)

Running number	Title of periodical
(Source number only)	Abbreviated titles of periodicals as in *DIN 1502*
	Publisher and place of publication
	Sponsor (H.), editor (Sch.)
	How issued.

Cards for (2) and (3) are reproduced automatically from the photographic contact-printing card.

IV. *Notation for Informational Characteristics*

Extent

0 = One page or less
1 = More than one but not more than three pages inclusive
2 = More than three but not more than five pages inclusive
3 = 6 to 10 pages
4 = 11 to 20 pages
5 = 21 to 50 pages
6 = 51 to 100 pages
7 = 101 to 200 pages
8 = 201 to 500 pages
9 = over 500 pages

Number of bibliographical citations

0 = 0
1 = 1
2 = 2 to 5
3 = 6 to 10
4 = 11 to 15
5 = 16 to 20
6 = 21 to 30
7 = 31 to 50
8 = 51 to 100
9 = 100 to 200 and over 200.

Where there are over 200 bibliographical citations, 'Bibliography' (1/6) is to be punched in the properties system also.

C. *Instructions for Plugboard Connections, I. Card Reproducer (mark-sensing automatic punch)*

Connections 1: Front of mark-sensing card
Marking columns 1–27 on
Punching columns 1–27 connected (without check)

Connections 2: Back of mark-sensing card
Marking columns 1–27 on
Punching columns 28–54 connected (without check)

Connections 3: Direct copying of all 80 columns with check of columns 46–80 where not multiple-punched.

II. Card Collator

Connections 1: for searching multiple-digit numbers on both card units (searching for hierarchically subdivided objects)
Columns 46–54

Numerical: Columns 47, 49, 50
Alphabetical: Columns 46, 48, 51, 52, 53, 54

Connections 2: for searching multiple-digit numbers on both card units (searching by author's name)
Columns 55–64 (alphabetical).

III. Punch-to-print Interpreter

Connections 1: Normal punch-to-print translation on line 2

Punching columns on	55 – 63	64	65 – 69	70 – 72	73 – 74	75 – 78	79	80
printing positions	1 – 9	11	13 – 17	19 – 21	23 – 24	26 – 29	31	33

Punching columns on	46	47	48	49 – 50	51 – 52	53 – 54
printing positions	35	37	39	41 – 42	44 – 45	46 – 47

Additional punching columns on	65 – 69	73 – 74	75 – 78
printing positions	49 – 53	55 – 56	57 – 60

IV. Tabulator

Connections 1: Printing of bibliographical lists

Punching columns on	55 – 63	64	65 – 69	70 – 72	73 – 74	75 – 78	79	80
printing positions	1 – 9	11	15 – 19	23 – 25	29 – 30	34 – 37	42	44

Punching columns on	46	47	48	49 – 50	51 – 52	53 – 54
printing positions	49	51	54	56 – 57	60 – 61	63 – 64

Observations on the reference card system for biology and physiography—Be it remarked, first of all, that obviously the classification and method of referencing here described cannot be and are not claimed as the only possible solution. Unfortunately, there is no such thing as an ideal system without any weak points or disadvantages. As already fully explained, the system here described is the outcome of several years work. Above all, it is not a system built in the air but one which has been tried out in practice and organically evolved on the basis of the experience so obtained. In a separate major tome (*Literaturanalyse des Archivs für Hydrobiologie*, Scheele, 1958 c) it is shown to work well and to be fully capable of meeting the demands made upon a modern referencing method using punch-cards. It is not, however, only in limnology that the system has been tried out. On the contrary, as an experiment, all the research papers embodied in five annual reports of the Deutsche Forschungsgemeinschaft relating to the fields of biology, geography, geology, medicine, agriculture and forestry were systematically gone through and coded; these included over 4000 titles, and provide indisputably a complete cross section of all conceivable subjects of research to which our code extends.

Should any reader of this book himself intend to introduce and apply the system which has here been described in detail, I would strongly advise him to take it over as it stands and not make any more changes. In it the relations between basic scientific theory along with technical requirements on the one hand, and the necessity for the successive working stages within the field of documentation on the other, have been hammered out and tried in practice one by one, so that any further change must inevitably upset the balance and work to the detriment of the whole. Finally, the user needs continually to be reminded not to expect more from the punch-card method than it is capable of yielding. This point has already been stressed here many times. If too much is demanded, and it is sought inexorably to free the method from even the very last little esthetic blemish, it becomes irrational and ends by failing to meet its own purpose. Sooner or later a point in the development is reached when a halt must be called to changing and improving, for otherwise the experiment has no end and there is no sense in it.

The considerations which have played a part at each state in bringing the system to its definitive form will now be reviewed in detail.

(i) *Nomenclature and terminology.* The system is based on concepts, not on names or terms; that is to say, it is founded on the *meanings* of the names and terms. This principle secures it a great advantage over the Uniterm system in that it is independent of the languages used and in that it also enables the synonyms which exist in a language to be circumvented. The various designations applied, for instance, to the breathing organs of various organisms (lungs, gills, trachea, etc.) are here brought together at a single and definite punching position. As it was not possible, for reasons purely of convenience, to list every possible designation alongside each place in the coding tables those designations of biological objects which people most often apply to them have been preferred; but in a separate list, which for lack of space is not reproduced here, all the technical expressions that relate to this field of work are arranged in alphabetical order so as to constitute a kind of special dictionary or key to the system. This can be consulted whenever there is any lack of clarity or any doubt as to the proper place to code any particular expression. The whole system is consistently divided into two systems, respectively for objects (denoted by names) and for properties (denoted by terms) The conceptualization associated with terms is regulated here from the point of view of function, as has already been fully explained in Chapter 5.

(ii) *Classification.* In collecting the chosen basic concepts along particular dimensions, advantage was taken of the fact that the technical peculiarities of the IBM system bring with them certain possibilities for grouping:

From the mechanical standpoint, punching columns have an advantage over punching lines—on this matter see Part I. For this reason, it is always within columns that the groups have been constructed (Example: column 28: Breathing system and nervous system). Wherever a branch of the classification requires more than one column the hole which represents the appropriate higher collective concept is always additionally punched in the other columns. Taking an example from inorganic chemistry (16/0), this ensures that any works referring to chemical factors can be selected in a single run.

The method here described takes account both of the principle of separating objects from properties and of the basic rule that wherever possible each fundamental concept is to be brought in only once. Thereby a very small number of fundamental concepts has been enabled to cover an extraordinarily wide range of scientific expressions, often extending into specialized divisions of the subject matter handled. The classification as reproduced, which lies at the basis of the whole system, is closely related to the attempt to establish a true scientific system of biology and physiography on which the author is at present engaged. That system, and the classification here set forth, have the property that any given convergences of concepts which otherwise might later give rise to particular difficulties in coding appear as independent dimensions. For instance, all relations of particular organisms to particular environmental factors are regarded as forming a special stage of organization within the framework of cenobiology (10/0 or 10/4: organism + environmental factor). Indeed, the whole field of cenobiology serves to express special relationships. Thus the classification system from its very nature eliminates immediately the difficulty that arises in expressing such relations by way of a complicated notation or codification.

It is not possible, within the limits of this book, to explain and comment on every detail of the system and its construction. That task must be left over for a separate publication, the first short summaries of which have already appeared elsewhere (Scheele, 1955b and 1956d).

(iii) *Notation.* For the purposes of the hierarchical object system, the bibliographical indications and the informational characteristics it has been found desirable to introduce a separate notation. The construction of this has already been described in detail. In the object system neither the underlying classification nor the notation built up on this follow quite consistently the natural system of the organisms. There are two reasons for this. In the first place the natural system, expressing as it does the present state of our knowledge, is always fluid and the very nature of our subject makes it impossible to crystallize it out in any definitive and generally

valid shape; but for our purpose in documentation such definitive formulation is necessary. Secondly, the natural system comprises too many
categories, whose orderly reproduction on the punch-cards would take up
too much space. This has been clearly shown by extensive experiment.

These considerations have led to a fully satisfactory compromise. Relying
to a very large extent on the most used groups in the natural system, a
classification and notation have been built up which on the one hand allow
no possibility of misundertanding and on the other hand provide a stable
system, which moreover takes up the smallest possible amount of space on the
punch-cards. Notation and coding are to a great extent mutually determined. For the whole of the properties system, any notation has been
shown to be an unnecessary detour, so this has been obviated.

(iv) *Primary recording*. This does not arise here.

(v) *Documentation*. The whole system here described is a method of
referencing for that branch of documentation which aims comprehensively
to survey those sciences which relate to the earth and to life. Whilst the
classification system which underlies this converges as far as possible with
the systematics of scientific theory, it has been completely adapted to the
practice of reference documentation. It can, therefore, also be used as
a stage on the way, or as a springboard, in various other directions such as
evaluative documentation and the documentation of results; but in the form
here presented it is *not* suited to those purposes.

After documentation based on bare titles and on abstracts had been tried
and neither of these bases had been found suitable, a referencing system
dependent on documentation by means of keywords (indications of contents)
in accordance with the German standard *DIN 1426* was adopted. It has
become more and more apparent that this is just what is best suited for the
application of punch-card methods. Thereby it becomes possible to set
out the punching instructions appropriate to each single publication in the
form of a 'guide' or standard form corresponding to the build-up of
the classification system in which the documentalist concerned can enter the
appropriate keywords so that these may then be coded directly by using the
'punching pattern method' and be transferred to the punch-cards without
the intervention of any notation. Conversely, the reference cards (Fig. 41)
which can be supplied to the customer enable the keywords to be read off
the punch-cards directly, with the aid of the code, by a very simple method
as described on page 224.

(vi) *Secondary recording*. Since the organization of recording and retrieval
of information by the use of punch-cards has already been discussed it will
be enough here to add a few general remarks.

The first point to be made is that after various other experiments a combination of photographic contact printing with punch-cards was adopted.
The original idea had been to punch the whole of the bibliographical
indications, including the full titles, into the cards themselves, and thereafter
use the punch-to-print interpreter and tabulating machine for reading them
off. In order to meet this requirement the 'contents card' for each publica-

tion was supplemented by two alphabetical cards to carry the bibliographical text, coupled to the contents card by means of a 'coupling number' (which was the same as the publication number). This method, however, proved unsuitable from many points of view (here see Chapter 10), its main disadvantage arising from non-observance of the principle that wherever possible only one punch-card should be used for each 'working unit'. There being three cards instead of one, a card mixing machine had to be interposed entailing three additional runs. A further disadvantage lay in the fact that the two alphabetical cards which carried the continuous text had always to be kept together and, therefore, could be sorted out only in accordance with aspects which had been punched in both of them (and in the same positions). As an example, if it were required to make the tabulating machine print out a list of titles arranged in the alphabetical order of authors' names a preliminary alphabetical sorting run was necessary and this could be carried out only when the authors' names were punched in the same position on both of the alphabetical cards—or, at least, if the second card had as many letters of the name punched in that position as were necessary for the sorting, which meant, in our experience, at least eight letters. Of course this disadvantage becomes still greater when more than two alphabetical cards have to be used to accommodate the continuous text. This brings us to the final disadvantage of the method originally adopted: by reason of the conditions governing the punch-to-print interpreter, a total of at most 120 letters or numerals can be punched in the two cards, including the necessary spaces between words, etc. For long titles this is not enough, so they have to be abbreviated which can lead to misunderstandings and which users do not like.

All these experiences and considerations led to the decision that the punch-card method should be used in accordance with its own main advantages, that is primarily for sorting and selecting rather than for the printing or reproduction of continuous text. This latter purpose is taken over by the photographic contact printing system which is particularly well adapted to it and which meanwhile has been further developed in a direction particularly advantageous here, in that a transparent card material has become available for use as a contact printing negative, which we have adopted.

Our system, therefore, now comprises keyword indications of both properties and objects, additional notations for objects, the most important bibliographical indications and two informational characteristics—all these brought together in a single punch-card with the possibility, at any time, of referring back via the publication number to the negative which can be reproduced by contact printing and its contents thereby made available to the user. If, therefore, the indications given on the punch-card are not in themselves sufficient to the user, he can always ask for a copy of a complete card containing the full title of the publication in question (Fig. 39).

In the absence of fuller experience, it can be assumed from a rough calculation that this device of combining the punch-card method with contact printing is the most efficient, but more accurate costing must await experiment on a larger scale.

The following considerations govern the choice of the indications to be incorporated in an IBM card:

(*1*) The whole of the properties and objects systems must always be given. For this purpose all available positions in the mark-sensing cards are used (columns 1–54). Here the punch-card may be regarded as a system of coordinates in which the x values correspond to the column numbers and the y values to the line numbers (see Fig. 33). In the code it is best to print the x values first, followed by the y values, so that, for instance, 17/2 means column 17, line 2.

(*2*) The remaining 26 columns are so arranged that the bibliographical indications follow as far as possible the order laid down in the German standard *DIN 1505*, but here certain concessions to the technical principle now firmly grounded in the punch-card process are unavoidable:

(*a*) Authors' names which have more than nine letters cannot be completely punched. In practice, however, the identification of an author by nine letters of his surname and the initial of one given name is enough to prevent any confusion when accompanied by the other bibliographical indications. This is enough also for alphabetical listing.

(*b*) On one card it is possible to mention only one author. If the publication mentions several authors, the first is named or, if it is considered essential to mention all of them, a corresponding number of cards must be provided. The fact of there being several authors is indicated by an asterisk in the column provided for the initial of a given name which, in that case, cannot be given.

(*c*) For the indication of sources, a special numerical notation has been found best as there is not room on the cards to give them in clear language. Apart from this, the indirect way of using a notation (see page 235) enables the sources to be much more accurately indicated than is possible by punching them in the card.

(*d*) The indications of volume, year and page number can be directly punched in the cards. These provide every loan library with a uniform means of reference to publications (in accordance with the German standard *DIN 1505*). By the elimination of the running number—sometimes called a 'telephone number'—and the incorporation in its place of the page number the card has been given still greater indicative possibility.

(*e*) It was a difficult question to decide what informational characteristics should be indicated on the punch-card in order to provide the user of a punch-to-print interpreted card with the maximum amount of information. Even with the greatest economy, only two columns were left available for these characteristics. It seemed necessary always to indicate the extent of the publication because, on the same grounds of economy, only the initial page number can be given. The first of these two columns has, therefore, been reserved for showing the number of pages and the second for the number of literature citations. It is, of course, open to argument whether this decision was right, or whether it would have been better to indicate, for instance, the number of illustrations or the language used, but the author is of the opinion that the number of literature citations in a publication is a particularly important piece of information.

Finally, a few examples will now be given to show how the code works, in which it is assumed for simplicity, except in the last example, that the title accurately indicates the contents in each case.

Example 1: Nervous control of the clotting of the blood in man.
Object system: Homo sapiens

Among the large groups (punching pattern)	. . . . .	43/12
Hierarchical subdivision:	. . . .	R8 D17 02 05
Properties system		
General:	main subject biology	1/1
Method:	—	
Time period:	present	3/9
Field of science:	main subject physiology (idiobiology, theory of data, antecedents)	4/0 4/2
Stage of organization:	tissue	7/0
Magnitudes, rhythms, physics, chemistry:	—	
Functional system:	blood, nerves	24/2 28/9
Bioses:	—	
Cenoses:	—	
Geography:	—	

The subdivision does not extend as far as 'clotting', but this publication will now be retrieved if searched for under any of the keywords mentioned above, or in any of their possible combinations.

Example: all works relating to
        (a) the blood of animals
        (b) the blood of mammals
        (c) physiology of tissues in man
        (d) interplay of nerves and blood in mammals
        (e) tissues in recent animals, etc., etc.
        (These examples are not systematically put together.)

By reason of the way the classification has been grafted on to the IBM technique this publication will, however, also be retrieved if searched for under the appropriate higher collective contents (idiobiology, circulation system, nervous system). It can be seen even from this simple example, containing only a few parameters, how very flexible the punching pattern method is by reason of the fact that any concepts can be freely joined to any others.

Example 2: Investigations into the morphology and evolutionary physiology of sperms in anthropoid apes.

Object system:	Summo-primates	
Major group:	Placentals	43/11
Hierarchical subdivision:	. . . .	R 8 D 16
Semaphorontes:	nuclear cells	39/0
	male	39/9
Properties system:		
General:	main subject biology	1/1
Method:	—	—
Time period:	Present	3/9
Field of science:	main subject morphology	4/0 4/1
	(idiobiology, theory of data, structure) and evolutionary physiology	
	(idiobiology, ontogenetics, antecedents) .	4/11 4/2
Stage of organization:	whole organism	8/0

Magnitude, rhythms, physics, chemistry —
Functional system: —
Bioses: —
Cenoses: —
Geography: —

Example 3: Development of the course of the river Main and historical evolution of the
Main valley since the miocene age.

Object system:	—	
Properties system:		
General:	main subject physiography . . .	1/2
Method:	—	
Time period:	Tertiary, quaternary	3/8 3/9
Field of science:	main subject: cenobiological evolutionary history (cenobiology, ontogenetics, structure)	5/11 5/1
Stage of organization:	main subject: cenoses	10/2
Magnitudes, rhythms, physics, chemistry:	—	
Functional system:	—	
Bioses:	—	
Cenoses:	Flowing water, valley	31/7 32/8
Geography:	Temperate zone, Europe	35/2 36/0
	Germany, Hesse	37/9 38/9

Example 4: (Contents are wider than the title indicates.)
The phytoplankton of the Seeburger lake and autecology of the plankton
organisms.

Object system:	Cyanophyceae, Dinoflagellata, Protococcales Desmidiales, Bacillariophyta	
Major groups:	(as above)	13/12 40/0 40/2 41/12 37/11
Hierarchical subdivision:	C	
Properties system:		
General:	main subject biology . . .	1/1
	minor subject physiography . .	1/4
Method:	new apparatus for preparation of plankton	2/4 2/8
Time period:	present	3/9
Field of science:	main subject cenobiology, theory of data, structure	5/0 5/1
Stage of organization:	main subject cenoses. Minor subject organism + environmental factor	10/2 10/4
Magnitudes, rhythms, physics, chemistry:		
	temperature	14/5
	alkalinity, pH	16/2 16/3
	chlorine, phosphorus, sulfur . .	16/6 16/7 16/9
	nitrogen	16/11
Functional system:		
Bioses:	—	
Cenoses:	Stagnant water, suspensions . .	31/8 34/1
Geography:	Temperate zone, Europe . .	35/2 36/0
	Germany, Hannover (Lower Saxony)	37/9 38/8

(4) MEDICINE (using Needle Punch-Cards)

(From Raettig, 1953.)   'As there are practically unlimited possibilities for
constructing numerical subject codes, and as every freedom must be allowed
to each scientist within his special field of research, it would be pointless to

R

set down here a complete coding system and still more so to imply that it was binding.   I shall merely illustrate by an example those general principles that should be observed in constructing such a code which have worked well in practice.

(*1*) The simplest way of designating a subject content on an edge-notched card is to utilize pairs of holes for a 'yes-no' indication, as appears in the top right corner of the example where shallow notching indicates that the work in question is available in the indexer's own collection, deep notching that it is held in the library he uses.   It is important that deep and shallow notching in any given position should indicate compatible answers to the same question, for when this pair of holes is needled the deep-notched cards fall out as well as the shallow-notched.   This is logical because it implies, in the present instance, nothing more than that the original text can quickly be obtained somewhere within the building.   In similar fashion any other kinds of indications may be marked, such as works containing extensive literature citations, those which are especially important, etc.

(*2*) It is of practical value to punch the year of publication, as it frequently happens that only very recent works are of interest.   Apart from this, the cards can be then sorted according to years, which I found useful in my own work.

(*3*) Next I have inserted a two-digit main concept.   In a separate code which can enumerate a maximum of 100 different keywords (numbered from 00 to 99), I have provided places for those concepts which serve also as main headings for major subdivisions in the abstracts card index previously maintained.   This makes it possible to carry out a preliminary sorting of the cards such as often is desirable, and should it turn out after the passage of some years that the three-digit code for detailed contents—see (*4*)—no longer is quantitatively sufficient the whole collection of cards can be split into two or more parts.

(*4*) Following this, on my edge-notched cards, come five three-digit fields wherein five indications of subject contents can be punched.   If still larger numbers of subject contents are desired, two cards are provided, thus making it possible to indicate ten subject contents.

(*5*) It is desirable to allocate a definite punching field to each suitable range of subject contents.   For instance, I have always punched 'infectious diseases' in field '1. Subject contents', so that when searching for any given infectious disease I need only search this particular field.   As, however, it often happens that several infectious diseases are discussed in the same publication I must indicate that fact by marking a guide hole in such cards. (See the top left corner of the card, Fig. 43.)   In all cards which are notched at this guide hole I must also needle the other punching fields if it is a particular infectious disease that I am searching for.

(*6*) It is important to reserve some unused holes on the card, as shown in our example, so as to be able to meet further punching requirements which may arise later.

(7) Finally, it has been found desirable to indicate how many subject contents have been punched—see the top of the vertical right hand side of the code card in Fig. 43.   This saves a lot of work in sorting, as it avoids unnecessary searching of those punching fields, other than '1. Subject contents', in which only one subject content has been punched.   For this reason, I arrange the edge-notched cards by years—see (2) above—and, within each year, according to the number of subject contents which have been punched in them.

The part of the work which is specially important, and needs much time spent on it, is the establishment of the code.   This work, however, has only

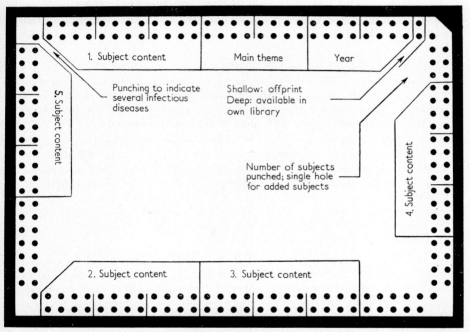

FIG. 43.   Edge-notched card with coding indications (mainly 7, 4, 2, 1 code) (Raettig, 1953). (From *Nachr. Dok.*, v. 4, n. 4.)

to be done once and it pays dividends over many years in the great advantages which an edge-notched card collection supplies. If it has been decided to start such a collection of cards and one is confronted with the problem of making a code it is a good idea to keep a list, for some months, of the kind of contents found in relevant publications which are useful for one's own scientific work or may become so, for which places should be provided. When it is believed that all the necessary subject headings have been collected in this way, they should next be scrutinized to make sure that they are conceptually clear and mutually exclusive. When this important preparatory work has been accomplished, the subject contents can be arranged in a suitable order and arranged as a code.

(*i*) First of all the scope of the code must be decided upon in accordance with the number of subject heads to be included.   My own work calls for a three-place code, as preliminary sorting had needed 600 subject headings and meanwhile the total had grown to nearly 800.   My work will not need more than 1000 and I think that total should generally be enough for the work of any individual scientist.   One hundred headings (represented in a two-figure code) will usually not be enough whereas 10000 (needing a four-figure code) are too many for any individual to control.

(*ii*) It is important not to fill up a code too much at the start, but to leave a sufficiency of numbers unoccupied as a reserve.   Thus, in our present example, one whole hundred-group of (800–899) is left free, and apart from this enough gaps had been left among the tens and units (for instance 028 and 029) to be able to accommodate a subject contents which may arise later.

(*iii*) It is a good plan to put certain content groups together.   Thus I have assigned a main subject to every hundredth place in my field of specialization; for instance, all the numbers from 400 to 499 relate to virus research.   Here care must be taken that 100 subdivisions of a main subject like this are enough; if not, they must be further subdivided.

(*iv*) Within each subject group, a number must be provided for 'general' and another number for 'other'.   Thus 020 serves to take up all works which refer quite generally to methods of staining or preparing bacteria, or which describe comparative investigations carried out by several methods. Under 'other', as for instance under 069, those publications are fitted in which describe a special influence exerted on bacteria, not provided for in the range 061 to 068.   This provision is necessary in order to be able to fit in absolutely any publication that may arise.

(*v*) There are large works which give a bird's eye view over so great a range of subject contents that it is impossible to include and punch all of the subjects.   For these works I have left the 00 within each hundreds group to receive 'surveys'.   Thus a work of this kind relating to virus research in general would be denoted by 400 and one relating to genetics by 700 (for bacteria 000—Author).

(*vi*) It is possible, of course, to form groups also at the tens and units in the same way as at the hundreds.   This produces very useful cross connections for sorting.   Thus, within each of the main subjects, the range 60–90 is uniformly reserved for effects due to radiation, so that for instance the following combinations are made available for answering enquiries:

064	effects of rays from radium on bacteria
764	effects of rays from radium in genetics
–64	all works relating to rays from radium
16–	all effects of radiation in the field of immunity
–6–	all works relating to radiation

(*vii*) When doing the preparatory work I discovered some further little tricks in sorting which offer special advantages.   When the sorting needle is inserted 'shallow' at the numbers 1, 2, 4 and 7, instead of 'deep' as the '1, 2, 4, 7' code demands, various cards fall out, namely the following:

> when 'shallow-needled' at '1', the cards notched 1, 3, 5 and 8
> when 'shallow-needled' at '2', the cards notched 2, 3, 6 and 9
> when 'shallow-needled' at '4' the cards notched 0, 4, 5 and 6
> when 'shallow-needled' at '7' the cards notched 0, 7, 8 and 9

as will easily be understood on making a sketch of the '1, 2, 4, 7' code. These irregular results can be turned to advantage by assigning contents groups to the above named groups of numbers as I did in the example of 'methods of preparation'. Here, at the hundredth place, I have used the numbers 0, 4, 5 and 6 for certain (four) main subjects of adequate range, namely 'virus' 'bacteriophages' and 'tumors'. This enables me to build up cross connections between those subject contents which are significant only under these four particular heads, as in the example 'methods of display', which give the following combinations of searching aspects (the parentheses meaning that the number is shallow-needled):

> 0 25   electron-optical display of bacteria
> 4 25   electron-optical display of viruses
> (4) 25   all works about electron-optical display
> (4) 2–   all works relating to methods of display

The great advantage of such a combination—which can, of course, equally well be inserted at the tens and units places—lies in the fact that the remaining hundreds positions in the same groups are not blocked. For instance '325' denotes scarlatina. (Main subject 3 = infectious diseases—Author.)

Let us now briefly summarize the whole procedure. The following steps are necessary in respect of each work, whether available in the original or as a reprint or in abstract:

(*a*) The publication is scanned, and any of its contents which are of importance to one's own work are noted.

(*b*) For each publication an author card (of *DIN A 6* format— 4 in. × 5¾ in.) is prepared bearing the author's names, the title of the work and where it is to be found. This card is filed alphabetically.

(*c*) An edge-notched card is prepared, on which reference or a whole abstract is added. (Endeavors are being made to persuade German abstracting services to provide copies printed on only one side of the paper so that abstracts can be cut out and pasted on edge-notched cards.)

(*d*) When reprints are available they are given serial numbers and filed under those, marked also on the corresponding author cards and edge-notched cards.

(*e*) The appropriate indications of subject contents are given in numbers according to the code, which are noted both on the author card and on the edge-notched card. In the case of the author cards this is necessary so that at any time the corresponding edge-notched cards can be found.

(*f*) The edge-notched card is punched and disposed of by year and subject contents numbers.'

(5) MEDICINE (using Visual Punch-Cards) with Example of a Photographic Archive

(From Derbolowsky, 1953.) 'A clinic or polyclinic maintains a Cordonnier card (= visual card—Author) collection in accordance with the methods of documentation hitherto in use. The headings on most of these cards are diagnoses, years of age and the two sexes. In this way it is made very easy to answer series of questions such as the following:

(1) How many patients suffering from bronchial asthma have we had?
Answer: The 'asthma bronchiale' card is taken and the holes in it are counted.

(2) Which patients were they?
Answer: The positions punched on the 'asthma bronchiale' card correspond with the registration numbers of the patients in question.

(3) Were they predominantly male or female patients?
Answer: Take either the 'male' or the 'female' card—for instance, the first mentioned—and place it over the 'asthma bronchiale' card. Those positions through which the light is seen to come correspond with the registration numbers of the male patients who had bronchial asthma, and these have only to be counted in order to obtain the male total. Subtracting this total from the answer to the first question gives the corresponding total of female patients.

(4) 'I remember there was one female patient who besides bronchial asthma was suffering from enurodermitis, obstipation and migraines. Who was that? Has that combination occurred often?'
Answer: The cards headed 'bronchial asthma', 'neurodermitis', 'obstipation', 'migraine' and 'female' all are superimposed. Where the same position has been punched in all five cards the light is seen to come through it and the numbers of the positions where it does so correspond to the registration numbers of the patients in whom this combination of symptoms occurred. If there are more than one of them, the remembered patient will be among them.

What subjects are chosen for recording on Cordonnier (visual) cards is, of course, a question for each user to decide, but the method is as well adapted for use in a laboratory as in private medical practice and equally for work on literature or on cases. For a medical practice, it means that 12500 patients can be recorded before the cards are full. As an example of its application to study of the literature, any practitioner interested in 100 subjects would need to have not more than 100 such cards until he had read 12500 publications; if and when he has read more than that he can start a second series of 100 cards, which can be of another color and immediately have room for another 12500 'objects' which, in this case, are publications.

A not inconsiderable advantage of this method is that the subjects do not need to be coded and that their range can be increased at any time simply by adding new cards. It is useful, however, to mark at the top of each added card how far the running number had already reached at the time of its addition. The reason for this is as follows: suppose that the head of a polyclinic is particularly interested in one of the symptoms shown by the 3400th patient and decides in future to punch this previously unrecorded symptom. In order to do so a new card, 'empty' up to now, is added with that symptom as its heading. The first position to be punched in it will be number 3400, corresponding to the patient registered under that number. It may, however, have been the case that one or more of the patients numbered between 1 and 3399 also showed this symptom, although no account has been taken of it on the existing cards. If, then, it should be desired at some time in the future to find out the frequency with which this symptom occurs it will be necessary to know that this particular card did not 'enter into play' until the number 3400 was reached. That is why it is useful when new cards are added, to mark on them how far the running number has gone at the time of their addition.

Before turning to the next method, let us again summarize what has been said:

(*i*) The visual (or Cordonnier) card provides a cheap and simple technical means for making the card records of a physician in private practice, or in an institute, searchable from numerous different aspects, thereby lessening the burden on his memory and saving time.

(*ii*) Its adoption does not entail any work of converting or rearranging card records which already exist as there is no difficulty in 'connecting up' these with the visual cards.

(*iii*) The user of such cards is not obliged to decide upon a predetermined program of work as he would if he were considering the adoption of a subject code. He needs no code at all, he can change the direction of his work as often as he wishes without having to make any change in the 'system' and without his existing collection of visual cards being thereby rendered worthless.

(*iv*) 'No mechanical aid is needed for evaluating the recorded data.' (Derbolowsky, 1953.)

I shall supplement this medical example with a short reference to the application of visual punch-cards in a photographic archive. Suppose that a photographic center has an archive comprising photographs of individuals and groups numbered and arranged in serial order. Suppose it is desired to be able to find those photographs which show the most important persons, either separately or together. For this purpose a collection of visual punch-cards is started, containing a card for each person, in which are punched the serial numbers of all the photographs in which that person appears. For instance, a card headed 'Miller' is punched at the positions corresponding to the numbers of all the photos in which Mr Miller appears. Should it be desired to find all the photos in which Mr Miller, Mr Carter and Mr Johnson are shown together, the visual cards corresponding to all three are superimposed on one another as described above, and the serial numbers of the wanted photos can at once be read off.

(6) DOCUMENTATION AND RELATED FIELDS

(From Scheele, here published for the first time.) The following system of classification and notation has been found to work well as a means of arranging and 'fixing' publications which treat documentation and allied subjects. This system is similar to the way the present book is subdivided. The numerical notation adopted can be used also for filing purposes.

Classification and notation for documentation and allied fields

0 = General
1 = Formulation and arrangement of knowledge (terminology and nomenclature, classification)
2 = Re-expression of knowledge in new symbols (translation, notation)
3 = Primary fixation of knowledge in 'documents' (publication)
4 = Collection and storekeeping of documents (librarianship and filing)
5 = Processing of documents (documentation)
6 = Secondary fixation of the contents of documents (documentation, information)
7 = Collection and storekeeping of secondary documents (librarianship and filing)
8 =
9 = Other

Subdivision 0 (General)

00 = General
01 = General questions of organization
02 = Questions of training
03 = Standardization
04 = Calculation, costs
05 = Institutions
06 = Meetings
07 = Legal questions
08 =
09 = Other

Subdivision 1 (Terminology and nomenclature, classification)

10 = General
11 = Terminology and nomenclature
12 = Scientific objects systems (natural systems)
13 = Scientific aspects of search or properties systems (Theory of knowledge)
14 = General systematics of science
15 = Universal Decimal Classification (UDC)
16 = Oxford system
17 = Other systems
18 =
19 = Others

Subdivision 2 (Translation and notation)

20 = General
21 = Translation exclusively between living languages
22 = Translation between living and dead languages
23 = Translation in Esperanto and other artificial languages
24 = Numerical notations
25 = Letter notations
26 = Combined numerical and letter notations
27 = Other kinds of notation
28 =
29 = Other

Subdivision 3 (Publication)
(Modes of recording)

30 = General
31 = Handwriting
32 = Typewriting and duplicating
33 = Letterpress printing
34 = Contact photocopying
35 = Photographic methods, television
36 = Visual punch-cards

37 = Needle punch-cards
38 = Machine punch-cards
39 = Other (tape recorders, sound film, braille)

Subdivision 4 (Librarianship, filing and archives)
(Kinds of primary documents)

40 = General
41 = Monographs and non-periodical collective works (also catalogs)
42 = Periodicals (journals, newspapers and related documents)
43 = Academic test documents (dissertations, etc.)
44 = Patent documents
45 = Trade publicity (including commercial prospectuses)
46 = Other single documents (e.g. photographs, minutes)
47 = Looseleaf collections and card records of non-periodical form
48 = Looseleaf collections and card records of periodical form
49 = Other

Subdivision 5 (Documentation)

50 = General
51 = No processing of the document: it remains as it is
52 = Title reference
53 = Indication of contents by way of keywords
54 = Short abstract
55 = Fuller description
56 = Extraction of all statistical and otherwise exploitable data: evaluation
57 = Compilation of handbooks and similar collective stores of condensed knowledge: processing of results
58 =
59 = Other

Subdivision 6 (Methods of secondary recording)

60 = General
61 = Handwriting
62 = Typewriting and duplicating
63 = Letterpress printing
64 = Contact photocopying
65 = Photographic methods, television
66 = Visual punch-cards
67 = Needle punch-cards
68 = Machine punch-cards
69 = Other (tape recorders, sound film, braille)

Subdivision 7 (Kinds of secondary documents)

70 = General
71 = Monographs and non-periodical collective works (also catalogs)
72 = Periodicals (journals, newspapers and related documents)
73 = Academic test documents (dissertations, etc.)
74 = Patent documents
75 = Trade publicity (including commercial prospectuses)
76 = Other single documents (e.g. photographs, minutes)
77 = Looseleaf collections and card records of non-periodical form
78 = Looseleaf collections and card records of periodical form
79 = Other

Besides being suitable for filing and to provide headings for needle punch-cards, this system can equally well be applied to machine punch-cards.

The author uses needle punch-cards as shown in Fig. 44, with a direct code. Wherever possible the numbers used for notation and those for

DK 002 : 535.33 — 1 (084.12)

Mecke, R., und **E. D. Schmid:** Das Dokumentationsproblem in der Ultrarotspektroskopie. (Angewandte Chemie 65, 1953; S. 253-56.)

Dokumentation von UR-Spektroskopien mit herkömmlichen Mitteln nur unvollkommen durchführbar. Randloch- u. IBM-Karten aber vermögen Dokumentationsanforderungen zu erfüllen, insbesondere neue Hinweise auf Zusammenhänge und Gesetzmäßigkeiten zu geben.

A – C + E – 37+ 38+ 57– u+

Randlochkarte Din A 5/209/N

Hersteller: Lochkarten-Werk Schlitz-Hessen

designating the holes are the same, the only exception being in the notation of 60–69 and 70–79 for which the pairs of holes 30–39 and 40–49 are deep-notched. (See the system itself.)

Generally speaking, the coding is done in accordance with the 'punching pattern' method. For instance a work relating to the costs of maintaining continuous documentation in the form of needle punch-cards with abstracts pasted on to them, using the Decimal Classification and at the same time a numerical notation, would be coded as follows:

pair of holes	4 shallow	pair of holes	37 deep
pair of holes	15 shallow	pair of holes	48 deep
pair of holes	24 shallow	pair of holes	54 shallow

In addition, the first letter of each author's name can be notched in the pairs of holes a to e by using the abridged code and notching table as described from page 79 onward).

Likewise, an abridged code was developed for subject fields on the basis of the notching table. The related classification here is similar to the Decimal Classification but uses a different sequence and a different notation. This notation, too, can be used to provide marks for filing. On the needle punch-cards the pairs of hole A–K are used for coding.

Code for branches of knowledge

Notation:	Classification	Coding (key)
		+ = deep-notched
		− = shallow-notched
	I. General and Philosophy (UDC 0 and 1) . .	A +
1 =	General	A + B − C −
2 =	Librarianship, documentation	A + B − D −
3 =	Philosophy	A + B − E −
4 =		
5 =		
6 =		
	II. Moral and social sciences	B +
7 =	Theology (UDC 2)	A − B + C −
8 =	Social sciences (U.D.C. 3)	A − B + D −
9 =	Linguistic sciences (UDC 4)	A − B + E −
10 =	Art, applied art (UDC 7)	B + C − D −
11 =	Literary sciences (UDC 8)	B + C − E −
12 =	History, biographies (parts of UDC 9) . .	B + D − E −
	III. Natural sciences (UDC 5)	C +
13 =	Mathematics (UDC 51)	A − B − C +
14 =	Physics (UDC 53)	A − C + D −
15 =	Chemistry (UDC 54)	A − C + E −
16 =	Astronomy (UDC 52)	B − C + D −
17 =	Earth sciences (UDC 55)	B − C + E −
18 =	Biology (UDC 56 to 59)	C + D − E −
	IV. Applied sciences (UDC 6)	D +
19 =	Engineering, technology (UDC 62) . . .	A − B − D +
20 =	Various industries including building (UDC 67 to 69)	A − C − D +
21 =	Chemical industry and technology (UDC 66) .	A − D + E −

22 =	Domestic economy, commerce and communications										
	(UDC 64, 65) .	.	.	.	.	.	.	B —	C —	D +	
23 =	Agriculture, forestry, fishing (UDC 63)		.	.	B —		D +	E —			
24 =	Medicine (UDC 61) .	.	.	.	.	.	C —		D +	E —	

(UDC = Universal Decimal Classification, which is
basically similar to Dewey Classification—Translator.)

The pairs of holes marked L–U, f–u and 60–63 as well as the two holes y and z then remain free and can be used for further indications of any kind whatever. The author's own use of these holes would appear to be of less general interest and is not, therefore, described here.

14.   EXAMPLES FROM SYSTEM THEORY

(1) **CHEMISTRY**

(From Steidle, 1957.)   As already pointed out in Chapter 7, chemistry is in the fortunate position that its structural formulas provide it with a ready-made notation whereby the properties (or at least the structure) of chemical objects (compounds) can be read off directly.   Whilst it is clear that other

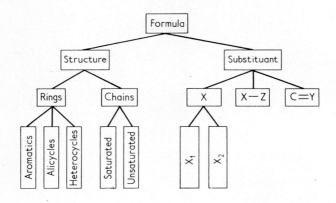

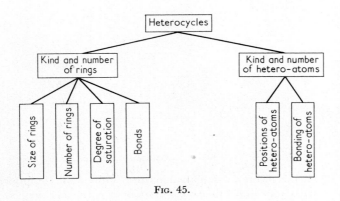

Fig. 45.

authors (Dyson, 1949; Gruber, 1950; Wiswesser, 1954) have evidently been misled through not being clear as to the difference between notation and coding and have not appreciated the possibilities latent in the use of punch-card method, and consequently have applied themselves to the task of creating a new linear notation for formulas, Steidle on the other hand has directly attacked the problem of how to code formulas on machine punch-cards. In doing so he has based himself on the 'punching pattern' principle,

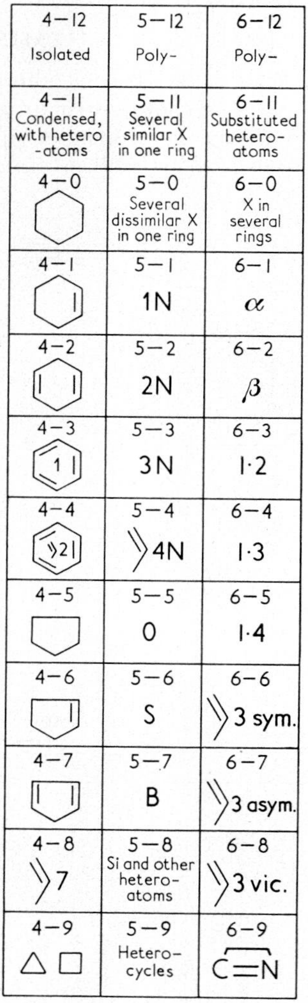

FIG. 46. Part of coding for chemical formulas

4—12 Isolated	5—12 Poly-	6—12 Poly-
4—11 Condensed, with hetero-atoms	5—11 Several similar X in one ring	6—11 Substituted hetero-atoms
4—0	5—0 Several dissimilar X in one ring	6—0 X in several rings
4—1	5—1 1N	6—1 α
4—2	5—2 2N	6—2 β
4—3	5—3 3N	6—3 1·2
4—4	5—4 4N	6—4 1·3
4—5	5—5 0	6—5 1·4
4—6	5—6 S	6—6 3 sym.
4—7	5—7 B	6—7 3 asym.
4—8 7	5—8 Si and other hetero-atoms	6—8 3 vic.
4—9	5—9 Hetero-cycles	6—9 $C \equiv N$

breaking down the formulas into their natural individual components and assigning a particular hole to each component. In this way an object code is created, applicable not only in reference documentation but also in evaluative documentation, the documentation of results and system theory. With its aid, far-reaching correlation research can be undertaken through the use of punch-cards, such as Steidle has already tried out in

15. CONCLUDING REMARKS

In bringing this book to an end we cannot but ask ourselves what is likely to be the eventual outcome from the developments and possibilities which have here been adumbrated. On this question the author would like once again to quote the words of two notable writers:

> It has become one of the most urgent concerns of mankind to discover some technical means whereby to keep pace with the rate at which knowledge is now accumulating. Unless we succeed in finding a way to maintain our mastery over the luxuriant growth we shall be suffocated by it. The jungle which is life itself has intergrown with what originally was planted as a cultivation to clear it and has now in its turn become a jungle also. If science has brought order into life, now order has to be brought into science (Ortega y Gasset, 1952).

Another has written:

> The present situation in science might be summed up as follows: the most important parts of the picture have already been painted or are in process of being sketched, but the decisive stage of synthesizing them into a whole has nowhere been completed. Knowledge of natural science increases at a rate which is exponential, but it is subject to two restraints: on the one hand the limits to the intellectual capacities of men, on the other hand limits of another kind, which affect all thought.
>
> The evolution of the natural sciences shows some parallels with that of organic life. It is an evolution which ramifies ever wider, producing new sciences almost every day, and any gaps left open at first are rapidly filled in by a specializing tendency which is, indeed, excessive. In this way many branches of science have become so specialized as to lose all connection with those from which they originally stemmed, or even the capacity to regraft themselves thereon. Territories of knowledge have been conquered wherein the traditional methods of science are in fact no longer applicable, but wherein 'mutation' has not yet brought about an adequate substitute for those methods, and wherein 'natural selection' operates only timidly.
>
> Civilization in general, and science in particular, continue to develop because men collect and diffuse knowledge and discoveries and are able to build upon the existing foundations. Science, however, has hitherto been but little affected by modern methods of diffusion— telephone, radio, facsimile reproduction, television. Great advances are being made in accumulating the material of science by way of micro-film and new methods of printing: *but the methods we use for evaluating and exploiting these stockpiles of knowledge in our libraries and files are almost archaic.*

261

Maybe science will some day be suffocated under the weight of its own products; will, like a bacterial culture, be hindered in its further evolution by its own secretions.   In the field of physics alone, there are thousands of periodicals any one of which may total some 5000 printed pages in a year, full of mathematical matter difficult to understand. Who, then, is in a position to maintain his mastery and able, of set purpose, to discover in this huge mountain of material the elements which he needs for the next step forward?   Science becomes polyglot. It propagates itself by ever further 'divisions of cells'.   To achieve a synthesis of multiple areas becomes a task of great difficulty.   How, then, are we to make those future greater syntheses needed for us to win our way through to daylight?

In fact a great deal can be done.   Aids to the intellectual activity of man have meanwhile developed far beyond the stage of paper and pencil.   At present it is electronic digital and analog computers that hold the forefront of the field and it already becomes possible to imagine machines similar to these which would be able, for instance, to carry out the routine work in organic chemistry much better than can be done by men in laboratories.   Such machines might compute relations and derivations, and establish their limits, very much more accurately and comprehensively than a man.   They might even be able to learn from experience.   It is possible, at least on paper, to design a machine able to follow the principles of association from point to point as the human brain does, but without having to be informed by knowledge stored after the manner that now occurs in the pyramidal cells of the brain. There seems no apparent reason why man should not rely on the machine for all those phases in the thinking process which amount merely to recollection or which are bound by fixed rules.   On the contrary, we have every justification for handing over to machines the whole of the work of accumulating and retrieving scientific knowledge. Properly speaking, we have no alternative to so doing, if we aspire to mastery over the huge mass of material which mankind has heaped up. *It seems evident that now science stands in need of new methods, for the reason that science now is encountering problems that lie on the farther side of those simple relationships which have, to a great extent, been at the foundation of its success to date.*

These new methods can be evolved only through our finding out new ways and means of documentation such as will enable us, at the same time, to refer back to the current totals standing in the balance sheet of science.   But we need also new forms of collaboration so as to be able to achieve true knowledge in directions which transcend the bounds of highly specialized disciplines.   Along many of the roads which now lie open to us, we can proceed with good prospects of success, always provided that we can learn to link the intellectual systems of practised thinkers much more intimately together than now occurs by way of books, lectures and seminars.   But in so doing, quite decisive changes are bound to occur in the nature of the scientist's approach to his work, in the training of his successors and in the place which science occupies in society.   (Adapted from an article by Vannevar Bush, 1956.)

When, furthermore, we read the responsible pronouncements of Norbert Wiener (1952) no doubt can remain that it is not least by the methods explained in this book that we may hope to solve the problems brought out in these quotations, as in many other places.   But the goal is yet far off, attainable only through a great deal of further effort.

In the long run, if Germany is not to fall behind other nations in these respects, our scientists concerned will be unable to supply these efforts without powerful aid from the State and from the great scientific organizations.   Hence this book is addressed with a special emphasis to everyone on whom the cultivation and promotion of the sciences devolves.   It seems necessary that the problems and possibilities treated here should be viewed from a broad angle and it is immaterial what attitude is taken towards the present author's own opinions and suggestions.   What matters is the threat that exists of all science coming to a dead stop unless the problems of documentation in all their bearings are faced and considered from every side. And that surely is something which cannot be secured without the abandonment of many longstanding preconceptions and prejudices, nor without free acceptance of the challenge made to us in this age of automation.

BIBLIOGRAPHY

For the purpose of this book the author built up an extensive bibliography containing about 2 000 titles in all, in the form of visual punch-cards according to 30 different features which can be searched for in whatever combination with one another may be desired.

After completing the manuscript it became apparent, however, that to include that bibliography in the book itself would be to lengthen it by some 80 or 90 pages, upsetting all the arrangements that had been made for publication.

In view of this, and of the fact that no such bibliography for the subject field here treated has hitherto been available, the author decided to make it into a separate book which can be distributed and used independently. The bibliography accompanied by a set of visual feature-punched cards can be obtained from Verlag H. Guntrum II. KG, Schlitz (Oberhessen), German Federal Republic.

Consequently the bibliography here following refers only to those works which have been quoted from or cited in the present book. The asterisk * denotes books as distinct from articles in periodicals. *Nachr. Dok.* is the abbreviation for *Nachrichten für Dokumentation* published for the Deutsche Gesellschaft für Dokumentation at Schubertstrasse 1, Frankfurt-am-Main.

Aikele, E.: 'Was gibt es zu berechnen?' Translated from the book *Faster, Faster* by W. I. Eckert and R. Jones. *IBM-Nachrichten* (1956) 128, pp. 416–425.

Allform-Büroorganisation: commercial publicity.

*Ausschuss für wirtschaftliche Verwaltung: *Handbuch der Lochkartenorganisation.* Agenor Druck- u. Verlagsges. mbH., Frankfurt/M. 1957.

*Bertalanffy, L. von: *Auf den Pfaden des Lebens (Ein biologisches Skizzenbuch).* Umschau-Verl. Frankfurt/M. 1951.

Bethge, W.: Dokumentation der Tonbandaufnahmen deutscher Sprache und Mundarten. MS.

Braband, C.: 'Einige Vorschläge für die Ausgestaltung des Sichtlochkartenverfahrens.' *Nachr. Dok.* 8 (1957), 1, pp. 42–44.

Busa, R.: Die Elektronentechnik in der Mechanisierung der sprachwissenschaftlichen Analyse.' *Nachr. Dok.* 8 (1957), 1, pp. 20–26.

Bush, V.: 'Der Mensch in seiner Beziehung zum Universum.' Newspaper *Die Tat* of 17.6.1956.

Carlé, R.: 'Beiträge zur vergleichenden Städteepidemiographie.' *Zbl. Bakteriol., Parasitenkunde, Infektionskrankheiten u. Hygiene* 163 (1955), pp. 560–570.

*Casey, R. S.; Perry, J. W.: *Punched Cards. Their applications to science and industry.* Reinhold Publ. Corp., New York, 1st edn. 1951, 2nd edn. 1958.

Clarke, S. E.: 'A multiple-entry perforated-card key with special reference to the identification of hard woods.' *New Phytologist* 37 (1938), pp. 369–374.

Danilof, H.: 'Vergleichende Zeitstudie verschiedener Verfahren zur Dokumentation von Patentschriften.' *Nachr. Dok.* 8 (1957), pp. 179–182.

Derbolowsky, U.: 'Zur Mechanisierung der Dokumentation auf dem Gebiet der medizinischen Psychologie.' *Nachr. Dok.* 3 (1952), 1, p. 23.

Derbolowsky, U.: 'Das geistige Quantitativproblem in der Medizin und die mechanisierte Dokumentation als Lösungsversuch: Über die Verwendung von Lochkarten in der Medizin.' *Klin. Wschr.* **31** (1953), pp. 825–831.

Deutsche Checker GmbH.: commercial publicity.

Deutscher Forschungsdienst: *Das Bild als Dolmetscher.* **5** (1958), Februar.

Deutscher Normenausschuss: 'Wissenschaftliche Zeitschriften. Richtlinien für die Gestaltung. Bibliothekswesen.' *Normblatt 1503*, Beuth-Vertrieb GmbH., Berlin, Krefeld-Uerdingen 1938.

— (Fachnormenausschuss Bibliotheks-, Buch- und Zeitschriftenwesen): 'Titelangaben von Schrifttum.' *Normblatt 1505*, Beuth-Vertrieb GmbH., Berlin-Köln 1939.

Deutscher Normenausschuss: 'Richtlinien für die Gestaltung technisch-wissenschaftlicher Veröffentlichungen.' *Normblatt 1422*, Beuth-Vertrieb GmbH., Berlin-Köln 1952.

Deutscher Normenausschuss (Fachnormenausschuss Bibliotheks-, Buch-, und Zeitschriftenwesen): 'Schrifttumsberichte. Richlinien.' *Normblatt 1426*, Beuth-Vertrieb GmbH., Berlin-Köln 1953.

Dezimalklassifikation: Deutsche Kurzausgabe. 2nd ed. revd. and enlgd. Beuth-Verl., Berlin 1941 (Ausg. 1945) (Veröff. Int.d. Verb. f. Dok. 182) and Stockholm: Fritze 1945.

Draheim, H.: 'Benennungen von Lochkarten.' *Nachr. Dok.* **8** (1957), 2, pp. 94–97.

Draheim, H. und Gdaniek, O.: 'Was leisten 10 Löcher einer Randlochkarte?' *Nachr. Dok.* **5** (1954), 4, pp. 201–210.

*Dyson, G. M.: *A New Notation and Enumeration System for Organic Compounds.* Longmans, Green and Co., New York 1947 and 2nd ed., London 1949.

*Elsenhans, T.: 'Psychologie und Logik.' *Samml. Göschen* **14**, Walter de Gruyter and Co., Berlin W 35, 1936.

Exacta Continental-Büromaschinen-Werke: 'Firmenprospekte des Bull-Lochkartenverfahrens.'

Faegri and Iversen: *Textbook of Modern Pollen Analysis.* Copenhagen 1950.

Fairthorne, R. A.: 'Theorie der Mitteilung (The Theory of Communication).' *Nachr. Dok.* **7** (1956), 1, pp. 2–11.

Farradane, J.: 'Classification and mechanical selection.' *Proc. Internat. Study Conf. Classif. Information Retrieval*, Pergamon Press, New York 1957, pp. 65–69.

*Frank, O.: *Die Dezimalklassifikation. Zweck, Aufbau, Anwendung.* Beuth-Verl., Berlin 1946.

*— *Grundlagen der Ordnungstechnik.* Beuth-Verl., Berlin 1948. (Handb. d. Klassifikation **3**.) 2nd ed. enlarged 1957.

Gray, C. J.: 'A new method of using the physical characteristics of minerals for their identification.' *Trans. Geol. Soc. S. Afr.* **23** (1920) pp. 114–117.

Grobe, G.: 'Eine Randlochkarte mit drei Lochreihen als Element einer Schrifttumskartei.' *Nachr. Dok.* **3** (1952), 4, p. 195.

— 'Internationale Dezimalklassifikation und Randlochkarte.' *Nachr. Dok.* **5** (1954), **3**, pp. 141–146.

— 'Was leisten zehn Löcher einer Randlochkarte?' *Nachr. Dok.* **6** (1955), 2, pp. 68–69.

Grolier, E. de: Concluding survey, in *Proc. Internat. Study Conf. Classif. Information Retrieval.* Pergamon Press, New York 1957 a, pp. 81–85.

— 5. 'Bericht des Mit-Berichterstatters des Comités FID/CA.' Paris 025.4 (04) 1957 b.

— 'What have we done at Dorking?' Referat 1957 c. (Mimeographed by Deutsche Gesellschaft für Dokumentation.)

— 'Après Dorking.' *Rev. Doc.*, 's-Gravenhage **25** (1958), 1, pp. 12–20.

Gröttrup, H.: 'Stellungnahme zur der Arbeit "Die Terminologie der Lochkartenverfahren" von Dr M. Scheele.' 1957. MS.

Gruber, W.: 'Die Genfer Nomenklatur in Chiffren und Vorschläge für ihre Erweiterung auf Ringverbindungen.' Beihefte 58 (1950) zur *Z. Angew. Chemie*.

Gülich, W.: 'Die Einheit der sozialwissenschaftlichen Dokumentation—Sozialwissenschaftliche Dokumentation durch bibliothekarische Organisation.' *Nachr. Dok.* **4** (1953), pp. 16–21.

*Guss, H.: *Die meteorologischen Lochkarten des Deutschen Wetterdienstes und ihre hauptsächlichen Auswertungsmethoden.* Verlag Dietr. Reimer, Berlin 1953.

— *Jahresbericht des Deutschen Wetterdienstes* (1955), Nr. 3.

Guss, H.; Reichel, E.: 'Anwendungen des Lochkartenverfahrens in der Meteorologie.' *Ber. dtsch. Wetterdienstes US-Zone.* Nr. 12, Bad Kissingen 1950, pp. 141–151.

Haldenwanger, H.: 'Über die Klassifizierung und Registrierung heterogener Stoffgebiete der wissenschaftlichen Literatur.' *Nachr Dok.* **6** (1955) 2, pp. 56–60.

Hartung, J.: 'Die dermatologische Begriffsbildung und ihre Dokumentation.' *Wiss. Z. Ernst-Moritz-Arndt-Univ., Greifswald,* Math.-naturwiss. Reihe Nr. **1/2** (1956/57), **6** pp. 21–24.

Havermann, H.: 'Forschungsaufgaben und Forschungsmethoden in der Tierzucht und Tierernährung—Anwendung des Lochkartenverfahrens.' *Hochschuldienst* **IX** (1956), 16, p. 23.

Heimerdinger, W.: 'Maschinelle Voraussetzungen für die Verwendung von Hollerith-Lochkarten mit der Ordnung nach der Dezimalklassifikation (UDC).' *Nachr. Dok.* **6** (1955), pp. 171–176.

*Hennig, W.: *Grundzüge einer Theorie der phylogenetischen Systematik.* Deutscher Zentral-verlag, Berlin 1950.

Heumann, K. H.: 'Die Informationstheorie im Bereiche des Bibliotheks- und Dokumenta-tionswesens.' *Nachr. Dok.* **6** (1955), 2, pp. 79–80.

Holmstrom, J. E.: 'The language problem of science', in *Research, Lond.,* **7** (May 1954), pp. 190–195.

— 'How translators can contribute to improving scientific terminology.' *Babel,* Bonn, **1** (1955) 2, pp. 73–79.

*— *Records and research in engineering and industrial science.* 3rd ed. Chapman and Hall, London 1956. 492 pp.

— 'Mehrsprachige Wörterbücher und Dokumentation.' *Nachr. Dok.* **8** (1957), 1, pp. 7–13.

Hörnicke, H.: 'Randlochkartei und Zettelkasten im Vergleich. Eine Darstellung am Beispiel einer Literaturkartei für die Atmungsphysiologie.' *Nachr. Dok.* **7** (1956), 1, pp. 25–30.

Hosemann, H.: 'Das Lochkartensystem und einige wichtige statistische Resultate auf gynäkologisch-geburtshilflichem Gebiet.' *Fortschr. Geburtshilfe u. Gynäkologie* **II** (1951), pp. 77–149.

— 'Plan einer gemeinsamen Karzinomstatistik der Gynäkologischen Kliniken in Deutsch-land.' MS.

Hustedt, F.: 'Die Diatomeenflora der Eifelmaare.' *Arch. Hydrob. Rybact.* **48** (1954), pp. 451–496.

IBM Deutschland: *Der IBM-Zahlenschlüssel.* (Commercial Publicity.)

Jans, W.: 'Diskussionsbeitrag zur Arbeitstagung des Deutschen Zentralausschusses für Krebsbekämpfung und -Forschung und der Deutschen Gesellschaft für Dokumentation.' Aussch. für Medizin in Göttingen am 4./5. Mai 1956. MS.

Kern, L.: 'Grundfragen der Dokumentation mit besonderer Berüchsichtigung von Wirtschaft und Technik.' *Nachr. Dok.* **1** (1950), 2, pp. 42–47.

Kistermann, F.: 'Über die Kostenfragen in Bibliotheken und Dokumentationsstellen. Eine kurzgefasste bibliographische Übersicht über das ausländische Schrifttum.' *Nachr. Dok.* **8** (1957), 4, pp. 191–193.

— 'Zur Geschichte und Entwicklung des Sichtlochkarten-Verfahrens.' *Dok. Fachbibl., Werksb.,* Hannover, **6** (1957/58), pp. 7–12.

Kistermann, F.; Uhlein, E.: 'Die Sichtlochkartei. Zur Technik der wissenschaftlichen Arbeit.' *Diskus, Frankf. Stud. Ztg,* **7** (1957 a), 5, pp. 185–186.

— 'Die Sichtlochkarte. Vereinfachte Auswertung von Literatur und Untersuchungsergeb-nissen.' *Umschau,* Frankfurt/Main. (1957 b) **12**, pp. 370–371.

Klewitz, O. von: 'Beispiele und Erfahrungen aus der betrieblichen Information.' *Nachr. Dok.* **8** (1957), 2, pp. 78–82.

Knappe, W.: 'Einige Gesichtspunkte zur Anwendung von Sichtlochkarten.' *Nachr. Dok.* **7** (1956), 3, pp. 140–145.

Knese, K. H.; Voges, D.; Ritschl, I.: 'Untersuchungen über die Osteon- und Lamellen-formen im Extremitätenskelett des Erwachsenen.' *Z. Zellforsch.* **40** (1954 a), pp. 323–360.

Knese, K. H.; Voges, D.; Ritschl, I.: 'Quantitative Untersuchung der Osteonverteilung im Extremitätenskelett eines 43 jährigen Mannes.' *Z. Zellforsch.* **40** (1954 b), pp. 519–570.

Knigge, H. J.: 'Mikrofilm und Lochkarte.' *Nachr. Dok.* **3** (1952), 3, pp. 125–128.
Koller, S.: 'Die Eigentypisierung einer medizinischen oder naturwissenschaftlichen Veröffentlichung durch den Autor.' *Nachr. Dok.* **6** (1955), 3, pp. 117–120.
Kreithen, A.; Gull, C. D.; Miller, E. E.: 'Klassifizierung nach dem System gleichwertiger Grundbegriffe.' *Nachr. Dok.* **5** (1954), pp. 6–11.
*Lecomte de Nouy, P.: *Die Bestimmung des Menschen.* Union Deutsche Verlagsges., Stuttgart 1948.
Lochkartenwerk Schlitz (Oberhessen): commercial publicity.
Loosjes, Th. P.: 'Die Deltakarte. Eine weitere Entwicklung der Sichtlochkarte.' *Nachr. Dok.* **8** (1956a), 2, p. 90.
*— *Documentatie van wetenschappelijke Literatuur.* N. V. Noord-Hollandsche Uitgeversmij. Amsterdam 1957 b. XVI.
Luhn, H. P.: *Superimposed coding with the aid of Randomizing Squares for use in Mechanical Information Searching Systems.* IBM-Engin. Labor. Poughkeepsie, NY, Code: 001011605. 1956.
— 'Self-demarcating code words.' IBM Corp.-Eng.-Lab. Poughkeepsie NY.
— *A Serial Notation for Describing the Topology of Multi-dimensional Branched Structures (Nodal Index for Branched Structures).* IBM Res. Rep. RC-27, IBM Res. Publ., Poughkeepsie, N.Y.
— 'A statistical approach to mechanized encoding and searching of literary information.' *IBM J. Res. Dev.* **1** (1957), 4, pp. 309–317.
Mansfeld, R.: 'Nomenklaturregeln und Nomenklatur in der Botanik und in der Zoologie.' *Ber. dtsch. bot. Ges.* (1942 a) 60, pp. 373–383.
— 'Werden und Wesen der wissenschaftlichen Pflanzenbenennung und ihrer Regelung.' *Verh. bot. Ver. Brandenburg*, 82, 1942 b, pp. 1–82.
Mecke, R.; Schmid, E. D.: 'Das Dokumentationsproblem in der Ultrarotspektroskopie.' *Angew. Chemie* **65** (1953), 10, pp. 253–256.
Meyer, E.; Heimerdinger, W.: 'Wie ist heute die Erfassung des literarisch gegebenen Standes der Technik noch möglich?' *Nachr. Dok.* **9** (1958), 4, pp. 172–179.
Oppenheimer, C.; Pincussen, L.: *Tabul. biol., Berl.* W. v. Junk, Den Haag 1925 ff. (bis jetzt 22 Bde., 1956).
Orosz, G.: 'Neue Methode der Dokumentationsselektion vermittels Lochkartenmaschinen.' *Dok., Lpz.* **2** (1955), 2, pp. 21–26; 3, pp. 41–49.
*Ortega y Gasset: *Schuld und Schuldigkeit der Universität.* 1952.
Perry, J. W.: 'Indexing, classifying and coding the chemical literature.' *Industr. Engng. Chem. (Industr.)* (1948) March, 40, pp. 476–477.
Perry, J. W.; Kent, A.; Berry, M. M.: 'Machine literature searching IX. Operational functions of automatic equipment; Machine literature searching X. Machine language factors underlying its design and development.' *Amer. Docum.* **6** (1955a), 3, p. 166; 4, p. 242.
— 'Which notation?' Staff Rep., *Chem. Engng. News*, **33** (1955 b), pp. 2838–2843.
Philipps, E. W. J.: 'Identification of softwoods by their microscopic structure.' Dep. of Sci. and Ind. Res., London, *Forest Prod. Res. Bull.* 22 (1948).
Pietsch, E.: 'Neue Methoden zur Erfassung des exakten Wissens in Naturwissenschaft und Technik. *Nachr. Dok.* **2** (1951a), 2, pp. 38–44.
— 'Wie ist eine grosse Dokumentationsstelle für die Fachgebiete der Naturwissenschaften aufzubauen?—Die Lochkarte in der Dokumentation.' *Nachr. Dok.* **2** (1951b), 4, pp. 116–124.
— 'Mechanisierte Dokumentation—ihre Bedeutung für die Ökonomie der geistigen Arbeit, *Nachr. Dok.* **3** (1952 a), pp. 3–5.
Pietsch, E.: 'Mechanisierte Dokumentation—ein Weg zur Ökonomie geistigen Schaffens.' *Umschau* **52** (1952 b), 17, pp. 513–516.
— 'Grundfragen der Dokumentation.' *Schriftenreihe d. Arbeitsgemeinschaft f. Rationalisierung d. Landes Nordrhein-Westf.* (1954), 14, pp. 18–39.
Pietsch, E.; Mulert, G.: 'Bibliographische Hilfsmittel der Chemie zur Anwendung der Randlochkarte in der Bibliographie.' *Nachr. Dok.* **6** (1955), 2, pp. 60–65.

Proppe, A.; Wagner, G.: 'Die Verwendung maschineller Auswertungsverfahren in der Klinik.' *Ärztl. Wschr., Ber.* **12** (1957), 4, pp. 89–93.

Raettig, H.: 'Einige Hinweise für die Anlage einer Literatur-Randlochkartei.' *Nachr Dok.* **4** (1953), pp. 204–209.

*Ranganathan, S. R.: *Colon Classification.* Madras, London 1957.

*Remane, A.: *Die Grundlagen des natürlichen Systems der vergleichenden Anatomie und der Phylogenetik.* Akad. Verl. Ges., Geest and Portig KG., Leipzig 1952.

Remington-Rand GmbH.: commercial publicity for Powers punch-cards.

Richter, F.: 'Die Nomenklatur auf dem Gebiet der organischen Chemie.' *Naturwissenschaften*, **42** (1955), pp. 593–600.

Richter, R.: *Einführung in die Zoologische Nomenklatur durch Erläuterung der Internationalen Regeln.* Senckenberg. Naturforsch. Ges., Frankfurt/M. 1943.

Riegels, F.: 'Über Arbeiten zur aerodynamischen Dokumentation.' MS 1954.

— 'Moderne Methoden in der Aerodynamischen Fachdokumentation.' *Mitt. Max-Planck-Ges.* (1955) 1, pp. 38–41.

Rösch, S.: 'Der literarische Kritikschlüssel als Hilfsmittel der Dokumentation.' *Nachr. Dok.* **2** (1951), 4, pp. 133–135.

Rotschuh, K. E.: 'Das ungenutzte Wissen. Die Literaturflut und die medizinische Forschung.' *Nachr. Dok.* **6** (1955), 2, pp. 52–56.

Rothschuh, K. E.; Schäfer, A.: 'Quantitative Untersuchungen über die Entwicklung des Physiologischen Fachschrifttums (Periodica) in den letzten 150 Jahren.' *Centaurus*, **4** (1955), 1, pp. 63–66.

Ruston, W. R.: 'Die Randlochkarte als Hilfsmittel für die wissenschaftliche Dokumentation. *Nachr. Dok.* **3** (1952), 1, pp. 5–12.

Samas-Lochkartenmaschinen: commercial publicity.

Scheele, M.: 'Die Bedeutung des Lochkartenverfahrens für die Biologie.' *Nachr. Dok.* **2** (1951), 3, pp. 100–102.

— 'Systematisch-ökologische Untersuchungen über die Diatomeenflora der Fulda.' *Arch. Hydrob. Rybact.* **46** (1952), pp. 305–423.

— 'Über einige Grundfragen der Dokumentation mit Lochkarten.' *Nachr. Dok.* **6** (1955a), 3, pp. 111–116.

— 'Neue Wege zur Einheit der Wissenschaften.' *Stud. gen.* **8** (1955 b), 7, pp. 435–443.

— 'Codifizierung auf dem Gebiet der Biologie.' Paper presented at a meeting of Committee FID/S (Mechanical Selection) of the International Federation for Documentation (FID). S.-A. IBM Deutschl. (1956 a).

— 'Verbreitung und Ökologie der Kieselalgen der Werra mit besonderer Berücksichtigung der Halophyten.' *Arch. Hydrob. Rybact.* **51** (1956 b), pp. 425–456.

— 'Zur Terminologie der Lochkartenverfahren.' *Nachr. Dok.* **7** (1956 c), 1, pp. 31–34.

— 'Die Bedeutung des Menschen als Voraussetzung wissenschaftlicher Systemkunde.' *Beitr. z. Festb.*: Aus d. Dt. Forsch. d. letzten Dezennien. Georg Thieme Verl., Stuttgart 1956 d, pp. 45–55.

— Maschinelle Lochkartenverfahren.' *Beitr. f. Handb. d. geistigen Arbeitsmeth.* MS.

*Scheele, M.: **50** *Jahre Archiv für Hydrobiologie, eine Literaturanalyse der Limnologie, dargestellt an den Bänden 1–50, 1906–1955.* Verl. Schweizerbart, Stuttgart, 1958 b, V.

Scherpenhuijsen, G.: 'Amerikanische Forschung auf dem Gebiet der Literaturdokumentation—Zugleich ein Beitrag zur Kostenanalyse von Katalogsystemen.' *Nachr. Dok.* **8** (1957), 3, pp. 120–124.

Schmalfuss, H.: 'Stoff und Leben.' *Bios*, **6**, 1937.

Schürmeyer, W.: *Der Begriff der Dokumentation.* Deutsche Gesellsch. f. Dokum. e. V. Ref. auf der 5. Jahresversamml. in Goslar am 6. 11. 1953.

Steidle, W.: 'Möglichkeiten der mechanischen Dokumentation in der organischen Chemie.' *Pharm. Ind. Berl.*, **19** (1957), pp. 88–93.

Totok, W.: 'Zur Anfertigung von Fachbibliographien.' *Nachr. Dok.* **7** (1956), 2, pp. 49–52.

Uhlein, E.: 'Moderne technische Informationseinrichtungen in der Anwendung. Eine Übersicht über die Dokumentation in USA.' *Nachr. Dok.* **9** (1958), 1, pp. 51–53.

UNESCO: Monthly Bulletin on Scientific Documentation and Terminology [Mimeographed, now replaced by Bulletin on Bibliography, Documentation and Terminology].

Vickery, B. C.: 'Developments in subject indexing.' *J. Documentation* **11** (1955), 1.

— 'Relations between subject fields: Problems of constructing a general classification.' *Proc. Internat. Study Conf. Classif. Information Retrieval.* Pergamon Press, New York 1957, pp. 43–49.

Walther, A.: *Elektronische Rechenmaschinen in Wissenschaft und Technik.* MS., 13. 2. 1957, Bad Liebenzell.

Weizsäcker, C. F.von, : *Der begriffliche Aufbau der theoretischen Physik.* (MS of lecture, 1948.)

*Wiener, N.: *Mensch und Menschmaschine (The Human Use of Human Beings—Cybernetics and Society).* German translation by Gertrud Walther. Alfred-Metzner-Verl., Frankfurt/M. 1952; u. Ullstein-Buch 184, Ullstein-Taschenbücher-Verl. GmbH., Frantfurt/M. 1958.

*Wiswesser, W. J.: *A Line-Formula Chemical Notation.* New York 1954.

Woitschach, M.: 'Berechnung von Maschinenleistungen.' *IBM-Nachrichten* (1954) 118, pp. 88–91.

Name Index

(This index includes names of companies whose manufactures of equipment are so designated in the text. Names of authors whose works are cited in the Bibliography are printed here in *italics*.)

Subject Index

(For equipment designated by its manufacturer's name, see Name Index)